APPLIED
COMBINATORICS
with
PROBLEM
SOLVING

APPLIED COMBINATORICS
with
PROBLEM SOLVING

Bradley W. Jackson and Dmitri Thoro
SAN JOSE STATE UNIVERSITY

Addison-Wesley Publishing Company
Reading, Massachusetts • Menlo Park, California • New York • Don Mills, Ontario
Amsterdam • Bonn • Wokingham, England • Sydney • Singapore • Tokyo • Madrid • San Juan

Sponsoring Editor: *Charles B. Glaser*
Production Supervisor: *Karen Garrison*
Technical Art Consultant: *Loretta Bailey*
Design, Editorial, and Production Services: *Schneider & Company*
Illustrator: *Publication Services*
Manufacturing Supervisor: *Roy Logan*
Cover Designer: *Ned Williams*

Library of Congress Cataloging-in-Publication Data

Jackson, Bradley W.
    Applied combinatorics with problem solving/by Bradley W. Jackson and Dmitri Thoro.
      p. cm.
    Includes index.
    ISBN 0-201-12908-6
    1. Combinatorial analysis. I. Thoro, Dmitri. II. Title.
QA164.J33   1989
511', 6—do20

                                                    89-36075
                                                      CIP

Reprinted with corrections, June 1990.

3 4 5 6 7 8 9 10 DO 959493

PREFACE

This text contains topics in combinatorics and graph theory that we believe are important to all students in mathematics and computer science. They were developed for a course in combinatorics at San Jose State University and are intended to be used for a one-semester course in combinatorics at the junior or senior level. This text is generally self-contained, but a knowledge of calculus would prove beneficial in some sections of Chapters 2, 4, and 7, and a familiarity with linear algebra would be helpful in the last two sections of Chapter 8. The main prerequisite for the student is a mathematical maturity that includes not only a thorough knowledge of many basic mathematical concepts, but also a creativity in solving and analyzing problems.

It is not our intention to include in this text all the important ideas and applications of combinatorics and graph theory. Generally we have tried not to include an idea unless it could be used in some meaningful way. We have tried to be as precise as possible in presenting the mathematical concepts without being overly formal.

We like to think that our students not only learn some relevant mathematical tools and applications, but that they will also develop their ability to solve problems. Each student should learn the following three skills in this course:

1. **Combinatorial problem solving:** Problem solving is important in all areas of mathematics, but especially in combinatorics. Particularly useful are techniques such as induction, iteration, and recursion, in which solutions of smaller problems are used to obtain a solution for a related larger problem. These techniques are the basis for many algorithms in computer science, and the student should become adept at their use. In this course each student will be expected to solve many combinatorial problems. In addition, being able to

present and analyze the solutions of these problems is also considered important. A large number of exercises are given at the end of each section, ranging in difficulty from easy and straightforward to relatively hard and challenging. In addition, we have tried to include some supplementary computer projects in many of the sections.

2. **Counting and estimating:** One of the three main problems in combinatorics is the counting problem. Counting is a useful skill in many areas of mathematics as well as in computer science. It is important to be able to estimate the number of steps required for a particular algorithm in order to determine the feasibility of solving a problem on a computer or to determine which of several solutions is best.

3. **Elementary mathematical modeling:** Many problems in combinatorics will be expressed in everyday English, so it will be necessary to formulate the problem in terms of an appropriate mathematical model in order to apply the basic techniques that we learn. Occasionally there is more than one way to formulate a problem, and it is important to remember that one formulation may lead to a better solution than another.

This text is written from a mathematical standpoint but with computer science students in mind. We have tried to treat many of the topics from an algorithmic point of view, although we have not usually included actual computer programs (except in the supplementary computer projects). We assume that once students understand the basic concepts, they can easily translate them into computer science terminology or a specific computer language in other courses.

Various applications of combinatorial mathematics to several areas of mathematics and computer science are given. Some applications involving games and puzzles are meant to be recreational in nature. It is always our goal to teach our students some useful mathematics in an interesting way. We hope that the students who use this text will conclude as we have that combinatorics is both challenging and fun.

Acknowledgments

Writing a book is a long and challenging task, and we owe our thanks to a great number of people for their help. We would like to thank our reviewers, Professor G. R. Blakely, Wright State University, Professor Sharon Cabaniss, San Jose State University, Professor Phillip Hanlen, University of Michigan, Professor Herbert Kasube, Bradley University, Professor Joseph Klerlein, Western Carolina University, Professor Peter Tannenbaum, California State University at Fresno, Professor Andrew Vince, University of Florida, who patiently read the earlier versions of this book and gave us many helpful suggestions. We gratefully acknowledge Professor John Mitchem, San Jose State University, for his help in class testing this book, and we would also like to thank the many students at San Jose State University who helped us find and correct errors in the earlier versions of this book and Vivian Fink for assistance in proofreading. In addition, we would like to thank our editors, Tom Taylor and Chuck Glaser, our production team, Deborah Schneider of Schneider & Co., and our production supervisor, Karen Garrison, as well as the many other fine people at Addison-Wesley who helped us produce a book that not only looks good but also is as error-free as humanly possible. As authors we assume the full responsibility for any remaining errors and mistakes.

Note to the Instructor

In an elementary version of this course, an instructor can start with the basic counting techniques covered in Chapters 1–3. Chapter 1 reviews most of the basic ideas and problem-solving techniques needed throughout this course. A more advanced course could start from Chapter 2. A variety of different topic selections can be made for a one-semester course because Chapters 4, 5, 6, and 10, which cover many of the basic topics in graphs and algorithms, are for the most part independent of the remaining chapters. Generally, about two sections should be covered each week, and about seven or eight chapters can be covered in one semester.

Note to the Student

From a student's perspective, the most important objective in this course should be to try as many of the problems as possible. For convenience the problems have been divided into two sections. The problems in the first section are generally straightforward. Those in the second section (advanced problems) are more difficult, requiring some analysis, and of these the starred problems are generally the most difficult. Hints and answers to the odd-numbered problems (but not always complete solutions) are provided at the end of the book.

Ideally the student will also take courses in applied algebra, the theory of algorithms, and graph theory, which would expand on some of the topics covered in this book.

CONTENTS

COMBINATORIAL PROBLEM SOLVING

1.1 DEDUCTION

An Introduction to Combinatorics

Combinatorics is mainly concerned with the study of finite sets or discrete sets (like the set of positive integers) and various structures on these sets. Since the data stored in a computer must by necessity be finite and the algorithms performed by a computer must have a finite number of steps, many important applications of combinatorics are being discovered in the study of data structures and algorithms in computer science. Historically many applications of combinatorics also involve games and puzzles.

In combinatorics we will look at many different mathematical models that can be described using finite sets and their structures. We will study subsets, sequences, partitions, and so on, of the objects in these sets. For example, arrangements of 0's and 1's in a sequence are called binary sequences, and they are important in the study of computers and electrical circuits. We will also study assignments, distributions, relations, functions, and so on, between two sets. Most students have probably encountered, in one form or another, a one-to-one function from a finite set onto itself, which is called a permutation. Permutations are useful examples in combinatorics and many other branches of mathematics. We will also study the combinatorial version of a graph for relations and functions between two finite sets.

1

Since we look at finite sets in combinatorics, the techniques and models we encounter will in some sense be simple, however there will be many of these models and techniques. The end result is that few combinatorics problems can be handled routinely; that is, a combinatorics student must often be a creative problem solver. Also, combinatorics is often the right kind of mathematics to use to analyze computer algorithms. For that reason, problem solving and algorithms will be important topics throughout this course. In the remainder of Chapter 1 we look at problem solving in general, and then we review some basic facts pertinent to the study of combinatorics. We talk more about algorithms in Chapters 4, 6, and 10.

Problem Solving

Problem solving is part science and part art, but it is mainly hard work. This first chapter discusses a few basic problem-solving strategies. Throughout this course you will want to keep these in mind as you learn to solve the various kinds of problems that we encounter. However, any general problem-solving techniques that we learn will never compensate for a lack of knowledge and effort. The solution of any challenging problem often requires some crucial insight. Consequently you must work with the problem, observing patterns and facts, to put yourself in the right position to gain this insight. However, with each successful completion of a problem, your increased skill as a problem solver will make it that much easier to solve the next problem.

One of the two main mathematical methods of problem solving is called deduction. A deductive solution is a way of solving a problem or establishing the answer by a straightforward sequence of computations or logical deductions, working from the hypothesis to the conclusion.

DEFINITION **Deduction**

A deductive solution consists of three important parts:

1. Hypothesis: The start or setup of the problem.
2. Sequence of intermediate steps: Each step or calculation must be justified by previously established claims or other factual data.
3. Conclusion: The final statement that gives the answer to the problem.

When encountering a problem for the first time, we often know the start of the problem and the desired goal, and it is up to us to supply the sequence of intermediate steps. Some solutions occur naturally as a sequence, but in general it would be impossible to give a method for deriving all deductive solutions. Since problem solving is learned by looking at and analyzing the solutions of many problems, we start by giving the following examples of problems with deductive solutions.

Example 1   Consider the problem of slicing a 3 × 3 × 3 cube (like a Rubik's cube) into 27 smaller cubes. In Fig. 1.1, note that six cuts—two horizontal, two side to side, and two front to back—will suffice to cut apart the original cube. However, if the intermediate rearrangement of pieces (between cuts) is allowed, will fewer than six cuts suffice?

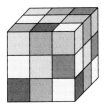

Figure 1.1

Solution
Concentrate on the 27 individual cubes and their positions in the original cube. One cut will make at most one new face on any individual cube. The corner cubes will thus require 3 cuts to be removed, since they start with three exposed faces. Similarly, the cubes in the center of an edge will require 4 cuts to be removed, the cubes in the center of a face will require 5 cuts, and the invisible center cube will require 6 cuts. Therefore no fewer than 6 cuts will suffice to cut apart the 3 × 3 × 3 cube, regardless of how the pieces are arranged between cuts. (See Problem 16 for a generalization of this example.)   ☐

The simple idea of parity is an important problem-solving concept with a wide variety of uses. In a typical application we divide a set of objects into two different types, for example, even or odd, and black or white (see also bipartite graphs in Chapter 5). However it can also be useful to divide a set of objects into more than two types; see equivalence relations and congruence modulo *n* in Section 1.3.

Example 2   The 64 squares of a regular chessboard can be covered easily by thirty-two 1 × 2 dominos in many ways. The chessboard in Fig. 1.2 is modified by removing diagonally opposite corners. Can the remaining squares of the modified chessboard be covered with thirty-one 1 × 2 dominos?

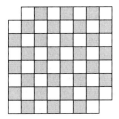

Figure 1.2

Solution

Since the squares of a chessboard are colored either black or white with adjacent squares receiving opposite colors, a single domino covers one white square and one black square no matter how it is placed. Thus 31 dominos would cover 31 squares of each color. However, diagonally opposite squares of a chessboard have the same color, so this modified chessboard must have 32 squares of one color and 30 of the other color. Therefore it is impossible to cover the squares of the modified chessboard with 31 dominos. (See Problem 18 for a variation of this example.)

$\square$

Example 3   Carl Friedrich Gauss was one of the most brilliant mathematicians of all time. As legend has it, young Gauss and his schoolmates were asked to compute the sum $1 + 2 + 3 + \cdots + 99 + 100$.

Solution

Gauss unexpectedly solved this problem in a few seconds using the following shortcut:

$$
\begin{array}{r}
1 + 2 + 3 + \cdots + 99 + 100 \\
100 + 99 + 98 + \cdots + 2 + 1 \\
\hline
101 + 101 + 101 + \cdots + 101 + 101 = 100(101) = 10{,}100
\end{array}
$$

Since twice the sum is $100(101)$, the solution to the original problem is $100(101)/2 = 5050$. In a similar manner, we can find the partial sum of any arithmetic sequence (see Problem 9).

$\square$

The Discovery of a Solution

In solving a problem, the discovery of the solution and the presentation of the solution are often two separate steps. In this chapter we will look at deduction and induction, the two main mathematical methods for presenting the solution of a problem. We will also encounter the following four important techniques for discovering the solution of a problem:

1. If possible, keep in mind both the hypothesis and the expected conclusion of the problem. Sometimes it is helpful to work forward from the hypothesis, and other times it is better to work backwards from the conclusion.

2. Experiment and search for a pattern. By working with small examples we sometimes gain insight into the general case.

3. Break a problem into smaller, related problems. A solution can be obtained sometimes by solving a slightly smaller problem and working up and other times by solving several smaller problems and combining them to obtain a solution to the original problem.

4. Reformulate the problem into another equivalent problem that is easier to solve. This is especially helpful if we are able to express the problem in terms of a basic mathematical model. Just using a convenient mathematical notation can be an important step.

Working Backwards

We usually encounter solutions written in their final polished form. Thus all the false starts and guesses have been eliminated. In writing a solution, the steps always proceed forward from the hypothesis to the conclusion. However, this sequence is often inappropriate for solving the problem because we often discover details in exactly the opposite order. Frequently the crucial insight is gained by looking at the goal and working backwards, rather than by working forward from the start. In either case, the solution is always written from start to finish and consequently may give no hint as to how the solution was discovered.

Example 4 A game involves a pile of 12 coins (as shown in Fig. 1.3) and two players who alternately take turns removing 1, 2, 3, or 4 coins from the pile. The player who removes the last coin(s) wins the game. How many coins should the first player remove in order to guarantee a win?

Figure 1.3

Solution

The game is hard to analyze from the start, so we concentrate on the end of the game. After his last turn, the first player would like to leave 0 coins remaining. To assure that he has the last turn, he should leave 5 coins on his next-to-last turn. The second player must remove at least 1 coin and no more than 4 coins, enabling the first player to win on the next move. On the turn before that, the first player should leave 10 coins to assure that he can leave 5 coins on his next turn. Thus on his first turn, the first player should remove 2 coins. (See problems 6 and 7 for other coin games.)

Example 5 Suppose we have empty 4-quart and 9-quart containers (as shown in Fig. 1.4) and an unlimited supply of water. If the containers can be used to measure 4 quarts and 9 quarts of water directly but not any intermediate amounts, give a sequence of steps that will allow us to measure out 6 quarts of water.

Figure 1.4

Solution
We let the ordered pair (i, j) represent the situation where i quarts of water are contained in the 4-quart container and j quarts of water are contained in the 9-quart container. From the start we can easily obtain the following situations:

$$(0,0) \to (0,9) \to (4,5) \to (0,5) \to (4,1) \to (0,1)$$

From the finish we can go back in the following manner:

$$(0,6) \to (4,6) \to (1,9) \to (1,0) \to (0,1)$$

It is easy to check that these can be joined to obtain the following overall solution:

$$(0,0) \to (0,9) \to (4,5) \to (0,5) \to (4,1) \to (0,1) \to (1,0) \to (1,9) \to (4,6) \to (0,6)$$

(See Problem 2 for another measuring problem, and consult the book by O'Beirne [8] for a variety of these problems.)   □

Example 6 Find all solutions of the equation $x + 1 = \sqrt{x^2 - 5}$.

Solution
First square both sides to eliminate the radical, and then solve the resulting equation $(x + 1)^2 = x^2 - 5$. The solutions of the original equation are always included in the solutions of the new equation, but not vice versa. The only solution of the new equation is $x = -3$, which is not a solution of the original equation. Thus we must not assume that backward steps can be performed in the forward direction, unless this is specifically checked.   □

1.1
PROBLEMS

1. Find all the roots of the equation $x + 2 = \sqrt{3x + 10}$.

2. Two men decide to share an 8-quart container of wine. Show how they can divide the wine into two equal parts if they are given unmarked, empty 3-quart and 5-quart containers (exactly one of each kind). [Tartaglia, 16th century]

3. Pick any number and perform the following sequence of operations. Add 6 to your number. Multiply the result by 2. Subtract 4. Divide by 2. Subtract your original number. What can you say about the result?

4. This number trick involves your favorite three-digit number and your age. Multiply your age by 7. Subtract 1 from the result. Multiply by 11. Add 8. Multiply by 13. Add your favorite three-digit number. Subtract your age. Add 39. Show that the last three digits are always your original three-digit number and the first digits are your age.

5. Consider a set of American coins. What is the largest amount of money in coins that we can have so that no subset of coins is worth exactly one dollar? *Hint:* It's greater than 99 cents. (For an answer to the question, how many different ways are there to make change for a dollar? See Section 7.2.)

6. One version of the game of Nim starts with two stacks of three coins. A player can remove any number of coins from one stack on their turn. The last player to remove a coin(s) wins the game. What strategy should the second player use so that she always wins the game?

7. In a certain game, two players take turns adding 1, 2, or 3 coins to a pile.
    a) Suppose that the pile starts with no coins and that the player who adds the 100th coin wins the entire pile. Which player should win and what strategy should he use?
    b) Repeat part (a) if the player who adds the 100th coin loses.

8. You are asked to find an integer someone else has chosen from the set $\{1, 2, 3, \ldots, 16\}$. You are allowed to ask any question that can be answered with a yes or a no. Show that you can always find the chosen number after your fourth question.

9. Compute the following sums:
    a) $1 + 2 + 3 + \cdots + n$
    b) $1 + 3 + 5 + \cdots + 2n - 1$
    c) $1 + 4 + 7 + \cdots + 3n - 2$
    d) $a + (a + d) + (a + 2d) + \cdots + (a + (n - 1)d)$

10.

n	1	2	3	4	5	6	7	8	9	10	11	12	13	14	15	16
$d(n)$	1	2	2	3	2	4	2	4	3	4	2	6	2	4	4	5

The preceding table contains values of $d(n)$, the number of different positive integer divisors of an integer n, for $1 \leq n \leq 16$. What can you notice about the integers with an odd number of divisors? Can you explain why this is always true?

ADVANCED PROBLEMS

11. Show that for any two positive real numbers a and b, $(a + b)/2 \geq \sqrt{ab}$, with equality holding if and only if $a = b$. (Arithmetic Mean–Geometric Mean Inequality)

12. Twenty-five students are seated in a square arrangement with 5 rows of 5 desks each. The teacher tells all the students to switch desks so that every student is switched to a desk either directly to the front, to the back, to the right, or to the left of their original desk. Can all the students switch to a new desk simultaneously?

13. A $3 \times 3 \times 3$ cube is cut into 27 small cubes that are 1 inch on each side. The 27 cubes are then glued to form thirteen $1 \times 1 \times 2$ bricks and then the extra cube is thrown away. Can these 13 bricks be used to reconstruct the original cube with an invisible hole in the center?

14. At a party there are truthtellers (people who always tell the truth), liars (people who always lie), and normals (people who sometimes lie and sometimes tell the truth). The following conversation between Brad (a known truthteller) and

Bob (a known liar) is overheard at a party:

> Bob: Tom is normal.
> Brad: One of Tom, Dick, and Harry is a truthteller, one is a liar, and one is a normal.
> Bob: Dick is a truthteller.
> Brad: Tom is a math major and he says $2^5 = 32$.
> Bob: Harry is a liar.

What can you deduce about Tom, Dick, and Harry?

15. At a party there are two truthtellers and one normal person. Assuming that the three know all about each other and each person must answer any yes-no questions that she is asked, show how to find the normal person using only two questions.

16. a) A $4 \times 4 \times 4$ cube is to be cut into sixty-four $1 \times 1 \times 1$ cubes. What is the minimum number of cuts needed if intermediate arrangement of the resulting pieces is allowed?

    *b) What is the minimum number of cuts needed to cut an $n \times n \times n$ cube into n^3 $1 \times 1 \times 1$ cubes?

17. There are n teams in a basketball tournament.
a) In a round-robin tournament, each team plays every other team exactly once. How many games are played?
b) In a single-elimination tournament, a team is eliminated from further play after its first loss. How many games are played until a single team (the champion) remains?
c) In a double elimination tournament, a team is eliminated from further play after its second loss. How many games must be played until a single team remains (there are two possibilities)?

*18. From an 8×8 chessboard, one black square and one white square are removed. Show that the remaining 62 squares can always be covered by 31 dominos.

1.1
SUPPLEMENTARY
COMPUTER
PROJECT

1. Wythoff's Game

Invented in 1907, Wythoff's Game for two players might remind you of the better known game of Nim. We start with two piles, each containing any number of coins. We denote by (x, y) the current status of the game if there are x coins in the first pile and y coins in the second pile. We might as well assume that $x \leq y$ because we can always interchange the two piles. The players

---

* Problems preceded by the symbol * are usually the most difficult of the advanced problems.

alternately remove coins from the piles in accordance with the following rules:

1. Remove an arbitrary number of coins from either the first or the second pile, or

2. Remove the same number of coins from both piles.

The winner is the person who takes the last coin.

To develop a winning strategy, we begin by saying that (x, y) is a winning position for you if regardless of your opponent's move on subsequent turns, you are guaranteed of ultimately winning (provided you follow an appropriate strategy). On the other hand, (x, y) is a losing position for your opponent if your next move can lead to a winning position for you.

We denote by W the set of winning positions. Wythoff showed that $W = \{(1, 2), (3, 5), (4, 7), (6, 10), \ldots\}$. If we let (c_n, d_n) represent the nth pair in W, Wythoff noted that this ordered pair could be determined in the following way. Let the first coordinate c_n equal the smallest positive integer that doesn't appear in the first $n - 1$ pairs and let $d_n = c_n + n$.

a) Show that $\Delta c_k = c_{k+1} - c_k$ always equals 1 or 2. Deduce that $c_{100} < 200$ and $d_{100} < 300$.

b) Use the fact that $d_{100} < 300$ to construct a program for listing the ordered pairs (c_n, d_n) up to $n = 100$. **Hint:** Let A be the vector $(a_1, a_2, \ldots, a_{200})$, initially set equal to $(0, 0, \ldots, 0)$. The coordinate a_i is set equal to 1 after i has been used in one of the ordered pairs, before the next pair is chosen.

c) Print the ratios c_j/j and d_j/c_j for $1 \le j \le 100$.

d) Let $C = \{c_1, c_2, \ldots, c_n, \ldots\}$ and $D = \{d_1, d_2, \ldots, d_n, \ldots\}$. Show that every positive integer is contained either in C or in D, but not both.

e) Show that (c_n, d_n) is a winning position for every positive integer n.

f) Let x and y be any positive integers. If (x, y) is not in W, show that (x, y) is a losing position.

g) We denote by t the quantity $(1 + \sqrt{5})/2$. Wythoff also noted that $c_j = [jt]$ and $d_j = [jt^2]$, where $[x]$ equals the greatest integer less than or equal to x. Use a computer to verify this observation for all positive integers $j \le 100$.

SECTION 1.2 INDUCTION

Another important technique used in problem solving is called induction. It is certainly one of the most useful techniques in combinatorial mathematics and computer science. Again, we differentiate between the discovery of a solution and its presentation.

In science we are often concerned with the search for facts by observation and experimentation, and this is usually called the experimental method.

DEFINITION   The Experimental Method

The experimental method consists of the following three steps:

1. Perform experiments and collect data.
2. Find a pattern in the data.
3. Make a conjecture explaining the pattern.

The experimental method is also useful in mathematics. When solving a problem, it is frequently useful to examine special cases and search for a pattern, which is the second technique for discovering the solution of a problem that we mentioned in Section 1.1. Often we arrive at a conjecture that appears to answer a problem for all positive integers n. However, the conjecture will need to be checked before we can put much faith in it. We cannot be absolutely certain that a conjecture is always true simply by verifying it for several integers, no matter how many integers we try.

Example 1   Find the sum of the first 100 odd integers.

Solution
Rather than immediately computing the entire sum, we first look at the partial sums and the following pattern emerges:

$$1 = 1$$
$$1 + 3 = 4$$
$$1 + 3 + 5 = 9$$
$$1 + 3 + 5 + 7 = 16$$
$$\vdots$$

The sums are squares of consecutive positive integers starting with 1. From our observation it appears likely that the sum of the first 100 odd numbers equals $100^2 = 10,000$. In general, we might conjecture (correctly, it turns out) that the sum of the first n odd numbers is n^2. (See Problem 9 in Section 1.1 and Fig. 1.5.) Therefore, $1 + 3 + 5 + \cdots + 199 = 10,000$. (Can you explain why the 100th odd number is 199? See Problem 3.)

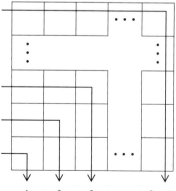

Figure 1.5 $1 + 3 + 5 + \cdots + 2n-1 = n^2$

To be sure that a statement is always true, it must be proved. It will never be enough to verify it for a number of cases. Sometimes patterns just stop or are more complicated than they first seem, as is illustrated by the following example.

Example 2   Suppose n mutually overlapping circles are drawn on a plane so that no three circles meet at a common point. How many regions are formed by these circles?

Solution
Let $r(n)$ stand for the number of regions formed by n circles. A little experimentation shows that $r(0) = 1, r(1) = 2, r(2) = 4,$ and $r(3) = 8$. We might conjecture from this experimental data that $r(n) = 2^n$. However this formula does not hold when a fourth circle is added, as in Fig. 1.6. The fourth circle must intersect each of the first three circles twice. Every time it intersects a circle, it enters a new region. Therefore, it goes through exactly six of the original regions. Since these regions are each divided into two smaller regions by the fourth circle, a total of 14 regions are created, not 16. In a similar way, the nth circle $(n > 1)$ drawn will always add $2(n-1)$ regions. By iterating this process, we see that $r(n) = 2 + 2 + 4 + 6 + \cdots + 2(n-1) = 2 + 2(1 + 2 + 3 + \cdots + n - 1)$. Thus $r(n) = 2 + 2n(n-1)/2 = n^2 - n + 2$, for $n \geq 1$.

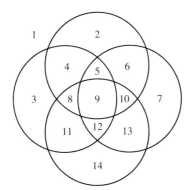

Figure 1.6

The preceding example shows why discovering a solution and proving it are considered to be separate parts of the problem-solving process. The technique of induction gives a powerful method for proving that certain conjectures are always true. Let k be a fixed integer, usually 1 for most problems. Suppose that for each integer $n \geq k$ we have a corresponding statement $P(n)$. The method of induction shows that $P(n)$ is true for all integers $n \geq k$ if the following statements are true.

DEFINITION   (Ordinary) Induction
An inductive solution consists of the following three steps:

1. **Initial step:** Verify that $P(k)$ is true.
2. **Induction hypothesis:** Assume that $P(n)$ is true for some $n \geq k$.
3. **Induction step:** Using the induction hypothesis, show that $P(n+1)$ is true.

Induction is thus an algorithmic method of proving that a solution is always correct. We start by showing that an initial statement is true, and then show how it is always possible to derive any statement (except the first) from the previous statements. If we thought of putting the preceding steps in a computer program, the computer could be used to prove that the statement $P(n)$ was true for any $n \geq k$ as long as the program was allowed to run long enough.

The program would first verify that $P(k)$ is true. Since $P(k)$ is true, it would then show that $P(k + 1)$ is true. Once $P(k + 1)$ was shown to be true, it would then show that $P(k + 2)$ is true, and so on, always proceeding one step at a time. Unlike the situation where we just tried a few values of n, every value of n would eventually be reached (in a finite amount of time), so we need not worry about some mysterious point where the pattern changes and $P(n)$ is no longer true.

The problems in the following examples can be solved inductively.

Example 3 Show that $f(n) = n^3 + 2n$ is a multiple of 3 for all positive integers n.

Solution
a) Note that $f(1) = 3 = 3(1)$ is a multiple of 3.
b) Assume that $f(n)$ is a multiple of 3.
c) In particular, $f(n) = n^3 + 2n = 3m$, for some integer m. Thus

$$f(n + 1) = (n + 1)^3 + 2(n + 1)$$
$$= n^3 + 3n^2 + 3n + 1 + 2n + 2$$
$$= f(n) + 3(n^2 + n + 1)$$
$$= 3(m + n^2 + n + 1)$$

This completes the inductive proof that $f(n)$ is always a multiple of 3 for any $n \geq 1$. □

Example 4 For any $n \geq 4$, show that $n! = n(n - 1)(n - 2)\cdots 1 > 2^n$.

Solution
a) $4! = 24 > 2^4 = 16$
b) Assume that $n! > 2^n$, for some $n \geq 4$.
c) Thus we see that $(n + 1)! = (n + 1)n! > (n + 1)2^n > 2(2^n) = 2^{n+1}$.
Therefore, the inequality is true for all $n \geq 4$. □

Example 5 **The Tower of Hanoi Puzzle**
A puzzle consists of three pegs and n circular disks of increasing diameter on one peg, with the largest disk on the bottom of the peg. (See Fig. 1.7.) The disks can be moved one at a time to another peg as long as a disk is not placed on top of one with a smaller diameter. The goal of the puzzle is to transfer the stack of n disks entirely from one peg to another, using a sequence of legal moves. Show that, for any $n \geq 1$, the Tower of Hanoi puzzle with n disks can be solved.

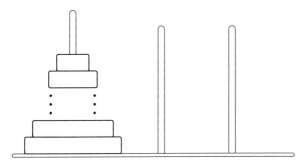

Figure 1.7

Solution
a) For 1 disk, the puzzle can be solved in one move.
b) Assume the puzzle can be solved for n disks.
c) Solve the puzzle for $n + 1$ disks.
First, transfer the top n disks to a vacant peg using the solution for the n-disk puzzle. Then, transfer the largest disk to the other vacant peg. Finally, restack the n disks on top of the largest disk, once again using the solution of the n-disk puzzle. By induction, any number of disks can be transferred from one peg to another. (We will return to this puzzle in Example 6. See Problem 28 for a variation of this puzzle.)

Sequences

In this book the word "sequence" often refers to an ordered list of real numbers. We usually consider sequences whose terms are numbered consecutively by non-negative integers. In the sequence $a_0, a_1, a_2, \ldots, a_n, \ldots$, the number a_0 is often called the initial term. Chapter 7 demonstrates why it is more convenient in combinatorics to think of a sequence starting with a_0 rather than a_1, which might seem more natural since the nth term would then be a_n.

Many facts about sequences can be proved using induction. The term a_n in a sequence is often described using a general formula $a_n = f(n)$. For example, the sequence $1, 2, 4, 8, 16, \ldots$ is described by the formula $a_n = 2^n$.

Arithmetic and Geometric Sequences

Another way of describing a sequence is by giving a general rule called a recurrence relation for computing a term from the previous ones. The following familiar kinds of sequences can be described in terms of recurrence relations. In an arithmetic sequence, one term is obtained from the previous one by adding a common difference d. In other words, $a_n = a_{n-1} + d$. In a geometric sequence, one term is obtained from the previous one by multiplying it times a common ratio r. In other words, $a_n = r(a_{n-1})$.

Another more complicated recurrence relation can be obtained by reexamining the Tower of Hanoi puzzle from Example 5. Let a_n represent the number of moves required to solve the n-disk puzzle using our recursive method. (In fact, it is easy to show that this sequence gives us the smallest number of moves needed to solve the n-disk puzzle.) The solution for the $n + 1$-disk puzzle involved using the solution of the n-disk puzzle twice to move the smallest n disks plus a single move of the largest disk. Thus we obtain the recurrence relation $a_{n+1} = 2a_n + 1$. Since it takes a single move to solve the 1-disk puzzle, we obtain $a_1 = 1, a_2 = 3, a_3 = 7, a_4 = 15, \ldots$. We would probably conjecture that a_n is always equal to $2^n - 1$, but to be certain, we must supply a proof.

Example 6 For the sequence defined by the recurrence relation $a_{n+1} = 2a_n + 1$ and $a_1 = 1$, show that $a_n = 2^n - 1$, for all $n \geq 1$.

Solution
a) $a_1 = 1 = 2^1 - 1$
b) Assume that $a_n = 2^n - 1$.
c) Thus $a_{n+1} = 2a_n + 1 = 2(2^n - 1) + 1 = 2(2^n) - 2 + 1 = 2^{n+1} - 1$, and the conjecture is proved for all $n \geq 1$.   □

Note that we can also see how the formula in Example 6 might be discovered systematically by iterating the recurrence. Repeated application of the recurrence shows that $a_1 = 1; a_2 = 2 + 1; a_3 = 2^2 + 2 + 1, \ldots, a_n = 2^{n-1} + \cdots + 2^2 + 2 + 1$, thus expressing a_n as the sum of a geometric sequence. A standard way of obtaining a formula for this sum directly starts with multiplying by the common ratio 2 to obtain the sum $2^n + \cdots + 2^3 + 2^2 + 2$. Taking the difference, we obtain $2a_n - a_n = (2^n + \cdots + 2^3 + 2^2 + 2) - (2^{n-1} + \cdots + 2^2 + 2 + 1) = 2^n - 1$ as before.

Finding formulas is definitely an important topic in combinatorics. We shall see later how to obtain such formulas for many sequences. However, at this point, it is sometimes more difficult to discover a formula than to prove that it is actually correct. As we learn more counting techniques, it will become easier to discover formulas. Some of these techniques such as generating functions (Chapter 7) and recurrence relations (Chapter 8) will naturally lend themselves to finding formulas. Sometimes we just need to compute the answer to a problem in two different ways to find an interesting formula.

Sigma Notation

Another frequently encountered problem concerns finding a formula for the partial sums of a sequence. We will often use the sigma notation $\sum_{i=j}^{k} f(i)$ to represent the sum $f(j) + f(j + 1) + \cdots + f(k - 1) + f(k)$.

Example 7 Consider the problem of finding the sum of the first n squares, $1^2 + 2^2 + \cdots + n^2$, which we represent by $S_n = \sum_{i=1}^{n} i^2$.

Solution
Remember that we have already encountered the sum $T_n = 1 + 2 + \cdots + n = n(n + 1)/2$. We give the following method of Polya for discovering a formula for S_n. List the values for n, T_n, and S_n in a small table.

n	1	2	3	4	5	6	7
T_n	1	3	6	10	15	21	28
S_n	1	5	14	30	55	91	140
S_n/T_n	$1 = 3/3$	$5/3$	$7/3$	$3 = 9/3$	$11/3$	$13/3$	$5 = 15/3$

In searching for a pattern, we might eventually try the ratio S_n/T_n. When this ratio is written as a fraction with denominator 3, the numerator increases by 2 each time. We might conjecture that $S_n/(n(n + 1)/2) = (2n + 1)/3$, and that $S_n = n(n + 1) \times (2n + 1)/6$. We now prove by induction that $\sum_{i=1}^{n} i^2 = n(n + 1)(2n + 1)/6$, for all $n \geq 1$.
a) For $n = 1$, we see that $1^2 = 1 \times 2 \times 3/6$.
b) Assume that $1^2 + 2^2 + \cdots + n^2 = n(n + 1)(2n + 1)/6$.
c) Then $1^2 + 2^2 + \cdots + n^2 + (n + 1)^2 = n(n + 1)(2n + 1)/6 + (n + 1)^2 =$
   $(n + 1)(2n^2 + 7n + 6)/6 = (n + 1)(n + 2)(2n + 3)/6$.
Therefore, the formula holds for all $n \geq 1$.   □

Strong Induction and Numbers (Optional)

Another technique that is useful for proving that a conjecture $P(n)$ is true for all $n \geq k$ is called strong induction. In this case the ordinary induction hypothesis is replaced by the following stronger hypothesis.

DEFINITION   **Strong Induction**
A proof by strong induction uses the following three steps:
1. Initial step: Verify that $P(k)$ is true.
2. Strong induction hypothesis: For some $n \geq k$, assume that $P(k), P(k + 1), \ldots, P(n)$ are all true.
3. Induction step: Use the induction hypothesis to show that $P(n + 1)$ is true.

We use strong induction to prove some basic results about integers.

Properties of Integers

Suppose $n \neq 0$ and m are integers. If an integer q exists such that $nq = m$, we say that n divides m, or n is a divisor of m, or m is a multiple of n. A positive integer p that has exactly two positive divisors is called a prime.

THEOREM 1.1   **(Division Theorem)**
If a and $b > 0$ are integers, there exists an integer q called the quotient and an integer r called the remainder such that $a = qb + r$ and $0 \leq r < b$.

Proof
First suppose that a is nonnegative. We proceed using strong induction on a. If $a < b$, then $a = 0(b) + a$. In particular, the result is true for $a = 0$. Assume

the result holds for all $0 \leq a \leq n$. Without loss of generality we can assume that $b \leq n$. In that case, $0 < (n + 1) - b = q'b + r'$. Therefore, $n + 1 = (q' + 1)b + r'$, and the division theorem holds for all nonnegative integers. If $a < 0$, then $-a = qb + r$. Thus $a = -qb - r$. When $r = 0$, $a = -qb$, and when $r > 0$, $a = (-q - 1)b + (b - r)$. If $b > r > 0$, then $b > b - r > 0$ and the division theorem holds for all integers. (We can also show that the quotient q and the remainder r are unique, but we omit this proof.)

When analyzing a problem involving an integer it is often helpful to express the integer as a product of primes.

THEOREM 1.2 **(Fundamental Theorem of Arithmetic)**

Every integer $n > 1$ can be expressed as $n = p_1 p_2 \cdots p_m$, where each p_i is a prime.

Proof

If n is itself a prime, the result is obvious and in particular the result holds for $n = 2$. Assume that the result is true for all $2 \leq k \leq n$. Either $n + 1$ is a prime or $n + 1 = ab$, where $2 \leq a, b \leq n$. In the second case, our assumption shows that both a and b can be expressed as a product of primes, so the combined product expresses $n + 1$ as a product of primes. (Note that it can also be shown that the preceding primes are unique where two factorizations are considered to be the same if they consist of the same primes in a different order.)

For any real number x, we denote by $[x]$ the greatest integer less than or equal to x. This notation is often used to simplify computations. For example, if n and d are positive integers, then $[n/d]$ of the integers $1, 2, 3, \ldots, n$ are divisible by d (see 1.2 Supplementary Computer Projects, number 3).

Example 8 Find the number of 0's at the end of 1000!.

Solution

Every terminal 0 corresponds to a factor of 10, so we write $1000! = 2^x 5^y z$, where z is a product of primes other than 2 and 5. Since each 10 consists of a single 2 and a single 5 multiplied together, the number of zeros at the end of 1000! equals the minimum of x and y. Clearly $x > y$ (see Supplementary Computer Projects, number 3(a)) so the required answer can be obtained by computing y. In the product $1 \times 2 \times 3 \cdots 998 \times 999 \times 1000$ every fifth number is a multiple of 5, so there are $[1000/5] = 200$ multiples of 5 that contribute a 5 to the product. There are also $[1000/25] = 40$ multiples of 25 that contribute an additional 5. There are $[1000/125] = 8$ multiples of 125 that contribute a third 5, and $[1000/625] = 1$ multiple of 625 that contributes a fourth 5. Therefore the total number of 5's in the prime factorization of 1000! is $200 + 40 + 8 + 1 = 249$, which means that 1000! ends with 249 zeros. ☐

Number Systems and Binary Numbers

In our usual decimal notation we represent a number by a sequence of the 10 digits $0, 1, 2, \ldots, 9$, and the position of each digit determines its contribution to the total value of the number represented. For example, 5314 is a shorthand way of representing the number $5 \times 10^3 + 3 \times 10^2 + 1 \times 10 + 4$. In a similar way, any positive integer b greater than 1 can be used as a base for a number system.

The **binary number system** is the system for representing numbers using the base b, where $b = 2$. In this system the only possible digits are 0 and 1. This base is widely used in computers since the choice of a 0 or a 1 can be indicated by the presence or absence of an electrical current flowing in a given circuit. Binary numbers are also useful in combinatorics.

The following theorem shows that it is always possible to represent an integer using any base b, where $b > 1$.

THEOREM 1.3

If b is any integer greater than 1, every integer $a > 0$ can be uniquely represented in the form $a = r_n b^n + r_{n-1} b^{n-1} + \cdots + r_1 b + r_0$, where $r_n \neq 0$, and $0 \leq r_i < b$ for $i = 0, 1, 2, \ldots, n$.

Proof
For any positive integer $a < b$ it is easy to represent a using base b, by taking $n = 0$ and $r_0 = a$, and this representation is obviously unique. Now suppose that $a \geq b$ and let us assume that every positive integer less than a has a unique representation using base b. By the Division Theorem, we have a unique remainder $0 \leq r < b$ and quotient $0 < q < a$ such that $a = q \cdot b + r$. If $q = s_m b^m + \cdots + s_1 b + s_0$ is the base b representation of q, then $a = (s_m b^m + \cdots + s_1 b + s_0)b + r = s_m b^{m+1} + \cdots s_1 b^2 + s_0 b + r$ is the base b representation of a. The uniqueness of this representation follows directly from the uniqueness in Theorem 1.1.

Just as we usually omit the powers of 10 in ordinary decimal notation, we may also do this when using a base other than 10. If $a = r_n b^n + \cdots + r_1 b + r_0$, we write $a = (r_n r_{n-1} \cdots r_1 r_0)_b$ to indicate the representation of a using base b. The proof of the preceding theorem suggests an easy way to obtain the representation of a number a using a given base b. It is only necessary to compute the remainders obtained from dividing a successively by b.

Example 9   Represent 115_{10} in base 3 notation.

Solution
We perform the successive divisions as follows, $115 = 3(38) + 1$, $38 = 3(12) + 2$, $12 = 4(3) + 0$, $4 = 3(1) + 1$, $1 = 0(3) + 1$. Thus the base 3 representation of 115_{10} is 11021_3. In other words, $115 = 1 \cdot 81 + 1 \cdot 27 + 0 \cdot 9 + 2 \cdot 3 + 1$.   □

1.2
PROBLEMS

1. A piece of paper starts out 0.03 inches thick. Its thickness is doubled each time it is folded in half. If it could be folded in half 12 times, how thick would it be?

2. The inventor of the game of chess requested a reward from the king of Persia. He requested a single cent on the first square of the board, two cents on the second square, four cents on the third square, and double the amount on each successive square.
    a) Find a formula for the number of cents on the nth square.
    b) Find a formula for the total number of cents on the first n squares.

3. a) Suppose that an arithmetic sequence starts with a_0 and satisfies the recurrence $a_n = a_{n-1} + d$ for every positive integer n. Show that $a_n = a_0 + nd$.
    b) Find the 200th number in the sequence $13, 16, 19, \ldots$.
    c) Find the 1000th positive odd integer.

4. Suppose that a geometric sequence starts with a_0 and satisfies $a_n = r(a_{n-1})$ for every positive integer n.
    a) Show that $a_n = a_0(r^n)$.
    b) Find the 20th number in the sequence $3, 6, 12, \ldots$.

Show by induction that the following formulas hold:

5. $\displaystyle\sum_{i=1}^{n} i(i!) = (n+1)! - 1$

6. $\displaystyle\sum_{i=1}^{n} i^3 = n^2(n+1)^2/4$

7. $\displaystyle\sum_{i=1}^{n} (2i-1)^3 = n^2(2n^2-1)$

8. $a + ar + ar^2 + ar^3 + \cdots + ar^{n-1} = (a - ar^n)/(1-r)$

9. $\displaystyle\sum_{i=1}^{n} i(i+1) = n(n+1)(n+2)/3$

10. Find a formula for $\displaystyle\sum_{i=1}^{n} 1/(i(i+1))$ and prove that it holds for all $n \geq 1$.

11. Find a formula for $\displaystyle\sum_{i=1}^{n} i/(i+1)!$ and prove that it holds for all $n \geq 1$.

12. A ball is dropped from a height of 4 feet, and each time it hits the ground it rebounds to 3/4 the previous height. What is the total distance the ball will have traveled (up and down) when it reaches the top of its tenth rebound?

13. At the beginning of each year, 100 dollars is deposited into a savings account. At the end of each year, 5% interest is paid on all the money that was in the account at the beginning of the year. Give a formula for the amount of money in the account at the beginning of year n.

14. a) Show that none of the integers $2, 3, \ldots, n$ divides $n! + 1$.
    b) Show that none of the $n - 1$ consecutive integers $n! + 2, n! + 3, \ldots, n! + n$ is prime.

15. Show that the terms of the sequence that satisfy $a_n = 5a_{n-1} - 6a_{n-2}$ and $a_1 = 5, a_2 = 13$ are given by the formula $a_n = 2^n + 3^n$, for all $n \geq 1$.

16. Express 373_{10}
    a) Using base 2 (binary) notation.
    b) Using base 8 notation.
    c) Using base 11 notation (with X to represent the digit 10).

ADVANCED
PROBLEMS

17. Let $f(n) = n^2 + n + 41$. Notice that $f(n)$, for each $n = 0, 1, 2, \ldots, 39$ is a prime number greater than or equal to 41.
    a) Show that $f(40)$ is not a prime.
    *b) Show that $f(x)$, x a nonnegative integer, has no prime divisors smaller than 41.

18. The sequence of Fibonacci numbers is defined by $F_1 = F_2 = 1$, and $F_{k+1} = F_k + F_{k-1}$, for each $k > 2$.
    a) Show that F_{5k} is always a multiple of 5.
    b) If $a = (1 + \sqrt{5})/2$ and $b = (1 - \sqrt{5})/2$, show that $F_n = (a^n - b^n)/(a - b)$. [Binet's Formula]
    c) Let $R_n = F_{n+1}/F_n$. Prove that $R_{2n-1} < R_{2n+1} < R_{2n+2} < R_{2n}$.

19. For any positive integer n and real number $x > -1$, show that $(1 + x)^n \geq 1 + nx$. [Bernoulli's Inequality]

20. For any positive integer n, show that $2^{2n} - 1$ is divisible by 3.

21. Using only three-cent and five-cent stamps show that one can always make n cents postage for any $n \geq 8$.

22. Show that the terms of the sequence that satisfy $a_n = 3a_{n-1} - 2$ and $a_1 = 4$ are given by the formula $a_n = 3^n + 1$, for all $n \geq 1$.

23. a) Show that for any $n \geq 5$, $n^2 > 4n + 1$.
    b) Show that for any $n \geq 5$, $2^n > n^2$.

24. Show that for all integers n (first show for all positive integers)
    a) $n^3 + (n + 1)^3 + (n + 2)^3$ is a multiple of 9.
    b) $n^3 + 5n$ is a multiple of 6.

25. Show by induction that, for any positive integer k, the product of k consecutive integers is always a multiple of $k!$.

26. a) Count the number of squares of all sizes $1 \times 1, 2 \times 2, 3 \times 3, \ldots, 8 \times 8$ that can be constructed from the squares of a regular 8×8 chessboard if all possible squares are counted.
    b) Count the number of squares of all sizes $1 \times 1, 2 \times 2, 3 \times 3, \ldots, n \times n$ that can be constructed from the squares of an $n \times n$ chessboard.

*27. Let $a_1, a_2, \ldots, a_n$ be positive real numbers. Show that

$$(a_1 + a_2 + a_3 + \cdots + a_n)/n \geq (a_1 a_2 \cdots a_n)^{1/n}$$

with equality if and only if $a_1 = a_2 = \cdots = a_n$. [Arithmetic Mean–Geometric Mean Inequality] (**Hint:** First prove for all integers $n = 2^m$.)

28. In a linear version of the Tower of Hanoi puzzle, all three pegs are in a straight line. The stack of n disks starts on one side and is to be transferred to the far side. This version of the puzzle allows only moves from one peg to an *adjacent* peg. Show that this linear version of the Tower of Hanoi puzzle can also be solved for any number of disks.

∗29. a) Show that any integer n can be expressed as a sum of powers of three, $n = y_i 3^i + \cdots + y_1 3^1 + y_0 3^0$, where each coefficient y_j is either $-1, 0$, or 1. (We refer to this as the balanced ternary system.)
   b) Show that with four well-chosen weights and an equal arm balance, we can weigh any integral weight from 1 to 40 pounds if weights can be placed on both sides of the balance.

∗30. For any positive integer n, show that a $2^n \times 2^n$ chessboard with a single corner removed can be completely covered by nonoverlapping L-shaped triominos.

31. Show that there are infinitely many primes. **Hint:** If $p_1, p_2, \ldots, p_n$ are primes, consider $p_1 p_2 \ldots p_n + 1$.

32. Show that any positive integer $i \geq 1$ can be represented uniquely as a sum of the form $a_1 1! + a_2 2! + \cdots + a_{n-1}(n-1)! + a_n n!$, where a_j is an integer satisfying $0 \leq a_j \leq j$, for $j = 1, 2, \ldots, n$.

1.2
SUPPLEMENTARY COMPUTER PROJECTS

1. A Gravity Sort
Sixteen 3×5 index cards are labeled A, B, C, ..., P. Four holes are punched in the upper right-hand corner of each card (as shown in Fig. 1.8).

Figure 1.8

Figure 1.9

   If the cards are in random order, we would like to return them to alphabetical order using the following procedure. Prepare the cards by slitting some holes as shown in Fig. 1.9. (You have to determine which holes to slit.)

   The cards are stacked in a deck, which is held vertically. A pencil is run through the rightmost hole and then lifted, permitting some cards to fall. These cards are placed in the back of the deck. Then the procedure is repeated using the next hole to the left and so on. (Gravity does all the work!)

a) Which holes should be slit?
b) Show that the procedure works for your choice.

2. **Converting to Binary**
    For a given decimal integer n, write a computer program that determines the binary representation of n.

3. **The Greatest Integer Function**
    For any real number x we denote by $[x]$, the greatest integer less than or equal to x. In combinatorics, the greatest integer function can often be used to simplify computations. For example, how many multiples of 5 does $S = \{1, 2, 3, \ldots, n\}$ contain? If $n = 50 = 5 \cdot 10$, the answer is clearly 10. When n is not a multiple of 5, we may write $n = 5t + r$, where $1 \leq r \leq 4$. Thus there are t multiples of 5, where $t = [n/5]$. In general, for positive integers n and d, $[n/d]$ of the integers $1, 2, 3, \ldots, n$ are divisible by d.

a) Find the highest power of 2 that divides 1000! (completing Example 8).

What information about a positive real number x can be determined by the following questions?

b) Is $x = [x]$?
c) Is $x = [\sqrt{x}]^2$?
d) Is $x = 3[x/3]$?

   To find $[x]$ when $x \geq 0$, simply discard the fractional part of x. Thus $[\pi] = 3$, $[7.0] = 7$, and so on. This procedure is called truncation. However $[-\pi] = -4$, not -3, since $-4 < \pi < -3$. Unfortunately, when the function $\mathrm{INT}(x)$ is used in Basic, FORTRAN, and in different programmable calculators sometimes it is the same as $[x]$ and sometimes you get truncation.

Some elementary properties of $[x]$ are suggested by the following questions. Let x and y be real and let m be an integer.

e) When will $0 \leq x - [x] < 1$?
f) When will $[x + m] = [x] + m$?
g) Compare $[x] + [y]$ and $[x + y]$.
h) When will $[x] + [-x] = -1$?
i) When will $[[x]/m] = [x/m]$?

Suppose you wish to write a code to "round" a given positive number x to a specific "decimal place" d as follows:

x	d	Desired Output R
π	4	3.1416
.01293	3	.013
23.67	0	24.

j) For a given x and d, describe a simple way to compute R.

k) Suppose n is a (large) positive integer "in memory." Use the greatest integer function to show that a single assignment statement may be used to obtain the number of decimal digits in n. **Hint:** Use another well-known function.

4. Fibonacci/Lucas Excursions

The Fibonacci numbers (F_i) and the Lucas numbers (L_i) are

$$\begin{array}{cccccc} F_1 & F_2 & F_3 & F_4 & F_5 & F_6 \cdots \\ 1 & 1 & 2 & 3 & 5 & 8 \ \cdots \end{array} \quad \text{and} \quad \begin{array}{cccccc} L_1 & L_2 & L_3 & L_4 & L_5 & L_6 \cdots \\ 1 & 3 & 4 & 7 & 11 & 18 \ \cdots \end{array}$$

where each number in either sequence is equal to the sum of the two preceding numbers.

a) Write a program that determines if a given positive integer n is a Fibonacci number.

b) Write a program that finds, for a given positive integer n, the number of terms in the Fibonacci sequence that are less than or equal to n.

c) Let a and b be given as in Problem 18(b) of this section. There we obtained the Binet form of $F_n = (a^n - b^n)/(a - b)$. Use a computer or calculator to discover a similar formula for L_n. **Hint:** Work with a^n and b^n. Can you prove that this formula always works?

d) For small values of n it appears that $F_n = [(a^n/(a - b)) + 1/2]$. (Note that only half as many multiplications are required.) Use a computer to investigate this conjecture for all $n \le 25$. Can you prove that this formula always works? **Hint:** What do you think is true for $|F_n - a^n/(a - b)|$? Find a similar formula that uses the greatest integer function to compute L_n.

e) Of course, $F_{n+1} = F_n + F_{n-1}$, for $n \ge 2$. But can we express F_{n+1} in terms of F_n alone? **Hint:** Try $F_{n+1} = [c_1 F_n + c_2]$.

SECTION
1.3 SETS AND RELATIONS

Sets

Any well-defined collection of objects A is called a **set**. An object x is either in the set A or it is not in the set A. (Some authors in combinatorics allow multisets, but we do not.) If x is in A, we will also say that x is an **element** of A, and write $x \in A$.

A set can be described by listing all its elements or by giving a defining property

$P(x)$ so that precisely the elements of A satisfy $P(x)$. In this case we write $A = \{x \mid P(x)\}$. For example, $A = \{1, 2, 3, 4, 5\}$ can also be denoted by $A = \{x \mid x$ is a positive integer and $x \leq 5\}$.

Subsets

We say that a set B is contained in A or that B is a **subset** of A, written $B \subseteq A$, if for every object $x \in B$ it is also true that $x \in A$. Any set A is a subset of itself and one set, $\varnothing$, called the empty set because it has no elements, is also considered to be a subset of any set A. We denote by 2^A the set consisting of all the subsets of A. For two sets A and B, we say that $A = B$ if A and B have precisely the same elements, that is, if $x \in A$, then $x \in B$, and if $x \notin A$, then $x \notin B$.

Venn Diagrams

There are several useful ways of combining sets to get other sets. They can best be pictured by the use of a special diagram called a Venn diagram. In general, it is convenient to assume that there is some large set X containing all the sets in question. This set is sometimes called the universal set, and, as shown in the diagrams in Fig. 1.10, this set is usually pictured as a large rectangle. All the other sets are drawn inside it. The union of two sets A and B is denoted by $A \cup B$. The set $A \cup B = \{x \mid x \in A$ or $x \in B\}$ is pictured by the shaded area in the diagram to the left. The intersection of two sets A and B is denoted by $A \cap B$, and the set $A \cap B = \{x \mid x \in A$ and $x \in B\}$ is pictured in the middle diagram. The complement of set A is denoted by $\bar{A}$, and $\bar{A} = \{x \mid x \in X$ and $x \notin A\}$ is pictured in the diagram to the right.

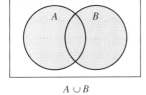
$A \cup B$

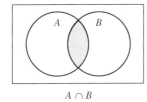
$A \cap B$

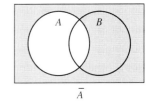
$\bar{A}$

Figure 1.10

In the diagrams in Fig. 1.10, we were able to represent two arbitrary sets by overlapping circles. Note that Venn diagrams can also be used to represent three or more sets. We use three mutually overlapping circles to represent three arbitrary sets. However, to represent four or more sets, it is not possible to use only circles (see Example 2 in Section 1.2).

Puzzle 1   The San Diego Puzzle

A number of years ago, while vacationing in the San Diego area, we visited a science exhibition in Balboa Park. One of the exhibits consisted of a game-playing console. You were invited to pick one of the following 16 numbers.

64	82	52	62
67	91	53	51
46	18	22	16
45	39	13	15

Next, you were asked to respond to four questions by flipping a switch (for each question) to a YES or a NO position.

1. Is your number greater than 50?   YES   NO
2. Is your number even?   YES   NO
3. Is the sum of its digits greater than 8?   YES   NO
4. Is the difference of the digits less than 3?   YES   NO

The machine responded by displaying your number. In testing this out, however, a discrepancy was discovered.

a) Complete the Venn diagrams in Fig. 1.11 to discover the error.

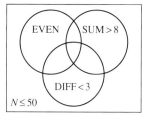 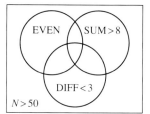

Figure 1.11

b) Show that the problem can be corrected by removing one number. (The remaining numbers could be arranged in 3 rows and 5 columns.)
c) Is your answer to part (b) unique? Explain.
d) In the original problem, suppose that in the last question "less than 3" is replaced by "less than 4." Will this version work?
e) Can you correct the original problem by replacing one of the given numbers by a two-digit number? Explain.   □

Sets and Counting

The **size of a set** A, denoted by $|A|$, is the number of objects contained in the set A. In this discussion, the sets under consideration will all have a finite (though possibly large) number of objects. Throughout the next few chapters, we will encounter many problems that involve counting the objects in some set. Usually the sets will be large and complicated, so listing the objects would be impractical.

In counting the number of objects contained in a large set of objects it may be easier to think of the set as being the union of two smaller sets, which are easier to count. In that case, the original problem can be solved using the following formula, which is called the Addition Principle.

THEOREM 1.4   (The Addition Principle for Arbitrary Sets)
> For any two sets A and B, $|A \cup B| = |A| + |B| - |A \cap B|$.

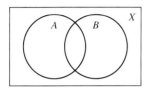

Figure 1.12

In other words, the number of objects in $A \cup B$ is equal to the number of objects in A plus the number of objects in B, minus the number of objects that were counted twice because they were in both A and B. A special case of the addition principle applies when A and B have no elements in common. When $A \cap B$ is empty, we say that A and B are **disjoint**. In this case the formula consists of one simple addition.

THEOREM 1.5   (The Addition Principle for Disjoint Sets)
> If A and B are disjoint sets, then $|A \cup B| = |A| + |B|$.

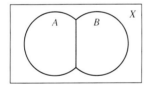

Figure 1.13

Since sets A and $\bar{A}$ are disjoint, a variation of the preceding is pictured in Fig. 1.14.

THEOREM 1.6   (Counting What You Don't Want)
> For any set A contained in X, $|A| = |X| - |\bar{A}|$.

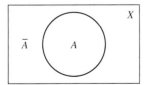

Figure 1.14

Generally, we are asked to count the number of objects in a larger collection of objects X, whose description depends on certain properties, say p_1 and p_2. We attempt to count the objects by applying several counting principles which help to break large complicated problems down into smaller, easier problems. This is, of course, one of the general problem-solving techniques we discussed earlier.

Describing Objects Using Properties

We have already indicated that a single set can be described in terms of a defining property that is satisfied by precisely those elements in the set. Let us denote by A_1 the set $\{a \mid a \in X$ and a satisfies $p_1\}$ and by A_2 the set $\{a \mid a \in X$ and a satisfies $p_2\}$. Counting the number of objects that satisfy property p_1 or property p_2 (or both) is the same as counting the number of objects in $A_1 \cup A_2$. The complementary problem is to count the objects that satisfy neither property p_1 nor property p_2. Finding the number of objects satisfying both of the properties p_1 and p_2 is equivalent to counting the number of objects in $A_1 \cap A_2$. Similar ideas hold when more than two properties are under consideration (see Chapter 3).

DEFINITION   Relatively Prime Integers

Two integers are said to be relatively prime if they have no common divisors greater than 1.

Example 1   Find the number of integers from 1 to 100 (inclusive) that are relatively prime to 100.

Solution

Two integers that are not relatively prime must have a common divisor that is a prime. Since the only primes dividing 100 are 2 and 5, this problem is equivalent to finding the number of integers from 1 to 100, which are neither a multiple of 2 nor a multiple of 5. If we let X be the set of integers from 1 to 100, A be the multiples of 2, and B be the multiples of 5, then the integers we need to count are in the complement of $A \cup B$. By the addition principle, $|A \cup B| = |A| + |B| - |A \cap B|$. Since A consists of the multiples of 2 between 1 and 100, inclusive, $|A| = 100/2 = 50$. Similarly, B consists of multiples of 5 and $A \cap B$ consists of multiples of 10, so $|B| = 20$ and $|A \cap B| = 10$. Therefore $|A \cup B| = 60$, and the number of integers from 1 through 100 that are relatively prime to 100 is $|X| - |A \cup B| = 40$.   □

DEFINITION   Cartesian Product

The Cartesian product of two sets A and B, denoted by $A \times B$, is the set $\{(a,b) \mid a \in A$ and $b \in B\}$ containing all ordered pairs with first coordinate in A and second coordinate in B.

Example 2   List the elements of $\{0,1\} \times \{a,b,c\}$.

Solution
For $A = \{0,1\}$ and $B = \{a,b,c\}$, we obtain

$$A \times B = \{(0,a),(0,b),(0,c),(1,a),(1,b),(1,c)\}$$ □

In general, if $|A| = n$ and $|B| = m$, then for each of n possible first coordinates there are m ordered pairs with that first coordinate, namely, one for each element of

B, so the ordered pairs in $A \times B$ can be listed in a rectangular array with n rows and m columns. Thus the total number of ordered pairs in $A \times B$ is $n \cdot m$.

THEOREM 1.7 (The Multiplication Principle)

For any two sets A and B, $|A \times B| = |A||B|$.

Example 3 A Pair of Dice

A die is a cube with 1, 2, 3, 4, 5, 6 dots, respectively, on each of its six faces. In various games of chance a pair of dice are rolled. If the two dice are different, say, one is colored green and the other is colored red, then how many different outcomes are possible when the two dice are rolled?

Figure 1.15

Solution

Think of recording each outcome as an ordered pair, the green die in the first coordinate and the red die in the second coordinate. Since there are six outcomes for each die, the total number of outcomes equals the total number of ordered pairs where each digit is an element of $\{1, 2, 3, 4, 5, 6\}$. Therefore, the total number of outcomes is $6 \cdot 6 = 36$. Note that this result will be different if the two dice are identical (see Example 7(b), Section 2.1). □

The Cartesian product $A_1 \times A_2 \times \cdots \times A_n$ can be thought of as the set of all ordered n-tuples whose ith coordinate comes from A_i, for $i = 1, 2, \ldots, n$. In this situation, the Multiplication Principle will state that (see Problem 9) $|A_1 \times A_2 \times \cdots \times A_n| = |A_1||A_2| \cdots |A_n|$.

Example 4 Binary Sequences

Consider the set of k-digit binary sequences, that is, the sequences of k digits where each digit is either a 0 or a 1. Since each sequence can be thought of as an ordered k-tuple, the total number of sequences is $2 \cdot 2 \cdot 2 \cdots \cdot 2 = 2^k$. The 3-digit binary sequences are listed in Fig. 1.16. □

Figure 1.16
Eight 3-digit binary sequences

	000	
100	010	001
110	101	011
	111	

DEFINITION Binary Relation

A binary relation on a set A is a subset $R \subseteq A \times A$. If $(x, y) \in R$, then x is usually related to y in a certain way and we write xRy.

Example 5   Let $X = \{1, 2, 3, 4, 5, 6\}$ and suppose R represents the relation "divides." In that case, R consists of the ordered pairs $R = \{(1, 1), (1, 2), (1, 3), (1, 4), (1, 5), (1, 6), (2, 2), (2, 4),$ $(2, 6), (3, 3), (3, 6), (4, 4), (5, 5), (6, 6)\}$.   □

Properties of Relations

There are certain useful properties that a relation R on a set A can satisfy.

1. If xRx for every $x \in A$, we say that R is reflexive.
2. If xRy implies that yRx for every x and y, we say that R is symmetric.
3. If xRy and yRz imply that xRz for every x, y, and z, we say that R is transitive.

Note the relation "divides" in Example 5 is reflexive since a number always divides itself. It is also transitive since x divides y, and y divides z implies that x divides z. However, it is not symmetric since, for example, 2 divides 4 but 4 does not divide 2.

DEFINITION   **Equivalence Relation**

A relation on A is said to be an equivalence relation if it is reflexive, symmetric, and transitive.

An equivalence relation can be thought of as a classification of the objects of A into different types (and vice versa, see Problem 18, Section 1.4). Since the insight necessary to solve a problem involving a large collection of objects might become more apparent when the objects are divided into a small number of types, where two objects of the same type are related in some crucial way, this notion is often useful in problem solving. The equivalence class of x is denoted by $\langle x \rangle$ and defined as follows:

$$\langle x \rangle = \{y \in X \mid yRx\}$$

DEFINITION   **Partition of a Set**

A partition of a set A is a collection of nonempty subsets of A that are pairwise disjoint and whose union is A. (See Fig. 1.17.)

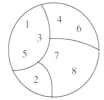

Figure 1.17
A partition of $A = \{1, 2, 3, \ldots, 8\}$

THEOREM 1.8
If R is an equivalence relation on A, the distinct equivalence classes with respect to R form a partition of A.

Proof
Since R is reflexive, each element x belongs to its own equivalence class $\langle x \rangle$. Thus the equivalence classes are nonempty and their union is the entire set A. It remains to be shown that two equivalence classes are disjoint or identical. If $\langle x \rangle \cap \langle y \rangle \neq \emptyset$, we can find an element $a \in \langle x \rangle \cap \langle y \rangle$. Since aRx and R is symmetric, then xRa. Since xRa and aRy, then xRy because R is transitive. For any $b \in \langle x \rangle$, bRx, but bRx and xRy implies that bRy. Therefore, $b \in \langle y \rangle$ and $\langle x \rangle \subseteq \langle y \rangle$. In a similar way we can show that $\langle y \rangle \subseteq \langle x \rangle$ and thus that $\langle x \rangle = \langle y \rangle$. (See Problem 19 in the problem set at the end of this section.)

Congruence Modulo n

An important relation on the set of integers can be defined using division. Two integers x and y are said to be congruent modulo n, written $x \equiv y$ (mod n), if they both have the same remainder when divided by n. Equivalently x and y are congruent modulo n if $x - y$ is divisible by n. Congruences are a powerful tool for attacking many problems in number theory. It is easy to see that congruence modulo n satisfies the three basic properties of an equivalence relation:

1. $x \equiv x$ (mod n)   [Reflexive Property]
2. $x \equiv y$ (mod n) implies that $y \equiv x$ (mod n)   [Symmetric Property]
3. $x \equiv y$ (mod n) and $y \equiv z$ (mod n) imply that $x \equiv z$ (mod n)
   [Transitive Property]

   Some useful arithmetic properties of congruence modulo n are given by the following theorem. (We will return to the study of congruence modulo n in Chapter 9.)

THEOREM 1.9
(Modular Arithmetic)
If $x \equiv y$ (mod n) and $a \equiv b$ (mod n), then

i) $a + x \equiv b + y$ (mod n)
ii) $ax \equiv by$ (mod n)

Proof
We see that $(x - y)$ and $(a - b)$ are both multiples of n. Thus $(a + x) - (b + y) = (a - b) + (x - y)$ is also a multiple of n, proving part (i). Similarly note that $ax - by = ax - ay + ay - by = a(x - y) + (a - b)y$. Therefore, $ax - by$ is a multiple of n, proving part (ii).

Example 6
Find the remainder when 2^{25} is divided by 7.

Solution
Clearly $2^3 \equiv 8 \equiv 1$ (mod 7). It follows that $2^{25} \equiv 2(2^3)^8 \equiv 2$ (mod 7).   □

1.3
PROBLEMS

1. Consider the set of integers from 1 to 500, inclusive.
   a) How many are a multiple of 3?
   b) How many are a multiple of 5?
   c) How many are a multiple of 3 or a multiple of 5?
   d) How many are neither a multiple of 3 nor a multiple of 5?

2. In a combinatorics class of 50 students, 32 are male students, 41 are right-handed, and 26 are right-handed males. How many left-handed females are in the class?

3. There are 87 tibbs. All 34 gibbs and 49 pibbs are tibbs. If exactly 9 tibbs are gibbs and pibbs, then
   a) How many gibbs are not pibbs?
   b) How many tibbs are neither pibbs nor gibbs?

4. Suppose two dice, one red and one green, are rolled.
   a) How many outcomes have a 1 or a 2 showing on at least one of the dice?
   b) How many of the outcomes have two different numbers appearing?

5. In Morse code, each symbol is represented by a sequence of dots and dashes. How many symbols can be represented by sequences of five or fewer dots and dashes?

6. Each digit in a ternary sequence is a 0, 1, or 2. Compute the number of n-digit ternary sequences.

7. If n different dice are rolled, how many different outcomes are possible?

8. a) Define $A - B$ to be equal to $\{x \mid x$ is in A but x is not in $B\}$. If $B \subseteq A$, show that $|A - B| = |A| - |B|$.
   b) Find a counting formula for $|A - B|$ that works for arbitrary sets.

9. Use the Multiplication Principle and induction to show that
   $|A_1 \times A_2 \times \cdots \times A_n| = |A_1||A_2|\cdots|A_n|$.

10. Determine which of the properties of relations—reflexive, symmetric, transitive—are satisfied by the following relations, defined by the ordered pairs (i, j) of positive integers for which
    a) $i + j$ is even
    b) $i + j$ is odd
    c) $|i - j| \leq 10$
    d) $i \geq j$

11. Let X be a set with n distinct elements. Define the following relation R on the subsets of X. Two subsets of X are said to be related if they have the same number of elements.
    a) Show that R is an equivalence relation on 2^X.
    b) How many distinct equivalence classes are there?

12. A relation R on a set A is called circular if aRb and bRc implies that cRa. Show that if R is reflexive and circular, it is an equivalence relation.

∗13. For a set X with n elements, show that it is possible to list all the subsets of X in a sequence, starting with the empty set, so that a subset is obtained from the previous one by adding or deleting one element.

14. a) Prove by induction that a set having $n \geq 2$ elements has exactly $n(n-1)/2$ two-element subsets.
b) Prove by induction that a set having $n \geq 3$ elements has exactly $n(n-1)(n-2)/6$ three-element subsets.

15. Compute the last two digits of 3^{123}.

16. a) Show that $(d_n d_{n-1} \cdots d_1)_{10}$ and $d_1 + d_2 + \cdots + d_n$ are congruent modulo 9.
b) Show that $(d_n d_{n-1} \cdots d_1)_{10}$ and $d_1 - d_2 + d_3 - d_4 + \cdots + (-1)^{n-1} d_n$ are congruent modulo 11.

17. When $n \geq 1$ different dice are rolled show that
a) For exactly one-half of the outcomes, the total sum of the dice will be even.
b) For exactly one-third of the outcomes the total sum of the dice will be a multiple of 3.

18. If $A \subseteq B$ and $C \subseteq D$, prove that
a) $A \cap C \subseteq B \cap D$. b) $A \cup C \subseteq B \cup D$.

19. Show that the relation "$\subseteq$" defined on the subsets of a set X satisfies
a) The reflexive property
b) The transitive property
c) The antisymmetric property; If $A \subseteq B$ and $B \subseteq A$, then $A = B$, (a relation of this kind is known as a partial ordering relation.)

20. a) For any two sets A and B, $A \subseteq X$ and $B \subseteq X$, show that $(\overline{A \cup B}) = \bar{A} \cap \bar{B}$ and $(\overline{A \cap B}) = \bar{A} \cup \bar{B}$. (DeMorgan's Laws)
b) Prove by induction that the following laws hold for any $n \geq 2$ sets,

$$\text{if } A_1 \subseteq X, A_2 \subseteq X, \ldots, A_n \subseteq X, \text{ then}$$
$$(\overline{A_1 \cup A_2 \cup \cdots \cup A_n}) = \bar{A}_1 \cap \bar{A}_2 \cap \cdots \cap \bar{A}_n \quad \text{and}$$
$$(\overline{A_1 \cap A_2 \cap \cdots \cap A_n}) = \bar{A}_1 \cup \bar{A}_2 \cup \cdots \cup \bar{A}_n.$$

1.3

SUPPLEMENTARY
COMPUTER
PROJECTS

1. ISBN Check Digit
In the last two decades every published book has been given an International Standard Book Number (ISBN) to identify it. Every ISBN number contains precisely ten digits. The first nine digits depend on the country, the publisher, and the title. The tenth digit is an error-detecting check digit. The check digit is a function of the first nine digits.
a) Describe an algorithm that will determine the tenth check digit if the first nine digits $(d_1, d_2, \ldots, d_9)$ are known. Write a program to check your

algorithm. ***Hint:*** Consider the function $d_1 + 2d_2 + \cdots + 9d_9$, and note that the check digit is always one of $0, 1, 2, \ldots, 9, X$.

b) Suppose that precisely one of the digits d_i is miscopied. Prove that the check digit will always be changed. ***Hint:*** If $ab \equiv ac \pmod{n}$, where a and n are relatively prime, then $b \equiv c \pmod{n}$.

c) Show that when two digits are miscopied, the error may not be detected.

d) Prove that if two adjacent digits are interchanged, the check digit will change, indicating an error.

e) What will happen to the check digit if two nonadjacent digits are interchanged?

2. Properties of Relations

Given a finite set of ordered pairs representing a relation, write a program to determine if the relation is

a) Reflexive

b) Symmetric

c) Transitive

FUNCTIONS

If f is a function from a set A to a set B, we write $f: A \to B$. In terms of ordered pairs, the function f can be thought of as a set of ordered pairs in $A \times B$, where each a in A is the first coordinate of exactly one ordered pair. If (a, b) is in f, we also write that $f(a) = b$ and say that b is the image of a. A function can also be thought of as an assignment or distribution of the objects in A to the objects in B, where each object of A is assigned to exactly one object in B. In general, each b in B is the image of zero, one, or more elements of A.

Types of Functions

We frequently encounter several types of special functions. Four different functions are pictured in Fig. 1.18 for A and B both equal to the set of nonnegative integers.

A function $f: A \to B$ is said to be a one-to-one function or an injection if each element of B is the image of at most one element of A. Functions (a) and (c) in Fig. 1.18 are one-to-one functions. A function $f: A \to B$ is said to be an onto function or a surjection if each element in B is the image of at least one element of A. Functions (b) and (c) in Fig. 1.18 are onto functions. Finally, a function f is said to be a one-to-one correspondence or a bijection if each element in B is the image of exactly one element of A. Thus a function is a bijection if and only if it is a surjection and an injection, like function (c) in Fig. 1.18.

Functions and Counting

When f is a function from a finite set A to a finite set B, it is not always possible to determine any information about the relative sizes of A and B. However, when f is

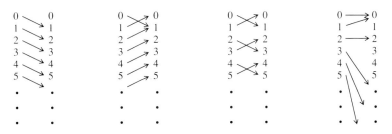

Figure 1.18   (i) $f(n) = n + 1$ (ii) $f(n) = |n - 1|$ (iii) $f(n) = n + (-1)^n$ (iv) $f(n) = n^2 - n$

an injection, every element of A has a different image in B; thus $|B| \geq |A|$. When f is a surjection, at least one element of A is assigned to every different element of B; thus $|A| \geq |B|$. When f is a bijection, it is an injection and a surjection; thus $|A| = |B|$. In particular, one important part of this relationship between functions and counting is known as the Correspondence Principle.

THE CORRESPONDENCE PRINCIPLE   If there is a bijection from set A to set B, then $|A| = |B|$.

Formulating an Equivalent Problem

The Correspondence Principle is often applied to counting problems when the objects in a set can be described in several different ways. In this context, the Correspondence Principle states that any change in the description of a set will not change the number of objects. Thus we often attempt to compare one set to another set of known size. This is a special case of the general problem-solving technique that involves reformulating a problem into a more easily solved equivalent problem. In applying the Correspondence Principle, it is often convenient to apply the following result, which we state without proof.

DEFINITION   **The Inverse Assignment**

If $f = \{(x, y) \mid y = f(x)\}$ is a function from X to Y, we denote by $f^{-1} = \{(y, x) \mid (x, y) \in f\}$ the inverse assignment of f. (See Fig. 1.19.)

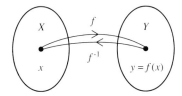

Figure 1.19

THEOREM 1.10 | A function $f: X \to Y$ is a bijection if and only if the inverse assignment f^{-1}: $Y \to X$ is also a function.

Example 1 Let $A = \{a, b, c, d\}$ and $B = \{1, 2, 3\}$. Compute the number of functions from A to B.

Solution
The Multiplication Principle can be used to count functions. In any function or assignment from the objects in A to the objects in B, there are three possible assignments for each element of A. Thus, for each function, there is a unique 4-tuple whose first coordinate is the image of a, whose second coordinate is the image of b, whose third coordinate is the image of c, and whose fourth coordinate is the image of d. The inverse assignment also takes each 4-tuple to a unique function. Thus there is a one-to-one correspondence between functions from A to B and 4-tuples whose coordinates are elements of B. Therefore, the total number of functions from A to B is $3^4 = 81$.   □

Example 2 Let $A = \{a_1, a_2, a_3, \ldots, a_n\}$ be a set with n elements and consider the problem of finding the number of subsets of A, that is, the size of 2^A.

Solution
One good way to look at this problem is to associate with each subset an inventory list of n digits (compare Fig. 1.20 with Fig. 1.16). The inventory list of a subset S is 1 in the ith digit if a_i is in the subset S and 0 if a_i is not in the subset S. We can easily show that any n-digit binary sequence is the inventory list of a unique subset, so there is a one-to-one correspondence between binary sequences of length n and subsets of A. Thus $|2^A| = 2^{|A|}$, and for this reason 2^A is sometimes called the power set of A.

$$\varnothing$$
$$\{1\}, \{2\}, \{3\}$$

Figure 1.20
Eight subsets of
$\{1, 2, 3\}$

$$\{1,2\}, \{1,3\}, \{2,3\}$$
$$\{1,2,3\}$$

□

The Pigeonhole Principle

In the previous examples we have seen that the Correspondence Principle is useful in many counting problems. The following principle is often used to solve a slightly different kind of problem, which might be classified as an existence problem. That is, under certain circumstances we are actually able to show that a particular kind of arrangement must always exist. This principle can be described most colorfully in terms of an assignment of pigeons to holes.

THE PIGEONHOLE PRINCIPLE   If $n + 1$ or more pigeons are assigned to n holes, at least two pigeons are assigned to the same hole.

The pigeons can be thought of as the objects of one set A and the holes as another set B of possible images. The Pigeonhole Principle states that if $|A| > |B|$, there is no injection from A to B.

Example 3   There is no way that a juggler can hold three balls in two hands unless one contains more than one ball. Note however, that this is not true if the balls are allowed to move.   □

Example 4   Consider a sequence of k integers: $a_1, a_2, a_3, \ldots, a_k$. Show that there is some subset of these terms whose sum is divisible by k.

Solution
First look at the k sums $a_1, a_1 + a_2, a_1 + a_2 + a_3, \ldots, a_1 + a_2 + a_3 + \cdots + a_k$. If one of these is divisible by k, we need not look any further. If not, each of these has a nonzero remainder when divided by k. Since the only possible nonzero remainders are $1, 2, 3, \ldots, k - 1$, two of these sums must have the same remainder r when divided by k. The difference of two such integers $qk + r - (pk + r) = (q - p)k$ is divisible by k. In that case, if $a_1 + a_2 + \cdots + a_n$ and $a_1 + a_2 + \cdots + a_m$ are the sums in question and $n > m$, then $a_{m+1} + a_{m+2} + \cdots + a_n$ is the required sum that is divisible by k.   □

Example 5   Suppose that we are given a set X of 10 positive integers, none of which is greater than 100. Show that there are two disjoint nonempty subsets of this set whose elements have the same sum.

Solution
Consider the $2^{10} = 1024$ different subsets of X. Each of the subsets has a sum ranging from 0 (the empty set) to $91 + 92 + \cdots + 100$. Since the number of possible sums is less than 1024, the Pigeonhole Principle states that two of these subsets must have the same sum. By throwing away their common elements, we obtain two disjoint subsets with the same sum, and they are both nonempty because no other subset of positive integers has the same sum as the empty set.   □

Example 6   In a basketball tournament each team plays 15 games in 10 days, playing at least one game every day. Show that no matter how the games are scheduled, a team must always play exactly 4 games during some period of consecutive days.

Solution
Let a_i be the number of games played in the first i days. Thus $0 < a_1 < a_2 < a_3 < \cdots < a_{10}$ and all the a_i's are distinct. We would like to show that for some i and j, $a_i = a_j + 4$. The 20 integers $a_1, a_2, \ldots, a_{10}, a_1 + 4, a_2 + 4, \ldots, a_{10} + 4$ are all between 1 and 19, so two of them must be the same. Since $a_1, a_2, \ldots, a_{10}$ are all distinct and likewise $a_1 + 4, a_2 + 4, \ldots, a_{10} + 4$ are all distinct, then some $a_i = a_j + 4$, as required. Thus, during the period of consecutive days starting with day $j + 1$ and ending with day i, exactly 4 games were played.   □

The simplest version of the Pigeonhole Principle states that when enough pigeons are assigned to n holes, at least two pigeons are assigned to the same hole. If the number of pigeons is large enough, we can say even more. A generalization of the Pigeonhole Principle states that if $kn + 1$ or more pigeons are assigned to n holes, at least $k + 1$ pigeons are assigned to the same hole. An alternate way of stating this is in terms of averages.

THE AVERAGING PRINCIPLE   Given a set of numbers, there is always a number in the set whose value is at least as large (at least as small) as the average value of the numbers in the set.

Example 7   A combinatorics student solves 29 problems in one week. Since the average number of problems solved is a little over 4 per day, on some day at least 5 problems were solved. Show that in some two-day period at least 8 problems were solved.

Solution
Let x_i be the number of problems solved on day i. Assume that at most 7 problems were solved in any two-day period. Then $x_1 + x_2 \leq 7$, $x_3 + x_4 \leq 7$, $x_5 + x_6 \leq 7$, $x_7 \leq 7$. Adding the inequalities, we obtain $x_1 + x_2 + x_3 + x_4 + x_5 + x_6 + x_7 \leq 28$, which is a contradiction since $x_1 + x_2 + \cdots + x_7 = 29$. Therefore, at least 8 problems were solved in some two-day period.   □

Example 8   Ten different integers are chosen from the set $\{1, 2, 3, \ldots, 99\}$. Show that there is a pair of these integers whose difference is at most 10.

Solution
Suppose $x_1 < x_2 < \cdots < x_{10}$ are the integers chosen. The sum of the 9 differences $(x_2 - x_1) + (x_3 - x_2) + \cdots + (x_{10} - x_9)$ equals $x_{10} - x_1$, which is at most 98. Thus one of these 9 differences is at most 10 since the average is less than 11.   □

1.4
PROBLEMS

1. If $|C| = 5$ and $|D| = 7$, use the multiplication principle to count the number of functions
    a) From C to D
    b) From D to C

2. If A and B are arbitrary sets, describe a bijection between the Cartesian products $A \times B$ and $B \times A$.

3. At a certain party there are n married couples. What is the largest subset of people that can be chosen not containing two people who are married to each other?

4. Show that among any 13 integers, not necessarily consecutive, there are at least two whose difference is a multiple of 12.

5. Show that among any $n + 1$ positive integers less than or equal to $3n$ there are two that differ by 2 or less.

6. At a dinner party there are 8 guests. The dinner takes place at a table shaped like a regular octagon. Each edge has one place setting that is labeled with the name of a different guest. Originally each person sits in the wrong place. Explain why the table can be rotated so that at least two persons are sitting in the right place.

7. a) The 10 digits $\{0, 1, 2, \ldots, 9\}$ are arranged in a straight line. No matter how they are arranged, show that there are always three consecutive digits whose sum is at least 13.

   b) If the 10 digits are arranged in a circle, show that there are always three consecutive digits whose sum is at least 15.

ADVANCED
PROBLEMS

8. A basketball team plays 30 games in 20 days playing at least one game every day.

   a) Show that there must be a period of consecutive days during which the team plays exactly 9 games.

   b) Is there necessarily a period of consecutive days when exactly 10 games are played?

9. From the set $\{1, 2, 3, \ldots, 100\}$, 51 different integers are chosen at random.

   a) Show that among the integers chosen, there exists a pair whose sum is equal to 101.

   b) Show that there does not have to be a pair whose sum is 100.

10. Show that among $n + 1$ different positive integers less than or equal to $2n$, there are always two that are relatively prime.

*11. Let $x_1, x_2, \ldots, x_{n^2 + 1}$ be a sequence of $n^2 + 1$ distinct integers. Show that there is some sub-sequence $x_{i_1}, x_{i_2}, \ldots, x_{i_{n+1}}$ $(i_1 < i_2 < \cdots < i_{n+1})$ of length $n + 1$ that is strictly increasing or strictly decreasing.

12. A lattice point in R^3 is a point whose three coordinates are all integers. Nine lattice points are chosen at random and a line segment is drawn between each pair. Show that at least one of the line segments has a lattice point in its interior.

*13. From the set $\{1, 2, 3, \ldots, 100\}$, 51 different numbers are chosen at random. Show that among the numbers chosen, there exists a pair such that one divides the other.

14. If a set X has n elements, show by induction that X has 2^n different subsets.

15. a) If a set X has $n > 0$ elements, show by induction that the number of subsets of X with even size is exactly equal to the number of subsets of X with odd size.

    b) Show that this is true by describing a bijection between the subsets of odd size and the subsets of even size.

*16. Let $a(n)$ be the number of representations of the positive integer n as a sum of 1's and 2's, taking order into account. Let $b(n)$ be the number of representations of n as a sum of integers greater than 1, again taking order into account (and counting the sum $n = n$). Thus $a(4) = 5$ and $b(6) = 5$.
   a) Show that $a(n) = b(n + 2)$ for every positive integer n by describing a one-to-one correspondence.
   b) Show that $a(1) = 1, a(2) = 2$, and for $n > 2$, that $a(n) = a(n - 1) + a(n - 2)$.

17. Prove that any subset of 53 numbers chosen from the set $\{1, 2, \ldots, 100\}$ must contain two numbers that differ by exactly 12, but need not contain a pair differing by 11.

18. Let $P = \{X_1, X_2, \ldots, X_k\}$ be a partition of a set X into k nonempty subsets. Define a relation R on X such that xRy if and only if x and y are in the same subset of the partition. Show that R is an equivalence relation and deduce that there is a one-to-one correspondence between partitions of X and equivalence relations on X.

19. Suppose 5 points are chosen at random inside an equilateral triangle with sides of length 1. Show that there is at least one pair of these points that are separated by a distance of at most $1/2$. **Hint:** Divide the triangle into 4 suitable regions.

20. Suppose that f is a function from A to B, where A and B are finite sets with $|A| = |B|$. Show that f is an injection if and only if f is a surjection.

1.4
SUPPLEMENTARY COMPUTER PROJECTS

1. A Digit Transfer Problem
   Let x be a positive integer containing $n \geq 2$ digits. We denote by $f(x)$ the integer obtained by removing the rightmost digit of x and placing it before the leftmost digit. Thus $f(1234) = 4123$. If $x = 35$, then $f(x) = 53$ represents an increase of a little over 51%. Is it possible for $f(x)$ to be exactly 50% greater than x?
   If x is a candidate with n digits, its rightmost digit is given by $R = x - 10[x/10]$ and the new number $f(x)$ becomes $y = R(10^{n-1}) + [x/10]$. We need to check whether or not $2y = 3x$.
   a) For $n = 2$, the program

```
FOR  x=10 TO 99
    R  =  x  -  10*INT(x/10)
    y  =  10*R  +  INT(x/10)
    IF  2*y  =  3*x    PRINT  x
NEXT  x
END
```

   when run on one programmable calculator took 25 seconds. There was no output. Show that a minor modification could cut the time in half.

b) Estimate the execution time for $n = 5$ if this strategy is used. (Note that $2y = 3x$ has no solution for $n \leq 5$.)

Now consider a mathematical approach to the problem. Let $I = [x/10]$. If $2y = 3x$, then $2R(10^{n-1}) + 2I = 3(R + 10I)$ or $R(2(10^{n-1}) - 3) = 28I$.

c) Explain why the preceding equation implies that R must be 4 or 8.
d) Test $M = 2(10^{n-1}) - 3$ for divisibility by 7 when $n = 2, 3, \ldots, 10$.
e) Use part (d) to find the two smallest values of x that have the desired property.

2. Some Missing Numbers
    For any positive integer n, let $a_n = [n + \sqrt{2n} + 1/2]$. Noting that $2 \leq a_n \leq 220$, for $1 \leq n \leq 200$, let

    $$U = \{1, 2, 3, \ldots, 220\}$$
    $$A = \{a_n \mid 1 \leq n \leq 200\}$$
    $$\bar{A} = U - A = \text{the complement of } A \text{ relative to } U$$

    a) Determine (it can be done easily) the number of elements in $\bar{A}$.
    b) Note that $a_2 - a_1 = 4 - 2 = 2$. Could $a_{k+1} - a_k$ be greater than 2 for some k? Justify your answer.
    c) Use a computer to list the numbers in $\bar{A}$. What pattern do you notice?

REVIEW PROBLEMS

1. In a certain game, two players take turns adding 2, 3, or 4 coins to a pile.
    a) Suppose the pile starts with no coins and the player who adds the 60th coin wins the entire pile. Which player should win and what strategy should be used?
    b) If the player who adds the 60th coin loses, how will this result change?

2. At the meetings of a friendly juggling club, each pair of m different members shakes hands exactly once. Explain why the total number of handshakes is exactly equal to $1 + 2 + \cdots + m - 1$.

3. Show that $3^{2n} - 1$ is divisible by 8 for any positive integer n.

4. Show that $1^2 - 2^2 + 3^2 - \cdots + (-1)^{n-1}n^2 = (-1)^{n-1}n(n+1)/2$, for any positive integer n.

5. a) In the set $X = \{1, 2, 3, \ldots, 600\}$, find the number of integers that are a multiple of 3 or a multiple of 4 (or both).
    b) Compute the sum of the integers in part (a).

6. Suppose $|A| = n$.
    a) Compute the number of functions from A to A.
    b) There is a bijection from the set of binary relations on A to the subsets of $A \times A$. Use this fact to compute the number of binary relations on A.

7. a) Find the number of ways to assign n different pigeons to $n + 1$ different holes.

 b) Repeat part (a) if no two pigeons are assigned to the same hole.

8. In the game of roulette, the numbers $0, 1, 2, \ldots, 36$ are placed randomly on the outside of a spinning wheel. Explain why there must always be three consecutive integers on the outside of the wheel whose sum is greater than or equal to 56.

9. There are 10 teams in a tournament. Each game involves two teams. If the teams play a total of 23 games, explain why some team must play five or more games.

10. Let S be the set of integers $\{1, 4, 7, 10, \ldots, 100\}$.

 a) Find the sum of all integers in S.

 b) Let A be any set of 18 distinct integers chosen from S. Show that there must be two integers in A whose sum is 101.

11. For any integer $n > 1$, show that $(.99)^n > 1 - (.01)n$.

CHAPTER

1   SUMMARY

In this chapter we started by talking about general problem-solving techniques, also known as heuristics. We discussed the two main mathematical methods for solving a problem, deduction in Section 1.1 and induction in Section 1.2. For more about problem solving see any of several books by Polya including [1]. See either of the books [2, 3] for interesting problems in many areas of mathematics, or any of the mathematical contest problem books [4, 5, 6]. Look at any issue of *American Mathematical Monthly* for even more new problems. The book by Lovasz [7] is a good source for challenging problems in combinatorics and graph theory.

Many games and puzzles are related to combinatorial mathematics. See any of the books [8–13] for a variety of mathematical puzzles. Especially recommended are any of the books by Gardner, including [9], and the older puzzle books by Dudeney [10] and Loyd [12].

A good problem solver must also have a thorough knowledge of many basic mathematical models. Sequences and numbers were discussed in Section 1.2, sets and relations were discussed in Section 1.3, and functions and the Pigeonhole Principle were discussed in Section 1.4. These models and their relation to counting will be discussed in greater detail in Chapter 2. Any of several number theory texts [14, 15], logic texts [16], or set theory texts [17] can be consulted for more about these areas.

BIBLIOGRAPHY

Problem Solving and Problems

1. Polya, G. *How To Solve It*, 2nd edition. Princeton, N.J.: Princeton University Press, 1973.
2. Newman, D. *A Problem Seminar*. New York: Springer-Verlag, 1982.
3. Larson, L. *Problem-Solving Through Problems*. New York: Springer-Verlag, 1983.
4. Hungarian Problem Books, I and II, translated by E. Rapaport. Washington, D.C.: Mathematical Association of America (MAA), 1963.
5. Gleason, A., R. Greenwood, and L. Kelly. The William Lowell Putnam Mathematical Competition—Problems and Solutions: 1938–1964, MAA, 1980.
6. G. Alexanderson, L. Klosinski, and L. Larson. The William Lowell Putnam Mathematical Competition—Problems and Solutions: 1965–1984: Washington, D.C.: MAA, 1985.
7. L. Lovasz. *Combinatorial Problems and Exercises*. New York: North-Holland, 1979.

Games and Puzzles

8. O'Beirne, T. *Puzzles and Paradoxes*. London: Oxford University Press, 1965.
9. Gardner, M. *Mathematical Puzzles and Diversions*. New York: Simon & Schuster, 1959.
10. Dudeney, H. *Amusements in Mathematics*. New York: Dover, 1970.
11. Coxeter, H., and W. Ball. *Mathematical Recreations and Essays*. Toronto: University of Toronto Press, 1972.
12. *Mathematical Puzzles of Sam Loyd*, Vols. 1 and 2. New York: Dover, 1960.
13. Berlekamp, E., J. Conway, and R. Guy. *Winning Ways*, Vol. I and II. New York: Academic Press, 1982.

Number Theory

14. Niven, I., and H. Zuckerman. *An Introduction to the Theory of Numbers*, 4th Edition. New York: Wiley, 1980.
15. Rosen, K. *Elementary Number Theory and Its Applications*. Reading, Mass.: Addison-Wesley, 1984.

Sets and Logic

16. Mendelson, E. *Introduction to Mathematical Logic*. Princeton, N.J.: Van Nostrand, 1964.
17. Halmos, P. *Naive Set Theory*. New York: Van Nostrand, 1960.

2

BASIC COUNTING PRINCIPLES

In studying the arrangements and structures of a finite set in combinatorics, three main kinds of problems that occur are counting, existence, and optimization problems. The **counting problem** involves computing the number of arrangements there are of a certain kind. In more difficult problems, we may be satisfied to know that at least one arrangement of a given kind actually exists. This is known as the **existence problem**. In many applications some arrangements are considered to be more efficient than others. The problem of finding the most efficient arrangement of a certain kind is called the **optimization problem**.

In the next two chapters, we will mainly be interested in problems that involve counting. Problems in many areas of mathematics and computer science require counting or at least estimating. We will encounter many applications of counting to probability, number theory, computer science, operations research, and so on. For example, to solve a problem on a computer, we usually need to know approximately how much storage will be required. Thus we must determine the number of objects of a particular type that need to be stored. We also must know approximately how many operations are necessary to perform an algorithm so we can compare different algorithms for efficiency as well as decide whether a particular solution is even feasible. The basic counting techniques needed to perform these computations are discussed in Chapters 2 and 3, and the analysis of algorithms is covered more fully in Chapter 4. The first principles we discuss, the Addition Principle and the Multiplication Principle, are specific techniques for dividing complex counting problems into smaller parts.

SECTION
2.1

SEQUENTIAL COUNTING

The most widely used counting technique is probably the Multiplication Principle. All sorts of objects can be thought of as sequences, lists, or other arrangements, which are essentially the same as ordered k-tuples. The Multiplication Principle was first introduced in Chapter 1 as a way of counting ordered pairs and k-tuples.

In order to count the number of objects of a certain type, we usually consider a counting procedure that is a series of steps for constructing or choosing the desired kind of object. If each of the distinguishable outcomes of the procedure corresponds to precisely one of the objects in question, we can count the number of objects by looking at the outcomes of that procedure.

Certain kinds of counting procedures can be thought of as filling in the coordinates of an ordered k-tuple. Such a counting procedure is called a **sequential counting procedure**. The Multiplication Principle counts the outcomes of a sequential counting procedure by looking at the outcomes of its individual steps.

THE MULTIPLICATION PRINCIPLE FOR COUNTING PROCEDURES   If a procedure can be described as a sequence of m independent steps, with i_1 possible outcomes for the first step, i_2 possible outcomes for the second step,..., and i_m possible outcomes for the mth step, then the total number of composite outcomes of the procedure is given by the product $i_1 i_2 \cdots i_m$.

Since in some sense the Multiplication Principle really deals with ordered k-tuples, we must make certain that the outcomes of our procedure can be accurately modeled by ordered k-tuples. In order for the Multiplication Principle to apply to a counting procedure, we must ensure that the steps of the procedure satisfy the conditions given in the following definition.

DEFINITION   A Sequential Counting Procedure

1. The steps are ordered, meaning that any two sequences of different outcomes represent distinguishable composite outcomes.

2. The steps are independent, meaning that the number of outcomes of one step is not affected by the outcomes of the preceding steps.

3. The steps are complete, meaning that each composite outcome consists of a complete sequence of individual outcomes, one for each step. This contrasts with the Addition Principle, discussed in Section 2.2, where a problem is broken up into different cases and each composite outcome occurs in exactly one case.

Example 1

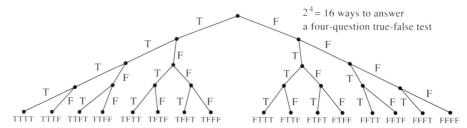

$2^4 = 16$ ways to answer
a four-question true-false test

Figure 2.1   TTTT TTTF TTFT TTFF TFTT TFTF TFFT TFFF   FTTT FTTF FTFT FTFF FFTT FFTF FFFT FFFF

Using the example given in Fig. 2.1 as a guide, find the number of ways to answer a true-false test with 12 different questions
a) If every question must be answered.
b) If instead any number of questions may be left unanswered.

Solution
Consider a counting procedure whose ith step is choosing an answer for question i. If every question is answered with a true or a false, the total number of possible answers is $2^{12} = 4096$. On the other hand, if we also allow the possibility of no answer on each question, the number of ways to answer the test increases to $3^{12} = 531,441$. □

Example 2

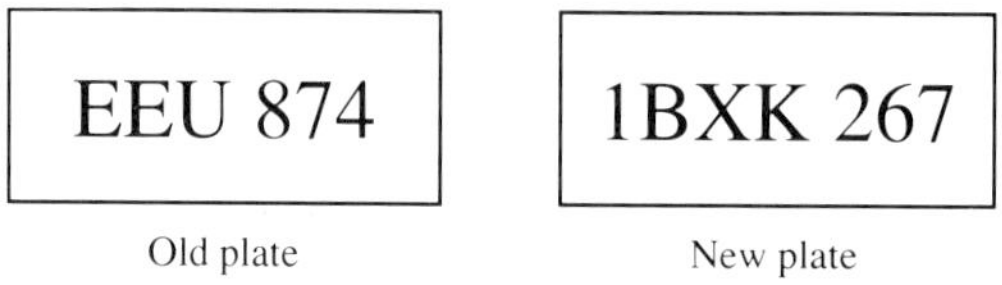

EEU 874   1BXK 267

Figure 2.2   Old plate   New plate

Old California license plates consisted of a sequence of three letters followed by three digits (see Fig. 2.2). Assuming that any sequence of letters and digits was allowed (though actually some combinations of letters were disallowed), how many license plates were available?

Solution
We use a counting procedure whose ith step chooses the ith character in the license plate. Since there were 26 choices for each letter and 10 choices for each digit, the total number of old California license plates was $26^3 \times 10^3 = 17,576,000$. Evidently the state ran out of license plates of this form because new California license plates consist of a digit, followed by three letters, followed by three more digits. Thus ten times as many new license plates are now possible. □

Example 3   Define a string to be any sequence of letters from the ordinary English alphabet.
a) How many seven-letter strings are there?

Solution
Since there are 26 choices for each letter, the total number of strings with exactly seven letters is 26^7.

b) A palindrome is a string that reads the same forwards as backwards. How many seven-letter palindromes are there?

Solution
The first and last letters are the same, as well as the second and the sixth letters, and the third and the fifth letters. There are 26 choices for each of the three pairs of identical letters as well as for the fourth letter. Thus the total number of seven-letter palindromes is 26^4. ☐

Ordered Steps

The Multiplication Principle can be used to compute the number of outcomes of various procedures that can be described mathematically as a sequence of **ordered steps**. Note that in this mathematical model, the term "order" has a slightly broader meaning than it does in everyday English. Some simple procedures can be thought of as a sequence of k steps where essentially the same step with n outcomes is repeated, as in Example 1. If the order of the steps is important and different sequences represent **distinguishable outcomes**, the total number of outcomes is n^k. On the other hand, steps are also considered to be ordered even if no particular order of the steps is important but the steps are naturally distinguishable in some other way.

Example 4   Find the number of distinct divisors of the integer 64,800.

Solution
The prime factorization of 64,800 is $2^5 3^4 5^2$. Any divisor of 64,800 must have a prime factorization of the form $2^i 3^j 5^k$, where $0 \le i \le 5, 0 \le j \le 4$, and $0 \le k \le 2$. Consider a procedure with three distinguishable steps, one choice for the exponent of each of the three different primes 2, 3, and 5. Since the number of choices for i is 6, for j is 5, and for k is 3, the total number of different divisors is $6 \times 5 \times 3 = 90$. ☐

Example 5   **Switching Functions**
Suppose that some component of a computer is a circuit with n different switches, which we label $1, 2, \ldots, n$. Each switch can be open or closed independently. For every switch, we represent open (meaning that no electricity can flow through it) by a 0 and closed (meaning that electricity can flow) by a 1. Thus each alignment of switches can be represented by a binary sequence of length n, with digit i representing the position of switch i. The net result of any alignment of the n switches is that either electricity flows through the circuit or it does not, which can also be represented by a 0 or a 1.

We define a switching function to be a function that assigns to each binary sequence of length n a 0 or a 1. Thus each switching circuit has an associated switching function, and two circuits with the same switching function are interchangeable. Every switching function can be realized in many ways by an electrical circuit so a computer engineer might like to have an inventory that lists, for every switching function, the most efficient electrical circuit realizing this switching function. For $n = 4$, compute the total number of circuits in the inventory.

Solution

We have seen that there are 2^n different binary sequences of length n. For each binary sequence we have two possible assignments, 0 or 1. Using the Multiplication Principle, we see that there are $2 \times 2 \times \cdots \times 2 = 2^{2^n}$ different switching functions. For $n = 4$, this turns out to be 65,536, which would make for quite a long inventory. In Chapter 9 we will see how to reduce this inventory substantially using symmetry.

□

Independent Steps

In any sequential counting procedure whose outcomes are to be counted by the Multiplication Principle, the steps of the procedure must be **independent**. We consider a step in a counting procedure to be independent of the preceding steps if the number of outcomes of the step in question is always the same, regardless of what has happened in the previous steps.

Example 6

Figure 2.3

Six different books are arranged on a bookshelf, as in Fig. 2.3.
a) How many distinguishable orders of arrangement are there?

Solution
Consider the following counting procedure:

1. Choose one book for the first position.
2. Choose a different book for the second position.
$\vdots$
6. Choose the last book for the sixth position.

The total number of outcomes for this sequence of steps is $6 \times 5 \times 4 \times 3 \times 2 \times 1 = 720$ different arrangements. Note that these steps are considered to be independent in the sense that the number of possible outcomes is always the same, regardless of the previous outcomes, even though the actual choices do depend on the previous outcomes.

b) Suppose that two of the six books are blue and should not be placed next to each other. How many different arrangements are there with the two blue books not adjacent?

Solution
Note that the counting procedure used in part (a) is not applicable here since the steps would not be independent. Choosing the first blue book in one step affects the number of choices in the next step. In fact, it is difficult to find a sequential counting procedure that counts these arrangements directly. However, we can count the

arrangements we do not want by the following sequential counting procedure:

1. Choose two consecutive positions for the blue books.
2. Arrange the blue books in these positions.
3. Arrange the four books left in the remaining four positions.

The total number of arrangements we do not want is $5 \times 2 \times 4 \times 3 \times 2 \times 1 = 240$. Therefore the total number of arrangements with no consecutive blue books is $720 - 240 = 480$. We consider more examples of this kind in the next section. □

Distinguishable Outcomes

When we are constructing a sequential counting procedure, another important consideration is that two different sequences of outcomes must always correspond to two distinguishable composite outcomes of the entire procedure. Since the Multiplication Principle counts each sequence as different, we must always be careful to check that the corresponding outcomes are also distinguishable. Outcomes are distinguishable when each step of the procedure is different from the others. Often this is indicated in the problem by the use of such words as "different," "distinct," or "distinguishable" as opposed to "identical" or "similar."

Example 7 Consider the problem of determining the number of outcomes when n dice are rolled.

   a) How many outcomes are possible when n dice are rolled if each die has a different color or is somehow different from the others?

Solution
In this case there are 6 possible outcomes for each die. Since each die is different, we can list the individual outcomes as an n-tuple with each n-tuple representing a distinguishable outcome. Thus there are 6^n different outcomes.

   b) How many outcomes are possible when two identical dice are rolled?

Solution
Even though there are 36 different ordered pairs whose coordinates are positive integers from 1 to 6, not all of them represent distinguishable outcomes. An outcome where one die is an i and the other is a j, for $i \neq j$, is represented by two different ordered pairs. There are 6 outcomes that are represented by a single ordered pair (i, i) and 15 outcomes that are represented by two ordered pairs, thus there are 21, not 36, different outcomes in this case. When applying the Multiplication Principle, we must always be careful to check that outcomes are distinguishable; otherwise, we may end up overcounting the objects in the set. See Section 2.4, Problem 7, for the number of outcomes when n identical dice are rolled. □

2.1
PROBLEMS

   1. How many ways are there to pick a man and a woman who are not married to each other from a group of n married couples?

2. a) Compute the number of distinct divisors of 112,000.

b) Compute the number of odd divisors of 112,000.

3. A three-digit (decimal) integer is any sequence of three digits chosen from $\{0, 1, 2, 3, 4, 5, 6, 7, 8, 9\}$ which does not start with 0 on the left.

a) How many three-digit odd integers with distinct digits are there?

b) How many three-digit integers with distinct digits are multiples of 10?

4. a) Five friends eat lunch on a long bench every afternoon. How many days in a row can they eat lunch without sitting in the same order?

b) In how many ways can a woman invite a group of one or more friends from a group of six friends out to dinner?

5. A valid telephone number consists of seven digits where neither of the first two digits is a 0 or a 1. How many valid telephone numbers are there?

6. A pizza parlor has five meat and five vegetable toppings that can be added to a pizza and individual pizzas come in three different sizes.

a) If any nonempty subset of the ten toppings can be added to each size of pizza, how many different individual pizzas can be ordered?

b) How many pizzas can be ordered that have at least one meat topping and at least one vegetable topping?

7. A man invites a nonempty subset of ten friends to a party.

a) In how many ways can he do it, if two of the friends are married to each other and must be invited together or not at all?

b) Repeat part (a) if instead the two friends are recently divorced and cannot both be invited at the same time.

8. The five officers of a juggling club line up for a photograph. If two are close friends and always stand together, in how many ways can all five officers line up for a photograph?

9. Three different math books and two different physics books are arranged on a bookshelf.

a) In how many different orders can they be arranged if all the math books are together and all the physics books are together?

b) In how many ways can they be arranged if no two math books are together?

10. On the menu of a Chinese restaurant there are 7 chicken dishes, 6 beef dishes, 6 pork dishes, 8 seafood dishes, and 9 vegetable dishes.

a) In how many ways can a family order if they choose exactly one dish of each kind?

b) In how many ways can they order if at most one dish of each kind is chosen?

ADVANCED PROBLEMS

11. Four married couples attend a party.

a) Suppose each man dances with each woman except his own spouse. How many different pairs dance together?

b) Suppose each person shakes hands with every other person, except their own spouse, exactly once. How many handshakes take place?

12. Twelve distinct books are lined up on a shelf. If four of the books are blue, how many of the arrangements have all four blue books together?

13. The combination of a certain combination lock consists of three numbers from 1 through 12 in a sequence with no two consecutive numbers the same. How many different combinations are possible?

14. A domino is a 1×2 rectangular tile divided into two square halves. The squares in a standard set of dominos are each marked with zero to six spots. If every domino is different, how many dominos are there in a complete set of dominos? In particular, explain why your answer is less than 49.

15. a) How many 10-digit integers (leading zeros are not allowed) have no consecutive digits that are the same?
    b) How many 10-digit integers have exactly one pair of consecutive digits that are the same?

16. A switching function of n variables assigns to each n-digit binary sequence a value of 0 or 1. A switching function is called self-dual if the assigned value of a sequence S is unchanged when the 0 digits of S are changed to 1 and vice versa. How many self-dual switching functions of n variables are there?

17. Suppose that $|A| = n$ and $|B| = m$.
    a) Compute the number of subsets of $A \times B$.
    b) Compute the number of functions from $A \times B$ to A.

18. An $m \times n$ matrix is a rectangular array of numbers containing m rows and n columns. If every number in the matrix is either a 0 or a 1
    a) How many $m \times n$ matrices are there?
    b) How many $m \times n$ matrices are there with a single 1 in each row?

19. Let S be a set of n distinct elements. Consider all functions f whose domain D (nonempty) and image $f(D)$ are both subsets of S. How many distinct functions of this kind are there?

*20. Let A be a set of n distinct elements. There is a one-to-one correspondence between binary relations on the set A and subsets $R \subseteq A \times A$.
    a) Compute the number of binary relations on A.
    b) A binary relation R is said to be symmetric if for every (a, b) in R, (b, a) is also in R. Compute the number of symmetric binary relations on A.
    c) A binary relation R is said to be antisymmetric if for every (a, b) in R $(a \neq b)$, (b, a) is not in R. Compute the number of antisymmetric binary relations on A.

*21. Let B be a set of m distinct elements. A binary operation $*$ on B can be thought of as a function $*: B \times B \to B$.
    a) Compute the number of distinct binary operations on B.

    b) A binary operation is said to be commutative if $*(x, y) = *(y, x)$ for all (x, y) in $B \times B$. Compute the number of commutative binary operations on B.

*22. Suppose that a positive integer n can be factored into primes $n = p_1^{i_1} p_2^{i_2} \cdots p_k^{i_k}$, where all the primes $p_1, p_2, \ldots, p_k$ are distinct and all the exponents $i_1, i_2, \ldots, i_k$ are positive. Compute the number of ways to factor n into two factors that are relatively prime, assuming that the order of the two factors is unimportant.

23. Find the smallest positive integer with exactly 18 positive divisors.

24. How many binary sequences of length n are palindromes? *Hint:* Two cases are needed.

2.2   CASE-BY-CASE COUNTING

The second fundamental rule for counting the number of objects in a set is called the Addition Principle and it was first introduced in Chapter 1 as a technique for computing the total number of objects in the union of two sets. We state the Addition Principle in the following general form, which can be applied to many counting procedures.

THE ADDITION PRINCIPLE FOR COUNTING PROCEDURES   If a procedure can be broken up into m events or cases whose sets of outcomes are mutually exclusive, with j_1 possible outcomes for the first event, j_2 possible outcomes for the second event, j_3 possible outcomes for the third event, ..., and j_m possible outcomes for the mth event, then the total number of outcomes of the procedure is the sum $j_1 + j_2 + j_3 + \cdots + j_m$.

    Like the Multiplication Principle, the Addition Principle is a technique for dividing complex counting problems into smaller parts. The Multiplication Principle breaks up a problem using a complete sequence of steps, each of which always happens, and counts the total number of outcomes by multiplying. On the other hand the Addition Principle breaks up a problem into different cases so that each composite outcome occurs in exactly one case and counts the total number of outcomes by adding. We often attempt to count objects that satisfy certain properties. In counting objects that have some variation of property 1, and some variation of property 2, ..., and some variation of property m, we normally use the Multiplication Principle. In counting objects that satisfy property 1, or property 2, or..., or property k, we would normally use the Addition Principle (or its generalization, the Principle of Inclusion-Exclusion, see Section 3.1).

Example 1 On a small bookshelf there are 5 different calculus books, 6 different linear algebra books, and 7 different combinatorics books.
a) In how many ways can a pair of books of different types be chosen?

Solution
Three mutually exclusive cases can occur, namely, a calculus–linear algebra pair can be chosen, a linear algebra–combinatorics pair can be chosen, or a combinatorics-calculus pair can be chosen. Thus a combination of the Multiplication Principle and the Addition Principle shows that there are $5 \times 6 + 6 \times 7 + 5 \times 7 = 107$ possible book selections.

b) In how many ways can a single book of each type be chosen?

Solution
This is a simple application of the Multiplication Principle. We have a sequence of three steps: 5 choices for a calculus book, 6 choices for a linear algebra book, and 7 choices for a combinatorics book. Thus we obtain a total of $5 \times 6 \times 7 = 210$ different book selections. ☐

Dividing Into Cases

In solving a counting problem, we often try to use the Multiplication Principle to break up the problem into a sequence of steps. However, if the objects under consideration are too varied, it may be difficult to find a sequence of independent choices that apply to all the different kinds of objects. Thus we may try to partition the objects into smaller sets of objects that are more alike.

Example 2 How many integers are there from 1 through 9999 that have distinct digits?

Solution
An integer can naturally be thought of as a sequence of digits, but in this case not all the sequences have the same length. Before choosing individual digits, we should divide the integers up into four types, namely, one-digit integers, two-digit integers, three-digit integers, and four-digit integers. Now choose individual digits starting from the left and going to the right. Each digit is chosen from the set $\{0, 1, 2, 3, 4, 5, 6, 7, 8, 9\}$ except that the first digit cannot be zero and each succeeding digit must be different from the previously chosen ones. Thus there are $9 \times 9 \times 8 \times 7$ four-digit integers with distinct digits, $9 \times 9 \times 8$ three-digit integers, 9×9 two-digit integers, and 9 one-digit integers, for a total of $9 \times 9 \times 8 \times 7 + 9 \times 9 \times 8 + 9 \times 9 + 9 = 5274$ integers with distinct digits. ☐

Example 3 How many four-digit integers are there that contain exactly one 8?

Solution
In this example each integer has four digits, however, there is another complication. A natural sequence of choices to consider would be first to choose one digit to be an 8 and then to fill in the remaining digits with some digit other than an 8. Unfortunately this sequence of choices would not be independent. The number of

ways to fill in the last three digits would depend on whether or not 8 was the first digit because the first digit has the added restriction that it cannot be zero. First we should count the four-digit integers whose only 8 is the first digit and then the four-digit integers whose only 8 is not the first digit. Thus the total number of four-digit integers with exactly one 8 is $1 \times 9 \times 9 \times 9 + 3 \times 8 \times 9 \times 9 = 2673$ integers.

Counting What You Don't Want

A set and its complement are mutually exclusive, so it is also possible to find the number of objects in a set by counting what you don't want. If the set of objects in question is contained in a larger set, you can count the objects you want by counting the total number of objects and subtracting from it the number of objects you don't want.

Example 4   A Deck of Cards

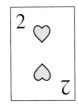

Figure 2.4

A standard deck of cards is partitioned into four types of cards called suits, namely, clubs, diamonds, hearts, and spades. (See Fig. 2.4.) A suit contains 13 cards one each of 13 different ranks, namely, 2, 3, 4, 5, 6, 7, 8, 9, 10, Jack, Queen, King, and Ace. Thus there are $4 \times 13 = 52$ different cards in the standard deck. Suppose we choose a sequence of four cards from the deck, with replacement. That is, one card at a time is chosen, and a card is always replaced in the deck after it is chosen, before the next choice.

a) In how many different ways can a sequence of four cards be chosen, with replacement, so that some card is repeated?

Solution
The total number of ways to choose a sequence, with replacement, is 52^4 since there are 52 choices for each card drawn. We are also familiar with counting sequences when no element is repeated. If no card is repeated, each card drawn must be different than the preceding ones, so the number of sequences with no repetition is $52 \times 51 \times 50 \times 49$. Thus the number of ways a sequence with some card repeated can be drawn is $52^4 - 52 \times 51 \times 50 \times 49 = 814,216$.

b) In how many ways can a sequence of four cards be chosen, with replacement, so that the fourth card is the first repeated card?

Solution

This problem can be dealt with directly using the Multiplication Principle. There are 52 choices for the first card, 51 remaining choices for the second card since it must be different than the first, 50 choices for the third card since it must be different than the first two, and three choices for the fourth card, which must be the same as one of the first three. Thus the fourth card is the first repeat in a total of $52 \times 51 \times 50 \times 3 = 397{,}800$ sequences.

c) In how many ways can a sequence of four cards be chosen, with replacement, so that the fourth card is a repeat, but not necessarily the first repeat?

Solution

The choices used in solving part (b) no longer work. They will not be independent since we do not know how many distinct cards there are among the first three cards. Again it is easier to count what you don't want. To choose a sequence where the fourth card is not a repeat, first choose the fourth card, and then choose the first three cards to be any cards different from the fourth. (Note that the natural order is not always the best for counting.) Since the fourth card is not a repeat in a total of 52×51^3 different sequences, it *is* a repeat in $52^4 - 52 \times 51^3 = 413{,}764$ sequences.   □

2.2
PROBLEMS

1. Old California license plates consisted of three digits followed by three letters or three letters followed by three digits. How many old California license plates were possible? How many old California license plates had a repeating letter or digit?

2. In one department there are 20 professors with a background in mathematics, 15 in computer science, and 5 in statistics.
    a) How many two-person committees can be formed from two people that have different backgrounds?
    b) How many three-person committees can be formed from three people with different backgrounds?

3. How many three-digit integers with distinct digits have all odd or all even digits?

4. In a computer science department there are three graduate students and ten professors.
    a) In how many ways can each student be assigned an advisor if no professor advises all three students?
    b) In how many ways if each student receives a different advisor?

5. a) How many four-letter strings chosen from the English alphabet contain at most one A?
    b) How many four-letter strings chosen from the English alphabet contain at least one A?

6. How many six-letter strings constructed from the English alphabet contain at least one of the vowels $\{a, e, i, o, u\}$?

7. a) Find the number of four-digit odd integers that have distinct digits.
   b) Find the number of four-digit even integers that have distinct digits.

8. A single die is rolled five times in a row.
   a) How many outcomes will result in five different numbers?
   b) How many outcomes will have the fifth number equal to an earlier number?

9. A sequence of five different cards is drawn from the standard deck.
   a) How many sequences will have exactly one Ace?
   b) How many sequences will have at least one Ace?

10. A sequence of five cards is drawn, with replacement.
    a) How many sequences will have at least one King?
    b) How many sequences will have at least one King or one Queen (or both)?

11. A professor has prepared seven questions for a two-page test. In how many different ways can the test be made up if at most four questions can fit on either page, the order of the questions is important, and all seven questions must be used?

ADVANCED
PROBLEMS

12. Six high school bands are lined up for a parade.
    a) In how many orders can the six bands be lined up if two of the bands have red uniforms and must be separated by at least one band?
    b) In how many ways can they be lined up if the two bands with red uniforms are put at opposite ends of the parade?

13. a) How many strings of length 8 that contain exactly two vowels (not necessarily distinct) can be constructed from the English alphabet?
    b) Repeat part (a) if the two vowels cannot be adjacent.

14. Four different dice are rolled.
    a) In how many outcomes will at least one five appear?
    b) In how many outcomes will the highest die be a five?

15. Show that the set of positive integers with distinct digits (in decimal notation) is finite by finding the number of integers of this kind.

16. How many five-digit integers with distinct digits
    a) Contain at least one 0?
    b) Contain at least one 9?
    c) Contain at least one 0 and at least one 9?

17. How many n-digit ternary sequences contain at least one pair of consecutive digits that are the same?

*18. a) How many positive integers are divisors of both 10^{40} and 20^{30}?
    b) How many positive integers are divisors of at least one of the integers 10^{40} and 20^{30}?

19. How many integers between 1 and 10,000 contain exactly one 1 and exactly one 9?

20. Compute the sum of all the integers from 1 through 200 that are a multiple of 3 or a multiple of 5.

21. a) How many n-digit decimal integers contain no consecutive digits that are the same?
   b) Of the integers in part (a), are there more even or more odd integers?

SECTION
2.3 SELECTIONS

This chapter has been concerned with problems of counting objects of a certain type. To do this we usually consider a counting procedure that is composed of smaller steps or events. Often a step in a counting procedure can be thought of as a choice or selection of k different objects from a set of n different objects. We now look at the two main models of such a selection. An ordered selection is known as a **permutation** and an unordered selection is known as a **combination**.

DEFINITION   **Permutation**

Let X be a set with n different objects. An arrangement of all the elements of X in a sequence of length n is called a permutation. An arrangement of k different elements, chosen from X, in a sequence of length k is called a k-permutation.

To describe a step in a counting procedure that involves the selection of objects as a k-permutation, k different objects must be selected and different orders of selection must lead to distinguishable outcomes. Mathematically this selection process can be described as an ordered selection, and each of its outcomes is called a k-permutation. The 3-permutations of $X = \{a, b, c, d\}$ are listed below.

$$
\begin{array}{cccccc}
abc & abd & acb & acd & adb & adc \\
bac & bad & bca & bcd & bda & bdc \\
cab & cad & cba & cbd & cda & cdb \\
dab & dac & dba & dbc & dca & dcb
\end{array}
$$

24 different 3-permutations of $\{a, b, c, d\}$

THEOREM 2.1 | The number of k-permutations or arrangements of k different objects chosen from a set of n different objects is $P(n, k) = n(n - 1)(n - 2) \cdots (n - k + 1)$.

Proof
We can count the number of permutations using the Multiplication Principle. Think of filling in the terms of a sequence with elements of X so

that each term selected is different from the previously chosen terms. Thus the number of permutations of X is $n(n-1)(n-2)\cdots 1 = n!$ and in general the number of k-permutations of X, denoted by $P(n,k)$, is $n(n-1)(n-2)\cdots (n-k+1)$.

Example 1 How many seven-letter strings with no repeated letters can be formed from the English alphabet of 26 letters?

Solution
Choose the letters in order, starting with the first letter and continuing to the last, so that each letter chosen is different from the previously chosen ones. The number of choices for the first letter is 26, for the second letter is 25, and so on. Thus the total number of strings with no repeated letters is $26 \times 25 \times 24 \times 23 \times 22 \times 21 \times 20 = P(26,7)$. Obviously these seven-letter strings are 7-permutations of the 26 letters since the order of the letters is important and no repeated letters are allowed.   □

Example 2 A computer center has to run nine different programs in a row. Four of them are written in FORTRAN and five of them are written in Pascal. Find the number of possible schedules for running the programs if the four FORTRAN programs must be run first and the five Pascal programs must be run after that.

Solution
First arrange the FORTRAN programs in the first four positions and next arrange the Pascal programs in the last five positions. There are 4! permutations of the FORTRAN programs and 5! permutations of the Pascal programs, making a total of $5! \times 4!$ different orders for the nine programs.   □

DEFINITION **Combination**
Let X be a set with n different elements. An unordered selection of a subset of k different objects from X is called a k-combination.

To describe a step in a counting procedure as a k-combination, k different objects must be selected, and all different orders of selection must be considered indistinguishable. If k-permutations can be used to count lists, sequences, ordered k-tuples, and other ordered arrangements, then k-combinations can be used to count subsets, groups, and other unordered arrangements of k objects. The 3-combinations of $\{1,2,3,4,5\}$ are listed as follows:

$$\{1,2,3\} \quad \{1,2,4\} \quad \{1,2,5\} \quad \{1,3,4\} \quad \{1,3,5\}$$
$$\{1,4,5\} \quad \{2,3,4\} \quad \{2,3,5\} \quad \{2,4,5\} \quad \{3,4,5\}$$

10 different 3-combinations of $\{1,2,3,4,5\}$

THEOREM 2.2 | The number of k-combinations or unordered selections of k different objects chosen from a set of n different objects is

$$C(n, k) = \frac{n(n-1)\cdots(n-k+1)}{k(k-1)\cdots 1} = \frac{n!}{k!(n-k)!}$$

Proof

The number of k-combinations of X is denoted by $C(n, k)$. The number of k-combinations can be computed indirectly from the number of k-permutations. A k-combination of a set X is a subset of k different elements chosen from the set X. Since any set of k elements can be arranged into exactly $k!$ sequences, $C(n, k) = P(n, k)/k!$. In other words, think of counting k-permutations using the following procedure:

1. Choose a subset of k different objects from X in $C(n, k)$ different ways.
2. Arrange the objects sequentially in one of $k!$ ways.

Thus the number of outcomes of this procedure is $C(n, k)k!$, which equals the number of k-permutations computed in the usual way, namely, $P(n, k)$, and the result follows.

Table 2.1 below summarizes the number of ways to select a subset from a set of n different objects.

TABLE 2.1

Counting Subsets Chosen from a Set of n Objects.

Type of subset	Number of choices
Any subset	2^n
Any nonempty subset	$2^n - 1$
Any k-element subset	$C(n, k)$

Example 3 | a) How many subsets of three integers can be chosen from the set $\{1, 2, 3, 4, 5, 6, 7, 8, 9, 10\}$?

Solution

The number of subsets is $C(10, 3) = 10 \times 9 \times 8/3! = 120$.

b) How many of the subsets in part (a) contain 3?

Solution

In this case choose 3 and any two of the nine remaining integers. Thus the total number of subsets containing 3 is $1 \times C(9, 2) = 36$.

c) How many of the subsets in part (a) contain at least one multiple of 3?

Solution
Here we count what we don't want and subtract. The number of subsets that do not contain any multiple of 3 is $C(7, 3) = 35$. Therefore the number of subsets that do contain at least one multiple of 3 is $120 - 35 = 85$. ◻

Example 4   A new club starts with n different members. If each member shakes hands with everyone else exactly once, how many handshakes take place?

Solution
The number of handshakes coincides with the number of pairs of different members, which is equal to $C(n, 2) = n(n - 1)/2$. ◻

Ordered versus Unordered Selections

We have seen that the main difference between a permutation and a combination is the difference between an ordered and an unordered selection. Note that it is not possible to count the number of k-combinations directly by a sequential counting procedure. Therefore when k identical selections from a single set are made in a counting procedure, we should consider these to be a single step with $C(n, k)$ outcomes to avoid overcounting. As a general rule of thumb, we should assume that order is unimportant unless it is naturally important or specifically stated to be so.

Example 5   Suppose that a certain juggling club has 17 members.
a) In how many ways can they choose four different members to be president, vice-president, secretary, and treasurer?

Solution
A set of officers is an ordered arrangement since each selection (office) is different. Thus there are $P(17, 4)$ different sets of officers that can be chosen.

b) In how many ways can they choose four different members to form a juggling team?

Solution
The four positions on the team are identical, so we use an unordered selection. Therefore the number of different teams is $C(17, 4)$.

c) In how many ways can a captain and three regular team members be chosen?

Solution
First choose a captain and then a group of three team members from the 16 remaining persons. By the Multiplication Principle, there are a total of $17 \times C(16, 3)$ different teams. ◻

Example 6   How many four-digit integers are there where each digit is greater than those to the right?

Solution
A digit-by-digit selection is probably inappropriate since these choices are not naturally independent for this problem. Since the four digits are distinct, consider

the following counting procedure:

1. Choose 4 distinct digits.

2. Arrange them in decreasing order from left to right.

By the Multiplication Principle, the total number of integers of this type is $C(10, 4) \times 1 = 210$ integers. Note that even though we are considering an arrangement where the order is important, our counting procedure uses an unordered selection.   ☐

Probability

One historically important application of counting is that of computing probabilities. Pascal used his famous triangle (See Section 2.5) around 1650 to try to compute certain gambling probabilities. Indeed any counting problem that asks for the number of outcomes of a certain type is closely related to the probability problem, which asks what fraction of outcomes there are of that same type. In probability we also begin by thinking of a procedure that has a number of possible outcomes. The set of all possible outcomes is called the **sample space** S. An event E consists of some subset of the outcomes. We will only concern ourselves with the computation of probabilities when the outcomes of the sample space are all equally likely to occur. In that case we say that S is an **equiprobable space**, and we have the following formula for the probability of an event E occurring. It was first developed over two hundred years ago by the French mathematician Laplace.

DEFINITION   If E is any event contained in an equiprobable sample space S, the probability of E is $|E|/|S|$.

In this case we see that a probability is always a fraction between 0 and 1. Intuitively the probability is close to 0 for an event that rarely occurs, close to 1 for an event that usually occurs, and close to .5 for an event that occurs about as often as it does not occur.

Example 7   Consider a procedure where a single coin is flipped four times in a row. The outcome of each flip is either a head or a tail, which we represent by an H or a T, respectively. Thus each outcome in the sample space can be represented by one of the 16 sequences of length 4, where each symbol is either an H or a T, thus $S = \{\text{HHHH}, \text{HHHT}, \ldots, \text{TTTT}\}$.

If we are mainly interested in the number of heads that occur during an outcome, there are five possibilities, namely, that 0, 1, 2, 3, or 4 heads can occur. Suppose that E is the event consisting of all outcomes where exactly 2 heads occur, then E is the subset of S consisting of sequences with 2 H's and 2 T's. The sequences of this kind can be counted by the following procedure:

1. Choose 2 H-positions to be filled, in $C(4, 2)$ different ways.

2. Fill in the remaining two positions with T's, for a total of 6 different sequences.

Since each sequence in S occurs equally often and E contains 6 sequences, the probability of E occurring is $6/16 = 3/8$. On the other hand, we could have considered the sample space consisting of the outcomes $\{0, 1, 2, 3, 4\}$, which correspond to the number of heads that can occur in the four flips. Clearly we would have made a mistake in assuming that the probability of 2 heads is $1/5$. In this sample space the outcomes are no longer equally likely, so the basic formula does not apply. □

Example 8   The Game of Poker

In the game of poker a player receives a subset of 5 cards, called a poker hand, from the standard deck of 52 cards. (See Fig. 2.5.) The order in which the cards are received is not important, just the actual cards themselves. Therefore the number of different poker hands is $C(52, 5)$. Certain combinations of cards occur less frequently than others and thus are considered more valuable in the game of poker.

a) A full house is a poker hand that has three cards of one rank and two cards of another different rank. What is the probability of receiving a full-house poker hand?

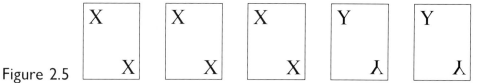

Figure 2.5

Solution

We use the following sequential counting procedure to count full-house poker hands:

1. Choose a three-card rank.
2. Choose three cards from that rank.
3. Choose a different two-card rank.
4. Choose two cards from the second rank.

Applying the Multiplication Principle, we see that the probability of receiving a full house is $(13 \times 12 \times C(4, 3) \times C(4, 2) = 3744)/C(52, 5)$.

b) A four-of-a-kind poker hand contains four cards of one rank and one card of another different rank. (See Fig. 2.6.) What is the probability of receiving a four-of-a-kind poker hand?

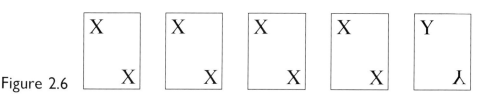

Figure 2.6

Solution
We use the following sequential counting procedure to count four-of-a-kind poker hands:

1. Choose a four-card rank.
2. Choose all four cards from that rank.
3. Choose one of the remaining cards.

Thus the probability of receiving a four-of-a-kind poker hand is $(13 \times 1 \times 48 = 624)/C(52, 5)$. Therefore a four-of-a-kind poker hand is better than a full house because it occurs less frequently.   ☐

2.3
PROBLEMS

1. Consider a contest among 20 people.
   a) If a \$100 prize, a \$50 prize, and a \$25 prize are awarded, how many results are possible, assuming that any person receives at most one prize?
   b) If three \$50 prizes are awarded, how many results are possible?

2. How many binary sequences of length n will contain exactly 3 digits that are 0's?

3. A subset of three distinct positive integers, each less than 20, is selected.
   a) How many subsets will contain all even numbers?
   b) How many subsets will contain exactly one even number?
   c) How many subsets will contain at least one even number?
   d) For how many subsets will the three integers selected add to an even number?

4. a) How many teams of 5 players can be chosen from a group of 10 players?
   b) How many teams will include the best player and exclude the worst player?

5. a) Count the number of arrangements of the letters in PHYSICAL.
   b) Count the number of arrangements of the letters in PHYSICS.

6. How many arrangements of the letters in DIGITAL have two consecutive I's?

7. An essay exam has 10 different questions. A student must choose to answer 7 out of 10 questions.
   a) In how many ways can the questions be chosen if the student must answer the first two questions?
   b) In how many ways can the questions be chosen if the student must answer at least four out of the first five questions?

8. A bag holds 24 different objects, of which 6 are orange, 6 are white, 6 are yellow, and 6 are red. If a juggler selects three objects to juggle, what is the probability that
   a) All 3 objects have the same color?
   b) All 3 objects have different colors?

9. A small computer company has 50 applicants for 6 jobs.
    a) Assuming that all 6 jobs are different and that each applicant can be hired for any of the 6 jobs, in how many ways can all 6 jobs be filled?
    b) Repeat part (a) if instead the company must fill 3 identical programming jobs and 3 identical engineering jobs.

10. Suppose that a club has eight male and nine female members. In how many ways can a four-person committee be chosen if
    a) Exactly two women committee members are to be chosen?
    b) At least two women committee members are to be chosen?

11. A three-of-a-kind poker hand contains three cards of one rank and two cards of other different ranks. What is the probability of getting a three-of-a-kind poker hand?

12. Twenty slips of paper are numbered from 1 through 20 and are placed in a hat.
    a) If two different slips are drawn, what is the probability that the two numbers drawn differ by just one?
    b) What is the probability that the two numbers differ by exactly k?

13. a) What is the probability that a three-element subset selected at random from $\{1, 2, 3, \ldots, 10\}$ contains the integer 7?
    b) What is the probability that a three-element subset has 7 as its largest element?

14. In a group of 30 ball bearings, 5 are defective. If 10 ball bearings are chosen, what is the probability that none of them is defective?

15. What is the probability that a poker hand of five cards has at least one pair (two cards of the same rank)?

16. If eight different books, five math books and three computer science books, are randomly arranged on a shelf, what is the probability that all three computer science books are together?

17. What is the probability that a randomly chosen three-digit integer is divisible by 3 or 4?

18. In a group of five randomly chosen people, what is the probability that exactly four were born on the same day of the week?

**ADVANCED
PROBLEMS**

19. At a dance there are 20 single women and 30 single men. In how many ways can they form 15 male-female couples to dance simultaneously?

20. On a certain weekend, 20 football games are played, and for each game three outcomes, win, lose, or tie, are possible. In how many ways can a football prognosticator predict one of these three outcomes for each game and end up predicting correctly on exactly 15 games?

21. In how many ways can 10 different books be distributed to three students so that each student receives at least 3 books?

22. In how many ways can eight identical rooks be placed on an ordinary 8×8 chessboard so that no two are in the same row or column? In how many ways, if each rook has a different color?

23. How many n-digit ternary sequences contain exactly k 0's?

24. a) How many poker hands contain exactly two hearts?
b) How many poker hands contain at least one card in each suit?

25. a) Explain why the number of five-card poker hands containing at least three spades is not $C(13, 3) \times C(49, 2)$.
b) Find the correct answer.

26. In one version of the game of poker, seven cards are dealt to a player (the order of distribution is unimportant). How many different poker hands have three different pairs (two cards of the same rank) and one card of a fourth different rank?

27. A subset of four distinct integers is chosen from the set $\{1, 2, \ldots, 25\}$.
a) In how many subsets will the highest integer chosen be greater than 20?
b) In how many subsets will the highest integer chosen be equal to 20?

28. Suppose a radio station name consists of four distinct letters, the first of which is a K. What is the probability that in a randomly chosen name, the letters are in alphabetical order?

29. If 15 players are separated at random into three teams of five each, what is the probability that two brothers will be on different teams?

30. In the situation described in Problem 29, what is the probability that three brothers will be completely separated, one on each team?

31. Eight different pairs of shoes are stored in a bag. If two right shoes and two left shoes are chosen at random, what is the probability that at least one matching pair of shoes is chosen?

32. In the game of KENO a player chooses a subset of eight different positive integers less than 100. Another subset of eight different integers is chosen by the house.
a) What is the probability that the two subsets have exactly five integers in common?
b) What is the probability that the two subsets have more than five integers in common?

33. A bridge hand contains 13 cards chosen from the standard deck.
a) What is the probability that two bridge hands chosen at random will have exactly k cards in common, for $0 \le k \le 13$?
b) For which value of k is this probability the greatest?

34. a) How many 4-tuples of integers (a, b, c, d) satisfy $0 < a < b < c < d < 20$?
b) How many 4-tuples of integers (w, x, y, z) satisfy $0 \le w \le x \le y \le z \le 20$?

35. a) Given n points in the plane with no three collinear, that is, no three lying on the same straight line, find the number of different lines that can be drawn through pairs of these points.

b) For an arbitrary set of n points, not all on one line, show that at least n different lines can always be drawn through pairs of these points.

*36. Given n points on a circle, all possible line segments with these points as endpoints are drawn.

a) If no three lines meet at a common point in the interior of the circle, find the number of intersection points of these lines inside the circle.

b) Show that the number of regions the interior of the circle is divided into by the line segments is $C(n,4) + C(n,2) + 1$.

*37. Let each of m distinct points on the positive end of the x-axis be joined by a straight line segment to each of n points on the positive end of the y-axis. Obtain a formula for the number of intersection points of these segments (not including the axis points), assuming that no three lines meet at the same point.

*38. Six points are chosen on a plane so that no three are collinear. If a straight line is drawn through every pair of points, what is the maximum number of different points at which these lines may intersect one another?

2.3
SUPPLEMENTARY COMPUTER PROJECTS

1. Calculating Permutations and Combinations

a) Write a computer program that calculates $n!$ for a given nonnegative integer n (starting with $0! = 1$).

b) Write a program that calculates $P(n, k)$, the number of k-permutations that can be chosen from a set of n objects, for a given pair k and n satisfying $0 \le k \le n$.

c) Write a program that calculates $C(n, k)$, the number of k-combinations that can be chosen from a set of n objects, for a given pair k and n satisfying $0 \le k \le n$.

2. The Birthday Problem

Write a program to determine the probability that in a group of n randomly selected people, at least two people will have the same birthday. Use this program to find the smallest integer n for which the probability is greater than .5. (To simplify the computation, you may ignore leap years and assume that all 365 birthdays are equally likely.)

SECTION 2.4 SELECTIONS WITH UNLIMITED REPETITION

Sometimes we need to select sequences of elements from a set X, and repeated selections are allowed.

DEFINITION   **Permutation with Unlimited Repetition**
If we select a sequence of k objects from a set with unlimited repetition allowed, such an arrangement will be called a k-permutation with unlimited repetition.

THEOREM 2.3
The number of k-permutations with unlimited repetition allowed chosen from a set with n objects is n^k.

Proof
If X is a set with n elements, the number of k-permutations with unlimited repetition is n^k, because there are n choices for each of the k selections.

A function $f: X \to Y$ can be thought of as an assignment of the different objects in X to images in Y. The process of choosing the images for a function $f: X \to Y$ can be thought of as a permutation with unlimited repetition since we are selecting one image for each of the different elements of X and unlimited repetition is allowed.

Example I   Let $A = \{1, 2, 3, 4, 5, 6\}$ and $B = \{a, b, c, d, e\}$.
a) Find the number of functions from A to B.

Solution
In selecting images for a function, arbitrary selections are allowed. Therefore the total number of functions from A to B is 5^6.

b) Find the number of injections from B to A.

Solution
In selecting images for an injection, no repeated selections are allowed. Thus there are 6 choices for the image of a, 5 remaining choices for the image of b, and so on. Therefore the total number of injections from B to A is $P(6, 5) = 720$.

c) Find the number of surjections from A to B.

Solution
An element by element selection of the images would not lead to a sequential counting procedure. However, since the size of A is one larger than the size of B, there is one element of B that is the image of two elements of A and every other element of B is the image of exactly one element of A. Thus the number of surjections from A to B can be counted by the following counting procedure:

1. Select a two-element subset of A.

2. Assign images without repetition to the two-element subset and the four remaining individual elements of A.

This shows that the total number of surjections from A to B is $C(6, 2)5! = 1800$. In general it is more difficult to count the surjections from one set to another (see Section 3.3).   □

DEFINITION   **Combination with Unlimited Repetition**

A k-combination with unlimited repetition is an unordered group of k objects chosen from n different types of objects, with an unlimited amount of each type available.

First we look at several different formulations of the basic model.

Nonnegative Integer Solutions of Linear Equations

A combination with repetition can also be described by saying that we select x_1 objects of type 1, x_2 objects of type $2, \ldots, x_n$ objects of type n for some n-tuple of integers $(x_1, x_2, \ldots, x_n)$. Each of the integers $x_1, x_2, \ldots, x_n$ is nonnegative, and the sum of these integers $x_1 + x_2 + \cdots x_n$ is equal to k. Each n-tuple of nonnegative integers that is a solution of the linear equation $x_1 + x_2 + \cdots + x_n = k$ corresponds to exactly one k-combination with repetition and vice versa, which means that the number of k-combinations with unlimited repetition is exactly equal to the number of nonnegative integer solutions of $x_1 + x_2 + x_3 + \cdots + x_n = k$.

Example 2   A student delivers an order for seven ice cream cones to an ice cream shop that carries three flavors: vanilla, chocolate, and strawberry. An order form with three columns, one column for each flavor, is used to help the student remember the order. The order is represented on the form by seven stars, each of which is positioned in one of the three columns. An order for 1 vanilla cone, 4 chocolate cones, and 2 strawberry cones is represented in Fig. 2.7.

Figure 2.7

vanilla	chocolate	strawberry
*	* * * *	* *

Our goal is to find the number of different seven-cone orders that are possible. We see that this is also equal to the number of different ways of placing 7 *'s in the three columns of the order form. Since the order can also be thought of as a sequence containing 7 *'s and 2 |'s, we see that the number of ways to place the *'s is $C(9, 7)$.
□

In general, think of constructing an order form for selecting a k-combination with repetition from n different types of objects. If we put the order on a single horizontal line, we need $n - 1$ |'s to divide the order form into n sections. In the first section (before the first |), we put x_1 *'s to represent the x_1 objects of type 1 we wish to choose. In the second section (between the first and second |'s), we put x_2 *'s to represent the objects of type 2 we want to choose, followed by x_3 *'s in the third section, and so on. Finally, in the nth section (following the last |), we put x_n *'s to represent the x_n objects of type n to be chosen. Since each integer x_i in the linear equation is now represented by a string of x_i *'s, we obtain a sequence of k *'s and $n - 1$ |'s. Also any sequence of k *'s and $n - 1$ |'s can be thought of as an order form for some k-combination with repetition because the $n - 1$ |'s divide the sequence into n subsequences of *'s (some of which may be empty) representing the number of objects of each type to be chosen. (See Fig. 2.8.)

Figure 2.8

$$** \,|\, *** \,|\, ** \quad \rightarrow \quad (2, 3, 2)$$

$$(4, 0, 3) \quad \rightarrow \quad **** \,|\,|\, ***$$

THEOREM 2.4

The number of k-combinations with unlimited repetition chosen from n different types of objects is exactly $C(k + n - 1, k)$.

Proof

The number of k-combinations with unlimited repetition is also equal to the number of sequences of length $k + n - 1$, consisting of k *'s and $n - 1$ |'s. The number of sequences of this kind can be computed by the following procedure:

1. Choosing k *-positions in $C(k + n - 1, k)$ ways.
2. Choose the $n - 1$ |-positions in $C(n - 1, n - 1)$ ways.

Thus the number of order forms is $C(k + n - 1, k)$. Note that by choosing the *'s and the |'s in the opposite order, this answer is also equal to $C(k + n - 1, n - 1)$.

Example 3 Find the number of nonnegative integer solutions of the equation $x_1 + x_2 + x_3 + x_4 + x_5 = 30$.

Solution

The number of solutions in nonnegative integers is $C(30 + 5 - 1, 30) = C(34, 30) = 46{,}376$. $\square$

Example 4 The expansion of $(x + y)^6$ contains 7 terms. Find the number of terms in the expansion of the multinomial $(x + y + z)^6$.

Solution

Each term of the expansion is a coefficient times a product of the form $x^{i_1} y^{i_2} z^{i_3}$, where each exponent is a nonnegative integer. Also the sum of all the exponents is 6 because each factor $(x + y + z)$ contributes a single symbol to the product. Thus the number of terms in the multinomial expansion also equals the number of nonnegative integer solutions of the equation $i_1 + i_2 + i_3 = 6$. We conclude that the number of terms in the multinomial expansion is $C(8, 6) = 28$. $\square$

In this section and later in Section 3.3, we encounter a variety of problems that can be modeled by distributions.

DEFINITION　Distribution

A distribution is an assignment from a collection of objects to a collection of recipients. Each object is assigned to exactly one recipient and the order of distribution is immaterial.

Note that the process for filling out an order form for a k-combination with unlimited repetition can also be explained naturally using a distribution. The $n - 1$ |'s divide the order form into n different sections, and the k identical *'s are distributed to these sections.

Example 5
a) Twelve identical juggling balls are distributed to three different jugglers. How many distributions are possible?

Solution
The number of distributions is equal to the number of nonnegative integer solutions of $x_1 + x_2 + x_3 = 12$, which is $C(14, 12) = 91$.

b) How many distributions are possible if five red, three blue, and four yellow balls (identical except for color) are distributed to three different jugglers?

Solution
In this case we first distribute the red balls, then the blue balls, and finally the yellow balls. Thus the total number of distributions is $C(7, 5)C(5, 3)C(6, 4) = 3150$. □

Positive Integer Solutions of Linear Equations

Consider our second formulation of the basic model in terms of integer solutions of the linear equation $x_1 + x_2 + x_3 + \cdots + x_n = k$, where each x_i is a nonnegative integer. We can also compute the number of solutions if certain simple restrictions are put on the values of x_i. Sometimes we want to consider only positive integer solutions, that is, solutions where each $x_i \geq 1$. In terms of selections we consider k-combinations with unlimited repetition, where at least one object from each of the n different types of objects is selected.

THEOREM 2.5

The number of k-combinations with repetition, where at least one object from each of n different types of objects is chosen, is $C(k - 1, k - n)$.

Proof
Since the order of selection is unimportant, consider the following counting procedure:

1. Choose a single object of each type.
2. Arbitrarily choose $k - n$ objects from the n different types of objects.

There is only one way to complete the first step and $C(k - 1, k - n)$ ways to complete the second. Therefore the number of positive integer solutions of $x_1 + x_2 + \cdots + x_n = k$ is $C(k - 1, k - n)$.

Example 6   In how many ways can 20 coins be selected from a bag containing an unlimited number of pennies, nickels, dimes, quarters, and half dollars?

Solution
The number of arbitrary selections is $C(24, 20)$. However, if at least one coin of each type must be selected, only $C(19, 15)$ selections are possible.   □

Example 7   A bookshelf holds 11 different books in a row. (See Fig. 2.9.) In how many ways can we choose 4 books so that no two consecutive books are chosen?

Figure 2.9

Solution
Represent the books by a sequence of *'s and |'s, where | represents a chosen book, and * represents an unchosen book. Thus we have a sequence of 4 |'s and 7 *'s. The 4 |'s divide the *'s into 5 subsequences, where the first and the last subsequences may be empty but the second, third, and fourth subsequences contain at least one * because no consecutive books may be chosen. (See Fig. 2.10.)

$$\{2, 4, 7, 10\} \quad \rightarrow \quad *|*|**|**|*$$

Figure 2.10 $|*|*|****|* \quad \rightarrow \quad \{1, 3, 5, 10\}$

It is also easy to see from Fig. 2.10 that each of the sequences we have just described corresponds to an allowable book selection, so it suffices to count the number of sequences of this type. Each sequence corresponds to exactly one 5-tuple $(x_1, x_2, x_3, x_4, x_5)$, where x_i represents the number of *'s in the ith subsequence. As we have seen, $x_1, x_5 \geq 0$, $x_2, x_3, x_4 \geq 1$, and $x_1 + x_2 + x_3 + x_4 + x_5 = 7$. A slight variation of the usual argument shows that we can distribute one * to each of the second, third, and fourth subsequences and then distribute the remaining 4 *'s at random to any of the 5 subsequences. Thus we conclude that the number of allowable book selections corresponds to the number of nonnegative integer solutions of $x_1 + x_2 + x_3 + x_4 + x_5 = 4$, which is $C(8, 4) = 70$.   □

Example 8   When three dice (Fig. 2.11) are rolled, what is the probability that the three dice add up to 10?

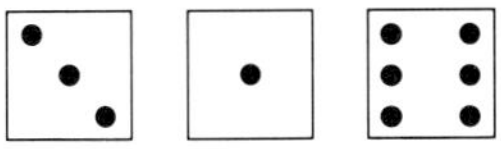

Figure 2.11

Solution

When several dice are rolled, it is easier to think of rolling different dice, even if they are not naturally different, because the probabilities remain the same and the computations are easier. When three different dice are rolled, the total number of outcomes is $6^3 = 216$, and each of these outcomes is equally likely. If the dice are numbered 1, 2, and 3, and x_i is the number appearing on die i, then $x_1 + x_2 + x_3 = 10$ and $1 \le x_i \le 6$. The number of integer solutions of this equation also equals the number of integer solutions of $x_1 + x_2 + x_3 = 7$, with $0 \le x_i \le 5$. By including all the nonnegative integer solutions and subtracting the ones with $x_i \ge 6$, we obtain $C(9, 7) - 3C(3, 1) = 27$. Thus the probability of rolling three dice and getting a 10 is $27/216 = 1/8$. $\square$

In this chapter we have looked at several counting models involving the selection of k objects from a set of n different objects. We differentiate between selections for different or ordered positions, which we call k-permutations, and selections for indistinguishable positions, which we call k-combinations. We also considered selections when unlimited repetition was allowed. Thus we can now complete the following table of selection models.

	Selections	
	Ordered	**Unordered**
No repetition	The number of selections is $P(n, k)$. An injection is an ordered selection of images without repetition.	The number of selections is $C(n, k)$.
Unlimited repetition allowed	The number of selections is n^k. A function is an ordered selection of images with repetition allowed	The number of selections is $C(k + n - 1, k)$. If at least one of each type is selected, the number of selections is $C(k - 1, k - n)$. A distribution from identical objects to different recipients is an unordered selection of recipients with repetition allowed.

2.4 PROBLEMS

1. A pastry shop has five kinds of pastries. In how many ways can a customer select a dozen pastries to buy if the order of selection is immaterial? In how many ways can a customer buy a dozen pastries if at least one of each kind is selected?

2. There are 12 chairs in a row on which we place five final exams, with at most one exam per chair. In how many ways can this be done if no two adjacent chairs can have an exam?

3. How many terms are there in the expansion of
    a) $(x + y + z)^n$ b) $(x + y + z + w)^n$

4. a) Find the number of nonnegative integer solutions of $x_1 + x_2 + x_3 + x_4 + x_5 = 24$.
    b) Repeat part (a) if each $x_i \geq 2$.
    c) Repeat part (a) if each x_i is even.

5. a) A domino is a 1×2 rectangular tile with $0, 1, 2, \ldots$, or 12 spots possible on each half, with possibly an equal number of spots on each half. How many different dominos are possible?
    b) How many different dominos are possible if $0, 1, 2, \ldots, n$ spots are allowed on each half?

6. An ice cream store has 30 flavors of ice cream. When 20 cones are selected, one flavor on each cone, how many selections are possible if
    a) No repetition is allowed?
    b) Repetition is allowed and at least half of the cones selected are chocolate?

7. a) How many results are possible when five identical dice are rolled?
    b) How many results if n identical dice are rolled?
    c) Repeat part (b) if each number 1, 2, 3, 4, 5, 6 appears at least once.
    d) How many results are possible when 5 white dice, 10 red dice, and 15 blue dice are rolled?

8. a) A small library contains 15 different books. If five different students simultaneously check out one book each, how many different book selections are possible?
    b) A catalog contains 15 different books. If five different students each order one book from the catalog (repetition is possible), how many different book selections are possible?

9. Consider the strings of length 7 formed from six distinct symbols.
    a) Explain why the number of strings that contain each symbol at least once is not $6 \times 5 \times 4 \times 3 \times 2 \times 1 \times 6$.
    b) Find the correct answer.

10. If 12 different candy bars are distributed to four children, what is the probability that the smallest child receives either one or two candy bars?

11. In how many ways can 40 identical cans of soup be distributed to five poor families if each family receives at least five cans?

12. If a collection of 10 pennies, 10 nickels, 10 dimes, and 10 quarters are distributed at random to five children, what is the probability that each child receives at least one coin of each type?

13. In how many ways can 100 identical chairs be distributed to five different classrooms if the two largest rooms together receive exactly half the chairs?

14. How many different functions are there from a set A, with n different elements, to a set B, with $n + 2$ elements? How many injections are there from A to B? How many surjections are there from B to A?

15. a) Find the number of positive integer solutions of $x_1 + x_2 + x_3 + x_4 + x_5 = 25$.
   b) Repeat part (a) if each x_i is odd.

16. How many 5-tuples of nonnegative integers $(x_1, x_2, x_3, x_4, x_5)$ satisfy $x_1 + x_3 = 6$ and $x_1 + x_2 + x_3 + x_4 + x_5 = 21$?

17. Find the number of nonnegative integer solutions of $x_1 + x_2 + x_3 + x_4 + x_5 + x_6 < 28$.

18. In how many ways can four blocks of four consecutive seats be chosen from 25 consecutive seats?

19. Suppose that k objects are chosen from n different types of objects with unlimited repetition allowed.
   a) How many selections are possible if exactly one type of object is not selected?
   b) How many selections are possible if exactly m types of objects are not selected?

20. Given n identical objects and n additional objects that are different from these and from each other, find the number of ways to select n objects out of these $2n$ objects.

21. In how many ways can 10 letters be selected from the English alphabet if repetition is allowed and each of the five vowels is selected at least once (order of selection is unimportant)?

22. a) Show that there are $C(y + 1, x)$ sequences of x 1's and y 0's with no two 1's adjacent.
   b) If r elements are chosen at random from the set $\{1, 2, 3, \ldots, n\}$, what is the probability that the resulting r-subset does not contain two consecutive integers?

23. How many ways are there to arrange the 26 letters of the English alphabet so that no two vowels $\{a, e, i, o, u\}$ appear consecutively?

24. A coded message is a sequence containing nine distinct nonzero digits and a total of thirty 0's. If there are at least two 0's between each pair of nonzero digits, how many messages are possible?

25. During a 12-hour day, a teacher is scheduled to teach for four 1-hour periods.
   a) In how many ways can the four hours be assigned so that no two consecutive hours are assigned?

b) In how many ways can the four hours be assigned if no block of more than two consecutive hours can be assigned?

26. A firefighter works three shifts, each of five consecutive days, in a month of 31 days. In how many ways can the shifts be scheduled if at least three days of rest must be scheduled between shifts?

27. In how many ways can $2n$ letters be selected from a collection of n a's, n b's, n c's, and n d's?

28. A stack of poker chips contains four blue, five red, and six white chips. How many stacks of this kind have no white chips together?

*29. The integer 3 can be expressed as an ordered sum of positive integers in four ways, namely, 3, 2 + 1, 1 + 2, and 1 + 1 + 1. Show that any positive integer n can be expressed as an ordered sum in 2^{n-1} ways.

2.5 BINOMIAL COEFFICIENTS

In the next two sections we shall see how combinatorics can be used to solve many problems related to binomial and multinomial coefficients.

Blockwalking

Consider the problem of traveling in the plane from the origin $(0, 0)$ to some other point $(k, n - k)$ in the first quadrant. We take only unit steps, and only in the positive x direction or the positive y direction, to avoid backtracking. The problem of walking from one intersection to another along the blocks of a city is similar to this problem of walking between points in the plane, hence the name "blockwalking." Each individual step can be represented by an x or a y, and the entire trip can be represented by a sequence of k x's and $n - k$ y's.

Example 1 A professor walks every day from his house to his school, which is 7 blocks north and 4 blocks west of his house. In how many ways can he walk the 11 blocks from his house to school?

Solution
This is equivalent to the problem of walking from $(0, 0)$ to $(7, 4)$ in the plane if only unit steps are allowed. (See Fig. 2.12.)

Figure 2.12
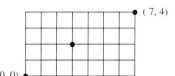

The following counting procedure can be used to compute the number of sequences of length 11 with 7 x's and 4 y's:

1. Choose 7 different x-positions from the 11 different positions.
2. Choose 4 different y-positions from the remaining 4 positions. A simple application of the multiplication principle shows that there are $C(11, 4)$ sequences of this type. Thus the total number of trips is $C(11, 4) = 330$.   □

Example 2   In how many ways can the professor in Example 1 walk to school if he first stops at a newsstand that is 3 blocks north and 2 blocks west of his house?

Solution
We can think of this as two trips in a row since he first walks from his house to the newsstand and then from the newsstand to school. The total number of different trips is thus $C(5, 2)C(6, 2) = 150$.   □

Expanding Binomials

A binomial is an algebraic expression with two summands, for example, $(x + y)$. While expanding the power of a binomial like $(x + y)^n$, sequences of x's and y's are again encountered. We are all familiar with the process of multiplying out such powers, specifically, say, $(x + y)^3$. First we apply the Distributive Law to show that $(x + y)^3 = (x + y)(x + y)(x + y) = xxx + xyx + yxx + yyx + xxy + xyy + yxy + yyy$, and then we combine like terms (since multiplication is commutative) and use exponents to obtain $x^3 + 3x^2y + 3xy^2 + y^3$. We consider some shortcut methods for computing the coefficients of the general binomial expansion, $(x + y)^n$, for any positive integer n.

THEOREM 2.6   **(Binomial Theorem)**

For any positive integer n, the expansion of the binomial $(x + y)^n$ is given by

$$(x + y)^n = \sum_{i=0}^{n} C(n, i)x^i y^{n-i}$$

Proof
In computing $(x + y)^n$ we have n factors of $(x + y)$ to multiply out. The expansion of $(x + y)^n$ is a sum containing many sequences of x's and y's multiplied together. Since each factor of $(x + y)$ can contribute either an x or a y to a product, the expansion will contain all the 2^n different sequences of n symbols, where each symbol is either an x or a y. Because the order in which numbers are multiplied has no effect on the outcome, the sequences with k x's and $n - k$ y's are combined to give a single term $\binom{n}{k} x^k y^{n-k}$. The binomial coefficient $\binom{n}{k}$ is equal to the number of different sequences with k x's and $n - k$ y's. Since there are $C(n, k)$ sequences of this type, $\binom{n}{k} = C(n, k)$, and these two symbols can be used interchangeably.

Example 3   Find the coefficient of x^7 in $(1 + 3x)^{10}$.

Solution
The term containing x^7 will be $C(10,3)1^3(3x)^7 = 3^7C(10,3)x^7$. Thus the coefficient of x^7 is $3^7C(10,3) = 262{,}440$. ☐

The number $C(n,k)$ can now be thought of as

1. A binomial coefficient
2. The number of sequences of k x's and $n - k$ y's
3. The number of k-element subsets of a set with n different elements
4. The number of ways to travel from $(0,0)$ to $(k, n - k)$ taking only positive unit steps in the x and y directions

Binomial coefficients also occur in many mathematical formulas and arise frequently in the analysis of algorithms, so any good mathematics and computer science student should become adept at their manipulation.

There are many interesting properties of binomial coefficients. It is easy to see that binomial coefficients are symmetrical since the counting procedure in Theorem 2.6 could just as well have started with the choice of $n - k$ y-positions. Therefore we see that $C(n,k) = C(n, n - k)$. Alternatively we could show this algebraically since $C(n,k) = n(n - 1)\cdots(n - k + 1)/k! = n!/(k!(n - k)!) = n(n - 1)\cdots(k + 1)/(n - k)! = C(n, n - k)$.

Another fact that is clear from the previous discussion is that the sum of the coefficients in the expansion of $(x + y)^n$, namely, $C(n,0) + C(n,1) + C(n,2) + \cdots + C(n,n)$, is equal to 2^n since there are 2^n sequences in the overall expansion of $(x + y)^n$. Another way to see this fact is to think of each individual term of the sum $C(n,k)$ as the number of k-element subsets of a set with n elements. We have already seen that, for any set with n elements, the total number of subsets is 2^n.

Pascal's Triangle

The mathematician Blaise Pascal noticed another pattern involving binomial coefficients. Suppose the binomial coefficients are arranged in a triangular array. There is one row and one column for each nonnegative integer, and the binomial coefficient $\binom{n}{k}$ is in the nth row and the kth column. This array is now known as Pascal's triangle, and the rows of the triangle for $n \le 6$ are as follows:

$n=0$	1	$k=0$						
$n=1$	1		1	$k=1$				
$n=2$	1		2		1	$k=2$		
$n=3$	1		3		3		1	$k=3$
$n=4$	1		4		6		4	1	$k=4$
$n=5$	1		5		10		10	5	1	$k=5$
Figure 2.13 $n=6$	1		6		15		20	15	6	1	$k=6$

In Fig. 2.13 the rows are horizontal and the columns go diagonally down from right to left. The first and the last terms in each row are 1 because $C(n, 0) = C(n, n) = 1$. Pascal noticed that the other terms in each row could be computed recursively from the terms in the preceding row. Two consecutive terms can be added together to get the term directly below them in the next row. Thus we have the following identity: $C(n, k) = C(n - 1, k - 1) + C(n - 1, k)$. This identity can be verified by noticing that $(x + y)^n = (x + y)(x + y)^{n-1} = x(x + y)^{n-1} + y(x + y)^{n-1}$. Thus the coefficient of $x^k y^{n-k}$ on the left, $C(n, k)$, equals the sum of the coefficients of $x^k y^{n-k}$ on the right, namely, $C(n - 1, k - 1) + C(n - 1, k)$, and we obtain the previous recurrence.

If we consider the partial sums of the columns of Pascal's triangle, the following formula is obtained:

$$C(k, k) + C(k + 1, k) + C(k + 2, k) + \cdots + C(n, k) = C(n + 1, k + 1)$$

This formula can be explained using blockwalking. First, the right side can be thought of as the total number of ways to travel from $(0, 0)$ to $(n - k, k + 1)$. Second, we count these trips in several cases depending on where they first intersect the line $y = k + 1$. If a trip first reaches the line $y = k + 1$ at the point $(i, k + 1)$, it first consists of a trip from $(0, 0)$ to (i, k), followed by one more step in the y direction to $(i, k + 1)$ and $(n - k - i)$ more steps in the x direction. Thus the number of trips of this type is $C(i + k, k)$. Adding these together for $i = 0, 1, 2, \ldots, n - k$, we obtain the left side of the preceding equation.

The basic formulas involving binomial coefficients are summarized as follows:

1. **Factorial Notation:** $C(n, k) = n!/(k!(n - k)!)$
2. **Row Summation:** $C(n, 0) + \cdots + C(n, n) = 2^n$
3. **Symmetry:** $C(n, k) = C(n, n - k)$
4. **Binomial Recurrence:** $C(n, k) = C(n - 1, k) + C(n - 1, k - 1)$
5. **Reduction Formula:** $C(n, k) = (n/k)C(n - 1, k - 1)$
6. **Column Summation:** $C(k, k) + \cdots + C(n, k) = C(n + 1, k + 1)$
7. **Binomial Theorem:** $(x + y)^n = C(n, n)x^n + \cdots + C(n, k)x^k y^{n-k} + \cdots + C(n, 0)y^n$

Many other useful sums and formulas can be computed using these basic formulas (See Problem 16). The study of such formulas and identities is a major topic in combinatorial mathematics of which we merely scratch the surface in this text.

Example 4   Compute the sum $(1 \times 2) + (2 \times 3) + (3 \times 4) + \cdots + n(n + 1)$.

Solution
The formula for the mth term of the series can be written using binomial coefficients because $m(m + 1) = 2C(m + 1, 2)$. Thus the sum equals $2(C(2, 2) + C(3, 2) + C(4, 2) + \cdots + C(n + 1, 2)) = 2C(n + 2, 3) = n(n + 1)(n + 2)/3$. (We shall see in Section 8.3 that any polynomial can be represented in a similar way using binomial coefficients, allowing partial sums of polynomials to be easily computed.)   □

Example 5   Evaluate $C(n, 0) + 2C(n, 1) + \cdots + 2^n C(n, n)$.

Solution

In Formula 7 from the preceding list, set $x = 1$ and $y = 2$ to obtain

$$C(n,0) + 2C(n,1) + \cdots + 2^n C(n,n) = (2+1)^n = 3^n.$$

Example 6 Evaluate $C(n,1) + 2C(n,2) + \cdots + nC(n,n)$.

Solution
Using Formula 5, we obtain

$$\begin{aligned}
C(n,1) &+ 2C(n,2) + \cdots + nC(n,n)\\
&= nC(n-1,0) + nC(n-1,1) + \cdots + nC(n-1,n-1)\\
&= n(C(n-1,0) + C(n-1,1) + C(n-1,2) + \cdots + C(n-1,n-1))\\
&= n2^{n-1}
\end{aligned}$$

Example 7 Evaluate $C(n,1) + 2^2 C(n,2) + \cdots + n^2 C(n,n)$.

Solution
A number of identities can be derived from the identity $(1+x)^n = \sum_{k=0}^n C(n,k)x^k$ by differentiating or integrating. Note that the identity in Example 6 can also be derived by first differentiating both sides of the identity with respect to x, yielding $n(1+x)^{n-1} = \sum_{k=1}^n kC(n,k)x^{k-1}$, and next setting $x=1$. Or we can continue, multiplying both sides by x to get $nx(1+x)^{n-1} = \sum_{k=1}^n kC(n,k)x^k$. Again differentiating both sides of this new equation by x, we obtain $n((1+x)^{n-1} + (n-1)x(1+x)^{n-2}) = \sum_{k=1}^n k^2 C(n,k)x^{k-1}$. Setting $x=1$ at this point gives us $n(n+1)2^{n-2} = \sum_{k=1}^n k^2 C(n,k)$, for any positive integer n.

Reliable Systems

One application of these ideas is in the study of system reliability. Suppose that a system has several different components, each of which works or fails to work independently. If a system has to be very reliable, it is likely to have built-in redundancy so that the system works even if some of the components fail to work. What is the probability that such a system works? We give a simple example.

Example 8 A rocket launch is monitored by five tracking stations around the world. Any one tracking station fails to work due to bad weather or other technical difficulties about half of the time. The spacecraft will be launched if at least two of the tracking stations are operational at the time of liftoff. What is the probability that the spacecraft will be allowed to take off during any attempt?

Solution
We use the symbol W to represent a tracking station that is working and an F to represent a tracking station that fails to work. The condition of the tracking stations at any one time can be represented by a sequence of five symbols, where each symbol is either an F or a W. The liftoff will not be allowed when the sequence has only 0 or 1 W's. There are 32 possible sequences, each of which is equally likely to occur. Thus the probability that the launch will occur during any attempt is $(32 - (C(5,0) + C(5,1)))/32 = 26/32$.

2.5
PROBLEMS

1. Show that the following formulas hold.
   a) $C(n, k) = (n/k)C(n - 1, k - 1)$
   b) $C(n, r)C(r, k) = C(n, k)C(n - k, r - k)$
   c) $C(n, 0) + C(n + 1, 1) + \cdots + C(n + k, k) = C(n + k + 1, k)$

2. Use the Binomial Theorem to expand $(2 + 3x)^5$.

3. Find the coefficient of $x^6 y^2$ in $(y - 2x)^8$.

4. Find the sum of all the coefficients in the expansion of $(3x + 4y)^6$.

5. Using the binomial expansion of $(1 + x)^n$, explain why a set S with n elements has the same number of subsets with even size as with odd size. **Hint:** Substitute $x = -1$.

6. Show that $m^2 = 2C(m, 2) + C(m, 1)$. Use this to compute the sum $1^2 + 2^2 + 3^2 + \cdots + n^2$.

7. a) Find three integers a, b, and c such that $aC(m, 3) + bC(m, 2) + cC(m, 1) = m^3$.
   b) Use this fact to compute the sum $1^3 + 2^3 + \cdots + n^3$.

8. Find the coefficient of x^5 in the expansion of $(2x + 3)(x + 1)^8$.

9. In a family with six children what is the probability of having three children of each sex? What is the probability of having two children of one sex and four of another?

10. A certain system has m components, each of which is equally likely to work or to fail independently. Suppose the system operates as long as k or more components are working.
    a) What is the probability that the system will work?
    b) What is the probability if the first component must work and at least $k - 1$ other components?

11. A restaurant needs at least one cook and at least one waitress to open. The owner hires three cooks and three waitresses, each of whom is equally likely to show up for work or call in sick. What is the probability that the restaurant will operate on any given day?

12. A player tosses a coin repeatedly. Heads is counted as one point, tails as two points. For example, if a player tosses H, T, T on his first three tosses, his score is first 1, then 3, then 5. A player tosses until his score equals or exceeds n. Show that the probability of scoring exactly n points is $(2 + (-1/2)^n)/3$.

13. What is the probability that an even number of ones turn up in a random toss of n dice?

14. Compute the probability that k tosses of a single coin are required before n heads or n tails are obtained, $n \le k \le 2n - 1$.

15. In the binomial expansion of $(5/6 + 1/6)^n$ show that the terms give the probabilities for obtaining $k = 0, 1, 2, \ldots, n$ sixes when n dice are rolled.

16. Evaluate the sums $m_0 \binom{n}{0} + m_1 \binom{n}{1} + \cdots + m_n \binom{n}{n}$ for the following sequences of multipliers.

a) $1\binom{n}{0} + 0\binom{n}{1} + 1\binom{n}{2} + 0\binom{n}{3} + \cdots + ((1 + (-1)^n)/2)\binom{n}{n} =$

b) $3\binom{n}{0} + 1\binom{n}{1} + 3\binom{n}{2} + 1\binom{n}{3} + \cdots + ((3 + (-1)^{n+1})/2)\binom{n}{n} =$

c) $1\binom{n}{0} + 2\binom{n}{1} + 1\binom{n}{2} + 2\binom{n}{3} + \cdots + ((3 + (-1)^{n+1})/2)\binom{n}{n} =$

d) $1\binom{n}{0} + 2\binom{n}{1} + 3\binom{n}{2} + 4\binom{n}{3} + \cdots + (n + 1)\binom{n}{n} =$

e) $1\binom{n}{0} - (1/2)\binom{n}{1} + (1/3)\binom{n}{2} - (1/4)\binom{n}{3} + \cdots + ((-1)^n/(n + 1))\binom{n}{n} =$

f) $1\binom{n}{0} + 3\binom{n}{1} + 5\binom{n}{2} + 7\binom{n}{3} + \cdots + (2n + 1)\binom{n}{n} =$

g) $\binom{n}{0} + \binom{n}{1}/2 + \binom{n}{2}/3 + \cdots \binom{n}{n}/(n + 1) =$

h) $1\binom{n}{0} + 1\binom{n}{1} + 2\binom{n}{2} + 3\binom{n}{3} + \cdots + F_{n+1}\binom{n}{n} =$

i) $0\binom{n}{0} + 1\binom{n}{1} - 4\binom{n}{2} + 9\binom{n}{3} - \cdots + (-1)^{n+1}n^2\binom{n}{n} =$

*17. Show that $C(n, 1)/(1 \times 2) - C(n, 2)/(2 \times 3) + \cdots + (-1)^{n+1}C(n, n)/(n(n + 1)) = 1/2 + 1/3 + \cdots + 1/(n + 1)$.

18. Find the number of ways to travel from $(0, 0)$ to $(5, 7)$ if any unit steps in the positive x direction and the positive y direction are allowed, except that it is not possible to travel from $(3, 2)$ to $(4, 2)$.

19. In the expansion of $(x + r_1)(x + r_2)(x + r_3)\cdots(x + r_n)$ where $r_1, r_2, r_3, \ldots, r_n$ are arbitrary real numbers, what can you say about the coefficient of x^i for $i = 0, 1, 2, \ldots, n$?

20. A committee of n students is chosen from a group of n males and n females.
a) How many committees of n persons can be chosen?
b) How many committees of k males and $n - k$ females can be chosen?
c) Use parts (a) and (b) to evaluate $C(n, 0)^2 + C(n, 1)^2 + C(n, 2)^2 + \cdots + C(n, n)^2$.

21. Find the value of k for which the following is as large as possible.
a) $C(2n, k)$
b) $C(2n - k, n)C(2n + k, n)$

22. In a city without one-way streets, a math professor drives to school, which is 8 blocks west and 5 blocks north of his house.
a) In how many ways can he drive to school without ever repeating his entire route if he always avoids a dangerous intersection 2 blocks west and 2 blocks north of his house?
b) In how many ways can he avoid two dangerous intersections: one 2 blocks west and 2 blocks north and the other 3 blocks west and 2 blocks north?

*23. a) Show that the number of odd terms among $C(n, 0)$, $C(n, 1)$, $C(n, 2), \ldots,$ $C(n, n)$ is a power of 2.
b) Determine the number of odd binomial coefficients in the expansion of $(x + y)^{1000}$.

24. Show that for $n \geq 2$, $0 = C(n, 1) - 2C(n, 2) + 3C(n, 3) - \cdots + (-1)^{n-1}nC(n, n)$.

*25. Show that $C(p, 1), C(p, 2), \ldots, C(p, p - 1)$ are all divisible by p if and only if p is a prime.

26. Show that $\sum_{j=0}^{n} \sum_{i=j}^{n} C(n, i)C(i, j) = 3^n$.

27. Show $C(m, 0)C(n, k) + C(m, 1)C(n, k + 1) + \cdots + C(m, m)C(n, k + m) = C(m + n, n - k)$.

28. Show that $1 = (1 + x)^n - C(n, 1)x(1 + x)^{n-1} + C(n, 2)x^2(1 + x)^{n-2} - \cdots + (-1)^n C(n, n)x^n$.

29. Show that the coefficient of x^n in $(1 + x + x^2)^n$ is $1 + \dfrac{n(n - 1)}{(1!)^2} + \dfrac{n(n - 1)(n - 2)(n - 3)}{(2!)^2} + \cdots$.

30. Show that $\dbinom{n}{0} - \dbinom{n}{1} + \dbinom{n}{2} - \cdots + (-1)^k \dbinom{n}{k} = (-1)^k \dbinom{n - 1}{k}$.

31. Let X be any set with n elements.
a) Find a set of $\dbinom{n - 1}{k - 1}$ k-subsets of X such that no two are disjoint.
b) Find a set of $\dbinom{n}{[n/2]}$ subsets of X with the property that no one of them is contained in another.

32. Let f be a function from $X = \{1, 2, \ldots, n\}$ into itself. If $x_1 \leq x_2$ implies that $f(x_1) \leq f(x_2)$ for every pair x_1 and x_2 in X, then f is said to be nondecreasing. How many functions from X into itself are nondecreasing?

2.6 PERMUTATIONS OF NONDISTINCT OBJECTS

As we have seen in Section 2.5, the binomial coefficient $C(n, k)$ can also be thought of as the number of arrangements of k x's and $n - k$ y's in a sequence. These ideas can also be generalized from two symbols to more than two and can be applied to the computation of multinomial coefficients.

Example 1 How many ways are there to travel from $(0, 0, 0)$ to $(3, 6, 5)$ taking only unit steps in the positive x, the positive y, and the positive z directions?

Solution
Each trip can be recorded by a sequence of 3 x's, 6 y's, and 5 z's. To choose such a sequence:

1. Choose 3 x-positions out of 14 positions.
2. Choose 6 y-positions out of the 11 remaining positions.
3. Choose 5 z-positions out of the remaining 5 positions.

Thus the total number of different trips is $C(14, 3)C(11, 6)C(5, 5)$. □

Example 2 In how many different orders is it possible to write the letters of the word MISSISSIPPI?

Solution
To count sequences consisting of 4 I's, 4 S's, 2 P's, and 1 M:

1. Choose 4 I-positions out of a total of 11 positions.
2. Choose 4 different S-positions.
3. Choose 2 different P-positions.
4. Choose 1 M-positions.

Thus the total number of orders for these eleven letters is
$C(11, 4)C(7, 4)C(3, 2)C(1, 1)$. □

In general consider sequences of n symbols of m different types, where there are i_1 symbols of type 1, i_2 symbols of type 2, ..., and i_m symbols of type m.

THEOREM 2.7 The number of sequences of length n consisting of m types of symbols, with $i_1, i_2, i_3, \ldots, i_m$ symbols of each type, respectively, is
$$C(n, i_1)C(n - i_1, i_2) \cdots C(i_{m-1} + i_m, i_{m-1})C(i_m, i_m) = n!/(i_1! i_2! \cdots i_m!).$$

Proof
We compute the number of sequences in two different ways. First we count the number of sequences by choosing, in order, positions for each of the different types of symbols as in the preceding examples. Thus we have the following procedure:

1. Choose i_1 type 1 positions.

2. Choose i_2 type 2 positions.
$$\vdots$$
m. Choose i_m type m positions.

Therefore the total number of sequences is
$$C(n, i_1)C(n - i_1, i_2) \cdots C(i_{m-1} + i_m, i_{m-1})C(i_m, i_m).$$
A second method of computing this number works by transforming the problem gradually into an easier one. First we consider the entire set of sequences containing i_1 indistinguishable symbols of type 1, i_2 indistinguishable symbols of type 2,..., and i_m indistinguishable symbols of type m. Next suppose that each of the i_1 symbols of type 1 is given a different subscript. We would obtain $i_1!$ new sequences from each of the original sequences by permuting the order of the now distinguishable symbols of type 1. Similarly give each of the i_2 symbols of type 2 a different subscript further multiplying the number of different sequences by $i_2!$. Proceed in this manner until we obtain $i_1 + i_2 + \cdots + i_m = n$ different symbols and $n!$ different permutations. Thus the total number of permutations originally must have been $n!/(i_1!i_2! \cdots i_m!)$.

When Theorem 2.7 is applied to sequences of length 5 consisting of 2 a's, 2 b's, and 1 c, we obtain the following $5!/(2!2!) = 30$ different permutations.

aabbc	aabcb	aacbb	ababc	abacb	acabb
abbac	abcab	acbab	abbca	abcba	acbba
baabc	baacb	caabb	babac	bacab	cabab
babca	bacba	cabba	bbaac	bcaab	cbaab
bbaca	bcaba	cbaba	bbcaa	bcbaa	cbbaa

permutations of aabbc

The methods of Section 2.5 used for computing binomial coefficients also carry over to the computation of multinomial coefficients.

THEOREM 2.8   (Multinomial Theorem)

In the expansion of the multinomial $(x_1 + x_2 + \cdots + x_m)^n$ there is one term for each product $x_1^{i_1}x_2^{i_2}x_3^{i_3} \cdots x_m^{i_m}$ with $i_1 + i_2 + i_3 + \cdots + i_m = n$ and each i_j nonnegative, whose coefficient is $\binom{n}{i_1, i_2, \ldots, i_m} = n!/(i_1!i_2! \cdots i_m!)$.

Proof

The expression $(x_1 + x_2 + \cdots + x_m)^n$ is the product of n factors $(x_1 + x_2 + \cdots + x_m)$. The expansion of this product consists of m^n sequences of length n since each factor contributes one of the symbols $x_1, x_2, \ldots,$ or x_m to each sequence. These sequences are then combined into like terms. If $i_1 + i_2 + \cdots + i_m = n$, the coefficient of $x_1^{i_1}x_2^{i_2} \cdots x_m^{i_m}$ equals the number of different sequences of length n with $i_1 x_1$'s, $i_2 x_2$'s,..., and $i_m x_m$'s. Therefore the multinomial coefficient of $x_1^{i_1}x_2^{i_2} \cdots x_m^{i_m}$ is $n!/(i_1!i_2! \cdots i_m!)$.

Example 3   a) Find the coefficient of $wx^2y^2z^3$ in the expansion of $(w + x + y + z)^8$.

Solution
The coefficient of $wx^2y^2z^3$ is $8!/(1!2!2!3!) = 1680$.

b) Compute the sum of all the coefficients in the expansion of $(w + x + y + z)^8$.

Solution
The sum of all the coefficients will equal the number of different sequences of length 8 consisting entirely of the four symbols w, x, y, and z, which is 4^8.   ☐

Example 4   a) Find the coefficient of x^5y^3 in $(3 + x + y)^{10}$.

Solution
The term containing x^5y^3 is $(10!/(5!3!2!))x^5y^33^2 = 22{,}680x^5y^3$. Thus the coefficient we seek is 22,680.

b) Compute the sum of all the coefficients of $(3 + x + y)^{10}$.

Solution
To sum up all the coefficients after the expansion and the combining of like terms, eliminate all the x's and y's by substituting $x = 1$ and $y = 1$. However, the same sum can be computed more easily by substituting $x = 1$ and $y = 1$ before the expansion. Therefore the required sum is 5^{10}.   ☐

Partitions of a Specified Size

A problem involving partitions is often equivalent to a corresponding distribution problem. In the following examples we see a set of different objects partitioned into subsets of a specified size.

Example 5   A math department has 35 professors. Each professor is assigned to advise students during one quarter. If 10 professors advise during the fall, winter, and spring quarters and 5 during summer quarter, how many different assignments are possible?

Solution
Advising assignments can be counted by the following procedure:

1. Choose 10 professors for fall advising.
2. Choose 10 of the remaining professors for winter advising.
3. Choose 10 of the remaining professors for spring advising.
4. Choose the remaining 5 for summer advising.

Thus the number of different possible assignments is $C(35, 10)C(25, 10)C(15, 10) \times C(5, 5)$.   ☐

Example 6   A student distributes 30 books to three indistinguishable boxes so that 10 books go in each box. Find the number of distributions that are possible.

Solution

If the boxes were different, the number of distributions would be $C(30, 10) \times C(20, 10)C(10, 10)$. However, in this case, the three boxes are indistinguishable, so the correct answer is obtained after dividing by 3!. Thus the number of distributions is $C(30, 10)C(20, 10)C(10, 10)/6$.   □

2.6

PROBLEMS

1. Use the Multinomial Theorem to expand $(x + y + z)^4$.

2. Determine the coefficient of $x^5 y^5 z^{10}$ in $(x + 2y - z)^{20}$.

3. How many sequences of $2n$ letters can be formed using n distinct symbols if each symbol is used twice?

4. In how many ways can n married couples line up for a photograph if every wife stands next to her own husband?

5. a) Compute the number of different sequences consisting of 3 x's, 4 y's, and 7 z's.
    b) Compute the number of different walks from $(1, 1, 1)$ to $(3, 5, 7)$ if only unit steps in the positive x, positive y, or positive z directions are allowed.

6. Consider sequences of length 8 formed from 2 a's, 2 b's, 2 c's, and 2 d's.
    a) How many of these have no consecutive a's?
    b) How many of these have 2 consecutive a's and 2 consecutive b's?

7. Find the number of ways $m + n$ different objects can be divided into two (indistinguishable) subsets containing m and n objects, respectively.

8. In how many ways is it possible to separate nm different objects into n subsets containing m objects in each subset?

9. In how many ways can $2n$ people form n pairs to play n simultaneous tennis matches?

10. What is the probability that a random $3n$-digit ternary sequence has an equal number of 0's, 1's, and 2's?

11. Determine the coefficient of x^4 in $(a + bx + cx^2)^7$.

12. Find the sum of all the coefficients of $(w + 2x + y + 2z)^6$.

13. Find the coefficient of $x^3 y^3$ in the expansion of $(x + y)(2 + x + y)^8$.

14. If the letters of the word ALGEBRA are randomly arranged in a sequence (of 7 letters), what is the probability that the two A's are together?

ADVANCED
PROBLEMS

15. Compute the number of sequences formed from 3 a's, 5 b's, and 8 c's
    a) That have no consecutive b's.
    b) That have no consecutive symbols the same.

16. a) Find the number of ways 5 males and 5 females can stand in a line if no one stands next to someone of the same sex.
    b) Find the number of ways 5 males and 5 females can stand in a line if everyone stands next to someone of the same sex (on at least one side).

17. How many sequences of 10 symbols can be formed from 4 a's, 4 b's, 4 c's, and 4 d's if each symbol must be used at least twice?

18. How many arrangements are there of 4 a's, 4 b's, and 4 c's in which each letter is next to an identical letter?

19. A single classroom is to be scheduled for 4 Calculus I, 4 Calculus II, and 4 Calculus III classes during 8 daytime periods and 4 evening periods. In how many ways can the schedule be made up if classes of the same type are considered to be identical and at least one evening class of each type must be scheduled?

20. If 3 X's and 2 0's are played in a game of tic-tac-toe, how many different positions are possible?

CHAPTER

2

REVIEW PROBLEMS

1. In the nth row of Pascal's triangle, $n \geq 3$, show that $\binom{n}{0} < \binom{n}{1} < \cdots < \binom{n}{[n/2]}$ and $\binom{n}{[n/2]+1} > \cdots > \binom{n}{n-1} > \binom{n}{n}$.

2. Four males and four females stand in a line.
   a) In how many ways can they stand if males and females alternate?
   b) In how many ways can they stand if everyone stands next to someone of the same sex on at least one side?

3. a) In how many ways can 20 objects be chosen from four different types of objects when unlimited repetition is allowed?
   b) Repeat part (a) if at least one object of each type must be chosen.

4. Find the number of nonnegative integer solutions of
   a) $x_1 + x_2 + x_3 + x_4 = 20$, with $x_1 \geq 2$ and $x_2 \geq 2$.
   b) $x_1 + x_2 + x_3 + x_4 = 20$ and $x_1 + x_2 = 5$.
   c) $x_1 + x_2 + x_3 + x_4 = 20$, with $x_1 \leq 3$ and $x_2 \leq 3$.

5. If A and B are disjoint sets with $|A| = 10$ and $|B| = 5$, compute the number of ways to select four objects from $A \cup B$ so that at least one object from each set is chosen.

6. How many permutations of the nine digits $1, 2, \ldots, 9$ have 1 somewhere to the right of 2 and 2 somewhere to the right of 3?

7. How many seven-card poker hands will contain
    a) Three cards of some rank, but not four cards of any rank?
    b) No more than five cards in any suit?

8. Explain the identity $\binom{m + n}{k} = \binom{m}{0}\binom{n}{k} + \binom{m}{1}\binom{n}{k - 1} + \cdots + \binom{m}{k}\binom{n}{0}$, for $0 \leq k \leq m$ and $0 \leq k \leq n$.

9. What is the probability that a randomly chosen five-digit integer contains 8 as its largest digit?

10. A stack of coins contains three pennies, four nickels, and five dimes. What is the probability that the first dime occurs before the first penny?

11. In how many ways can one select four pairs from a group of 30 people?

12. a) Find the coefficient of $x^3 y^4$ in $(2x - 5y)^7$.
    b) Find the coefficient of x^5 in $(3x - 1)(2x + 1)^8$.

CHAPTER

2 | SUMMARY

In Chapter 2 we studied the basic techniques for computing the number of objects in a set using sequential and case-by-case counting procedures. We also saw a variety of selection models, which are often used as the steps in these procedures, and how these models could be used to solve problems involving probabilities as well as binomial and multinomial coefficients. Section 2.3 introduced the two basic selection models, permutations and combinations, and Section 2.4 expanded these models to allow selections with unlimited repetition. Binomial and multinomial expansions were analyzed in Sections 2.5 and 2.6 using permutations of nondistinct objects. Selections with limited repetition and distributions will be discussed in greater detail in Chapter 3.

The book by Whitworth [1] was one of the first to contain a comprehensive treatment of permutation and combination problems. Since the modern advent of computing, many applications of combinatorics to computer science have been discovered and many other combinatorics books have been written. Any of the newer combinatorics books [2–9] can be checked for the basic combinatorial techniques as well as many of the other topics covered in this book. The book by Niven [5] is an excellent elementary book and the book by Roberts [8] is especially recommended for a variety of applications. For information on the history of combinatorics, see the book by David [10]. For further information about probability see either of the texts [11, 12].

BIBLIOGRAPHY

Combinatorics

 1. Whitworth, W. *Choice and Chance*, 5th edition. New York: Hafner Press, 1965.
 2. Brualdi, R. *Introductory Combinatorics*. New York: North-Holland, 1977.
 3. Berman, G., and K. Fryer. *Introduction to Combinatorics*. New York: Academic Press, 1972.
 4. Cohen, D. *Basic Techniques of Combinatorial Theory*. New York: Wiley and Sons, 1978.
 5. Niven, I. *Mathematics of Choice*. New York: Random House, 1965.
 6. Tucker, A. *Applied Combinatorics*, 2nd edition. New York: Wiley and Sons, 1984.
 7. Liu, C. *Elements of Discrete Math*. New York: McGraw-Hill, 1977.
 8. Roberts, F. *Applied Combinatorics*. Englewood Cliffs, N.J.: Prentice-Hall, 1984.
 9. Bogart, K. *Introductory Combinatorics*. Marshfield, Mass.: Pitman, 1983.
10. David, F. *Games, Gods, and Gambling*. New York: Hafner Press, 1962.

Probability

11. Feller, W. *An Introduction to Probability Theory*, 3rd edition. New York: Wiley and Sons, 1968.
12. Hoel, P., S. Port, and C. Stone. *Introduction to Probability Theory*. Houghton Mifflin, Boston, 1971.

CHAPTER

3

THE PRINCIPLE OF INCLUSION-EXCLUSION

3.1 THE UNION OF OVERLAPPING SETS

In Chapters 1 and 2 we discussed the Addition Principle, which was mainly used to compute the number of objects in the union of disjoint sets. However, we often need to consider the same problem when the sets overlap. Sometimes we try to count the number of objects in a set by breaking it up into smaller subsets, but there is no guarantee that the subsets will be disjoint. In this case we apply a generalization of the Addition Principle called the Principle of Inclusion-Exclusion. In fact we have already encountered the Principle of Inclusion-Exclusion for two overlapping sets. To count the number of objects in the union of two arbitrary sets A and B, which may overlap, we use the formula $|A \cup B| = |A| + |B| - |A \cap B|$. In other words, we include in the count the objects in A and the objects in B, and then we exclude from the count the number of objects in $A \cap B$ because they were counted twice in the first step (see Fig. 3.1). Therefore, in the final count, each object in $A \cup B$ is counted exactly once by the formula, whether it is in a single set or in both sets.

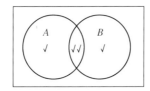

Figure 3.1

Example 1   Consider the permutations of $\{1, 2, 3, \ldots, 9\}$. Count the number of permutations that begin with 1 or end with 9.

Solution
Let A be the set of all sequences that begin with 1, and let B be the set of all sequences that end with 9. We would like to count the sequences in $A \cup B$. Since $|A| = 8!$, and $|B| = 8!$, and $|A \cap B| = 7!$, then $|A \cup B| = 2 \times 8! - 7!$.   □

Now consider the case of three overlapping sets A, B, and C. To count the number of objects in $A \cup B \cup C$, we start by counting the objects in A, the objects in B, and the objects in C. As before, objects in two or more sets are overcounted (see Fig. 3.2). Continue by excluding the objects in $A \cap B$, the objects in $A \cap C$, and the objects in $B \cap C$. At this point, objects in one or two of the original sets are counted exactly once, but it is also possible to have objects in all three sets, so we must continue. Those objects in all three sets have been included three times in the first step, excluded three times in the second step, and as a result have been included zero times in the overall count. By now including the objects in $A \cap B \cap C$ we get the correct total. Thus we obtain the formula, $|A \cup B \cup C| = (|A| + |B| + |C|) - (|A \cap B| + |A \cap C| + |B \cap C|) + (|A \cap B \cap C|)$. For three sets the procedure consists of three steps: one inclusion, one exclusion, and then another inclusion.

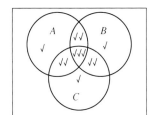

Figure 3.2

Example 2   Count the number of sequences consisting of 2 x's, 4 y's, and 3 z's that do not have all the symbols of one kind appearing in a single block.

Solution
In Chapter 2 we learned to count arbitrary sequences of 2 x's, 4 y's, and 3 z's. We know that there are $9!/(2!4!3!) = 1260$ sequences of this kind. Denote by X the set of all sequences consisting of 2 x's, 4 y's, and 3 z's. We want to exclude any sequences with 2 consecutive x's, or 4 consecutive y's, or 3 consecutive z's. Let A consist of all sequences with 2 consecutive x's, B consist of sequences with 4 consecutive y's, and C consist of sequences with 3 consecutive z's. Thus we wish to exclude from X all the sequences in $A \cup B \cup C$. To count the sequences in $A \cup B \cup C$, we apply the Principle of Inclusion-Exclusion.

First we count the number of sequences with 2 consecutive x's by the following procedure:

1. Choose 2 consecutive x-positions in one of 8 ways.
2. Arrange the 4 y's and 3 z's in the remaining 7 positions.

In other words we can think of arranging 8 symbols, one double x (xx), 4 y's, and 3 z's. Therefore the total number of sequences of this kind is $8!/(1!4!3!) = 280$. Similarly, to count sequences with 4 consecutive y's, think of arranging 2 x's, one quadruple y (yyyy), and 3 z's. There are $6!/(2!1!3!) = 60$ sequences of this kind. Finally, we count the number of sequences with 3 consecutive z's. The number of arrangements of $2x$'s, 4 y's, and one triple z (zzz) is $7!/(2!4!1!) = 105$. Thus, in counting $A \cup B \cup C$, we first include a total of 445 sequences.

In the next step we exclude from the count the objects in the intersection of each pair of subsets. The number of sequences with 2 consecutive x's and 4 consecutive y's is equal to the number of arrangements of one double x, one quadruple y, and 3 z's, which is $5!/(1!1!3!) = 20$. Similarly the number of sequences with 2 consecutive x's and 3 consecutive z's is $6!/4! = 30$, and the number of sequences with 4 consecutive y's and 3 consecutive z's is $4!/2! = 12$. In this step we exclude a total of 62 sequences from the count.

Finally, we include the sequences that are in all three sets. The number of arrangements with 2 consecutive x's, 4 consecutive y's, and 3 consecutive z's is $3! = 6$. We can now compute the total number of sequences in $A \cup B \cup C$, which is $445 - 62 + 6 = 389$. Therefore the answer to the original question is $|X| - |(A \cup B \cup C)| = 1260 - 389 = 871$. $\square$

To count the number of objects in the union of n overlapping sets, the Principle of Inclusion-Exclusion uses n alternating inclusions and exclusions. Suppose we have n sets $A_1, A_2, \ldots, A_n$. To compute the number of objects in $A_1 \cup A_2 \cup \cdots \cup A_n$, we start by including the objects in each individual set, excluding the objects in each pair of sets, including the objects in each triple of sets, and so on. More precisely, let

$$S_1 = |A_1| + |A_2| + \cdots + |A_n|$$
$$S_2 = |A_1 \cap A_2| + |A_1 \cap A_3| + |A_2 \cap A_3| + \cdots$$
$$S_3 = |A_1 \cap A_2 \cap A_3| + \cdots$$
$$\vdots$$
$$S_n = |A_1 \cap A_2 \cap \cdots \cap A_n|$$

In general, S_i is the total count of all the elements in the intersection of i sets, taken over all possible intersections, with each element counted once for every intersection in which it appears. The number of objects in $|A_1 \cup A_2 \cup \cdots \cup A_n|$ is given by the following formula, which is called the Principle of Inclusion-Exclusion.

THEOREM 3.1   (The Principle of Inclusion-Exclusion)

If $A_1, A_2, \ldots, A_n$ are n arbitrary sets, $|A_1 \cup A_2 \cup \cdots \cup A_n| = S_1 - S_2 + S_3 - \cdots + (-1)^{n-1}S_n$

Proof

We claim that each object x in $A_1 \cup \cdots \cup A_n$ is counted exactly once in the formula $S_1 - S_2 + \cdots + (-1)^{n-1}S_n$. To see this, suppose that x is contained in exactly m of the sets $A_1, A_2, \ldots, A_n$. In that case, x is included $C(m, 1)$ times in the first step, excluded $C(m, 2)$ times in the second step, excluded $C(m, 3)$ times in the third step, and so on for collections of 1 through m sets whose intersections contain x. Thus x is counted a total of $C(m, 1) - C(m, 2) + C(m, 3) - \cdots + (-1)^{m-1}C(m, m)$ times by the formula. We will show that this complicated expression simplifies to one for any value of m. We evaluate it by comparing it with the binomial expansion $(1 + x)^m = 1 + C(m, 1)x + C(m, 2)x^2 + \cdots + C(m, m)x^m$. Substituting -1 for x on both sides, we obtain $C(m, 1) - C(m, 2) + \cdots + (-1)^{m-1}C(m, m) = 1$. Therefore we have shown that the Principle of Inclusion-Exclusion is correct since it counts each object in the union exactly once.

Example 3   Find the number of five-card poker hands containing at least one card from each suit.

Solution

Let X be the set of all five-card poker hands and let A_1, A_2, A_3, and A_4 be the set of poker hands that contain no clubs, no diamonds, no hearts, and no spades, respectively. Since the poker hands in $A_1 \cup A_2 \cup A_3 \cup A_4$ are precisely those that we don't want, we compute the total number of poker hands, $C(52, 5)$, and subtract the ones we don't want. In computing $|A_1 \cup A_2 \cup A_3 \cup A_4|$, our computations are reduced by symmetry since

1. $|A_i| = C(39, 5) \to S_1 = 4C(39, 5)$
2. $|A_i \cap A_j| = C(26, 5) \to S_2 = C(4, 2)C(26, 5)$
3. $|A_i \cap A_j \cap A_k| = C(13, 5) \to S_3 = C(4, 3)C(13, 5)$
4. The intersection of all four sets is empty implying $S_4 = 0$.

By the Principle of Inclusion-Exclusion, $|A_1 \cup A_2 \cup A_3 \cup A_4| = 4C(39, 5) - 6C(26, 5) + 4C(13, 5)$. Thus the total number of poker hands we want is $C(52, 5) - 4C(39, 5) + 6C(26, 5) - 4C(13, 5)$. Note that this number can also be computed directly using the Multiplication Principle, as in Problem 24b, Section 2.3.   □

Describing Objects in Terms of Properties

Thus far we have stated the Principle of Inclusion-Exclusion in terms of over-lapping sets. However, we can also state it in the following form, which is often useful for applications. Let X be a set that contains all the objects under consideration. Objects to be counted are often described in terms of certain properties. For $i = 1, 2, \ldots, n$, suppose that A_i is a subset consisting of the objects in X that satisfy a property p_i. The Principle of Inclusion-Exclusion can be used to solve either of the following problems:

1. Compute the number of objects in X that satisfy at least one of the properties $p_1, p_2, \ldots, p_n$. This is exactly the same as the number of objects in $A_1 \cup A_2 \cup \cdots \cup A_n$, which is $S_1 - S_2 + S_3 - \cdots + (-1)^{n-1}S_n$.

2. Compute the number of objects in X that satisfy none of the properties $p_1, p_2, \ldots, p_n$. This is exactly the same as the number of objects in the complement of $A_1 \cup A_2 \cup \cdots \cup A_n$, which can be computed by subtracting the amount determined in the preceding problem from the total number of objects. Thus the number of objects we want is $|X| - S_1 + S_2 - S_3 + \cdots + (-1)^n S_n$.

Example 4   Count the number of ternary sequences of length n that contain at least one 0, at least one 1, and at least one 2.

Solution

Let p_1 be the property that a sequence contains no 0, p_2 be the property that a sequence contains no 1, and p_3 be the property that a sequence contains no 2. We use the second formulation of the basic principle to obtain the number of sequences that do not satisfy any of the three properties p_1, p_2, p_3. First, include in the count all 3^n ternary sequences of length n. A ternary sequence not containing any 0's consists entirely of 1's and 2's, so there are 2^n sequences in A_1, and a similar number in A_2 and A_3, respectively. Next, exclude these 3×2^n sequences from the count. Finally, notice that a sequence containing no 0's and no 1's consists entirely of 2's, so there is only one such sequence. Thus $|A_1 \cap A_2| = 1$, and similarly $|A_1 \cap A_3| = |A_2 \cap A_3| = 1$. We include these three sequences to obtain the final count. Using the Principle of Inclusion-Exclusion, we see that there are $3^n - 3 \times 2^n + 3$ ternary sequences of length n that contain at least one 0, at least one 1, and at least one 2. You may wish to compute the answers for $n = 3$ and $n = 4$ directly to see that they agree with this result.   ☐

Suppose that $p_1, p_2, \ldots, p_n$ are n properties and that $S_1, S_2, S_3, \ldots, S_n$ are defined as before. We have the following generalization of the Principle of Inclusion-Exclusion. Since it is more difficult, some readers may choose to skip it.

THEOREM 3.2   (Optional)

If X_m consists of the objects in X satisfying m or more of the properties $p_1, p_2, \ldots, p_n$, then $|X_m| = S_m - C(m, m-1)S_{m+1} + C(m+1, m-1)S_{m+2} + \cdots + (-1)^{n-m}C(n-1, m-1)S_n$.

Proof

Suppose that x is an object in X satisfying $k \geq m$ properties. Then x is included $C(k, m)$ times in the first term, excluded $C(m, m-1)C(k, m+1)$ times in the second term, included $C(m+1, m-1)C(k, m+2)$ times in the third term, and so on. Thus x is counted a total of $C(k, m) - C(m, m-1)C(k, m+1) + C(m+1, m-1)C(k, m+2) - \cdots + (-1)^k C(k-1, m-1)C(k, k)$ times by the formula. To complete the proof, we need to show that this sum always equals 1. This can be proved for $k \geq m$ by induction. For $k = m$, we obtain $C(m, m) = 1$, which is certainly true. If we assume that

$$C(k, m) - C(m, m-1)C(k, m+1) + \cdots + (-1)^{k-m}C(k-1, m-1)C(k, k)$$
$$= 1$$

then it suffices to show that

$$(C(k + 1, m) - \cdots + (-1)^{k+1-m}C(k, m-1)C(k+1, k+1))$$
$$- (C(k, m) - \cdots + (-1)^{k-m}C(k-1, m-1)C(k, k)) = 0$$

This difference equals

$$[C(k, m-1) - C(m, m-1)C(k, m)$$
$$+ C(m+1, m-1)C(k, m+1) - \cdots + (-1)^{k+1-m}C(k, m-1)]$$

Since $C(p, m-1)C(k, p) = C(k, m-1)C(k+1-m, p+1-m)$ [Problem 1b, Section 2.5], the preceding difference equals

$$C(k, m-1)(1 - C(k+1-m, 1)$$
$$+ C(k+1-m, 2) - \cdots + (-1)^{k+1-m}C(k+1-m, k+1-m))$$

This last product equals 0 since the right-hand side equals 0, as in the proof of Theorem 3.1. Thus

$$C(k+1, m) - C(m, m-1)C(k+1, m+1)$$
$$+ \cdots + (-1)^{k+1-m}C(k, m-1)C(k+1, k+1) = 1$$

which completes the proof of Theorem 3.2.

A similar formula can be derived for computing the number of objects that satisfy exactly m properties (see Problem 25).

3.1

PROBLEMS

1. In a group of 100 families, it was found that 83 subscribe to Time, 41 subscribe to Newsweek, and 32 subscribe to both. Find the number of families that
   a) Subscribe to neither.
   b) Subscribe to only one of the two.

2. A leap year is a year that is divisible by 4, but not divisible by 100 unless it is also divisible by 400. How many leap years are there from 1988 through 2400, inclusive?

3. Find the number of three-digit integers that are not divisible by 4, 5, or 6.

4. How many integers from 1 through 1000 (inclusive) are relatively prime to 1001?

5. How many arrangements of the letters in the word CALIFORNIA have no consecutive letters the same?

6. At one school, three computer languages, Basic, FORTRAN, and Pascal, are taught. Suppose that for each language 27% of the students know that language, for each pair of languages 12% of the students know that pair of languages, and 7% of the students know all three languages. How many of the students do not know any computer language?

7. a) How many four-digit integers are missing at least one of the digits 0 and 1?
   b) How many four-digit integers contain at least one of the digits 0 and 1?

8. How many permutations of the 26 letters in the English alphabet contain
   a) Neither the sequence ijk nor the sequence wxyz?
   b) Either the sequence abc or the sequence cde but not both?

9. a) How many arbitrary six-letter strings begin with a vowel (a, e, i, o, u) or end with a vowel?
   b) How many six-letter strings with no repeated letters begin with a vowel or end with a vowel?

10. Count the number of sequences consisting of three 0's, three 1's, and three 2's that have two but not three consecutive 0's.

ADVANCED
PROBLEMS

11. Find the number of permutations of $\{1, 2, \ldots, 9\}$ that contain at least one of the sequences 123, 456, or 789.

12. a) In how many different orders can the letters of the word TENNESSEE be arranged?
    b) In how many of the arrangements are no two E's adjacent?

13. a) How many different triangles can be formed using the vertices of a regular n-sided polygon?
    b) How many of these triangles do not contain any of the sides of the regular n-gon?

14. If four red, four white, four blue, and four gold poker chips are randomly arranged in a stack, what is the probability that the stack will contain a block of four consecutive chips that are the same color?

15. How many arrangements of the letters in the word LOUISIANA have both A's to the right of both I's?

16. Given $2n$ symbols, two each of n different types, how many arrangements are there with no pair of consecutive symbols the same?

17. Find the number of integers from one to one million, inclusive, that are not a square, a cube, nor a fifth power.

18. Twelve different dice are rolled. How many outcomes will have at least one of each number 1, 2, 3, 4, 5, 6 occurring?

19. Ten different offices are each painted one of the colors brown, blue, green, yellow, or white.
    a) How many ways are there to paint the offices if each color is used at least once?
    b) How many ways are there to paint the offices if each color is used at least twice?

20. Before leaving on a long trip, a person with eight friends invites two friends out

to dinner each night for a week. In how many ways can this be done so that all eight friends are invited at least once during the week?

21. How many seven-digit integers are there in which all three of the digits $0, 1, 2$ appear at least once?

22. How many 5-permutations of the set $\{1, 2, \ldots, 9\}$ contain at least one multiple of 3?

23. Three married couples are seated around a circular table. How many arrangements are there if no wife sits next to her own husband?

24. How many arrangements of exactly 3 X's, 3 Y's, and 3 Z's are there
    a) Having no three consecutive symbols the same?
    b) Having no two consecutive symbols the same?

25. a) Use Theorem 3.2 to find a formula for computing the number of objects in a set X satisfying exactly m out of n properties.
    b) Use part (a) to find the number of integers from 1 to 1000 that are divisible by exactly two of the integers in the set $\{4, 5, 6, 7\}$.

26. Consider N objects, of which N_a have a certain property a, N_b have a certain property b, and N_c have a certain property c. Let $N_{a,b}$ be the number having both properties a and b, and similarly for $N_{a,c}$ and $N_{b,c}$. Prove that $3N + N_{a,b} + N_{a,c} + N_{b,c} \geq 2N_a + 2N_b + 2N_c$.

27. An integer is called square free if it is not divisible by the square of a positive integer greater than 1. Find the number of square-free positive integers less than 100.

3.1

SUPPLEMENTARY COMPUTER PROJECTS

1. The Sieve of Eratosthenes
   The Sieve of Eratosthenes is the name given to the following method for finding all the primes less than or equal to a given positive integer n.

   1. Initially let S be the set of positive integers from 2 to n.

   2. The first integer p in S is a prime. Remove p and all remaining multiples of p from the set.

   3. If S is empty, stop; otherwise, return to Step 2.

   a) It is customary to designate the number of primes less than or equal to n by $\pi(n)$. Thus $\pi(10) = 4$. Write a program that uses the Sieve of Eratosthenes to find $\pi(n)$ for a given positive integer n.

   b) Use the Principle of Inclusion-Exclusion to count the number of integers remaining after three exclusion steps of the Sieve of Eratosthenes.

2. Sundaram's Sieve
   Let $U = \{1, 2, 3, \ldots\}$ and let T be the set of positive integers in the following

infinite array:

4	7	10	13	16	19	22	$\cdots$
7	12	17	22	27	32	37	$\cdots$
10	17	24	31	38	45	52	$\cdots$
13	22	31	40	49	58	67	$\cdots$
16	27	38	49	60	71	82	$\cdots$
$\vdots$	$\vdots$	$\vdots$	$\vdots$	$\vdots$	$\vdots$	$\vdots$	

The first row and the first column are identical, each forming an arithmetic sequence with common difference 3. All subsequent rows also form arithmetic sequences with common differences that are equal to the consecutive odd integers $5, 7, 9, 11, \ldots$, respectively. T is sometimes called Sundaram's Sieve after an East Indian student who proposed it in 1934.

a) Write a program that will determine whether or not a given positive integer N is in T. **Hint:** Look at remainders.

b) Modify the program in part (a) so that for a given positive integer N, the output will be $f(N)$, the number of positive integers less than or equal to N that are in T. Check that $f(20) = 8$ and $f(100) = 55$.

c) Prove the following remarkable theorem. For any positive integer N, N is in T if and only if $2N + 1$ is not prime.

SECTION
3.2

COUNTING RESTRICTED ARRANGEMENTS

As an application of the Principle of Inclusion-Exclusion, we consider some problems involving restricted arrangements.

Derangements

Consider the permutations of the set $\{1, 2, 3, 4, \ldots, n\}$. In some of these arrangements, which we call **derangements**, none of the n integers appear in their natural position, that is, 1 is not the first integer, 2 is not the second integer, 3 is not the third integer, and so on. We denote the number of derangements of n objects by $D(n)$. We will use the Principle of Inclusion-Exclusion to derive a formula for $D(n)$, which is valid for any positive integer n.

$D(2) = 1$	$D(3) = 2$	$D(4) = 9$		
21	231	2341	2143	4312
	312	3142	3412	2413
		4123	4321	3421

Example 1 A math professor has typed five letters to five different persons and has also addressed five different envelopes for these letters. At the end of a particularly long day, he absentmindedly stuffs the five letters into the five envelopes at random. What is the probability that no letter is stuffed into the right envelope?

Solution

To count the number of derangements of five letters using the Principle of Inclusion-Exclusion, we start by including all the arrangements of five different letters into five different envelopes, which is 5!. If p_i is the property that letter i is in envelope i, derangements are precisely those arrangements that satisfy none of the properties p_i, for $i = 1, 2, 3, 4, 5$. To apply the Principle of Inclusion-Exclusion, we first exclude all arrangements that satisfy one of the properties p_i, for $i = 1, 2, 3, 4, 5$. To construct an arrangement with letter i in its correct envelope, first place letter i in envelope i, and second place the other letters at random into the four remaining envelopes. In our next step we exclude these $C(5, 1)4!$ arrangements from the count. (Note that up to this point the overall count is zero.) Next we include arrangements that satisfy a pair of properties p_i and p_j. If two letters are placed in their correct envelopes, there are 3! ways to arrange the other three letters. Since there are $C(5, 2)$ pairs of the five properties, we include $C(5, 2)3!$ arrangements in this step. Similarly there are 2! arrangements with three specific letters in their correct envelopes and $C(5, 3)$ triples of the five properties. Thus we exclude $C(5, 3)2!$ arrangements in the third step. There are 1! arrangements with four specific letters in their correct envelopes, so we include $C(5, 4)1!$ arrangements in the fourth step. Finally, we exclude $C(5, 5)0!$ arrangements with all five letters in their correct envelopes, obtaining the following formulas for the number of derangements of five letters.

$$D(5) = 5! - C(5, 1)4! + C(5, 2)3! - C(5, 3)2! + C(5, 4)1! - C(5, 5)0!$$
$$= 5!(1 - 1/1! + 1/2! - 1/3! + 1/4! - 1/5!) = 44$$

The probability that an arrangement of five letters is a derangement is thus $D(5)/5! = 44/120$. $\qquad\square$

In general, we can compute $D(n)$, the number of derangements of n objects, in a similar way.

THEOREM 3.3

The number of arrangements of n different objects where no object is in its natural position is given by

$$D(n) = n! - n(n - 1)! + C(n, 2)(n - 2)! - C(n, 3)(n - 3)! + \cdots + (-1)^n C(n, n)0!$$
$$= n!(1 - 1/1! + 1/2! - 1/3! + \cdots + (-1)^n/n!)$$

Proof

If p_i is the property of an arrangement that object i is in its natural position, we wish to count the arrangements of n objects that satisfy none of the properties p_i, for $i = 1, 2, 3, \ldots, n$. As before there are $(n - k)!$ arrangements with k specific objects in their natural positions and there are $C(n, k)$ subsets of k objects. We apply the Principle of Inclusion-Exclusion by including all $n!$ arrangements, and then in each succeeding step we alternately exclude and include $C(n, k)(n - k)!$ objects to obtain the preceding formula.

Example 2   There are seven different pairs of gloves in a drawer. When seven children go out to play, each selects a left-hand glove and a right-hand glove at random.
  a) In how many ways can the selection be made so that no child selects a matching pair of gloves?
  b) In how many ways can the selection be made so that exactly one child selects a matching pair?
  c) In how many ways can the selection be made so that at least two children select matching pairs?
  d) Which of parts (a), (b), and (c) is most likely?

Solution
First consider distributing all seven left-hand gloves and then all the right-hand gloves. In each case there will be 7! ways that the left-hand gloves can be distributed. In part (a) the distribution of the right-hand gloves must be a derangement of the left-hand gloves, so the total number of selections is $7!D(7) = 7! \times 1854$. In part (b) one of seven children receives a matching right-hand glove and the remaining 6 right-hand gloves are a derangement of the corresponding left-hand gloves. Thus the total number of selections is $7! \times 7 \times D(6) = 7! \times 1855$. In part (c) the allowable distributions of right-hand gloves is the complement of those discussed in parts (a) and (b). Therefore the total number of selections is $7!(7! - D(7) - 7D(6)) = 7! \times 1331$. The most likely occurrence is part (b): exactly one child selects a matching pair of gloves. □

Many other restricted arrangement problems can arise. Often they can be solved using the Principle of Inclusion-Exclusion.

Example 3   Six Boy Scouts take a two-day hike. The trail is narrow so they must march in single file. On the second day they decide to switch positions so that no one follows the same person he followed on the first day. How many different orders are possible on the second day?

Solution
On day 1, label the Boy Scouts $1, 2, 3, 4, 5, 6$ from front to back. On day 2, we wish to have an order where $i + 1$ does not follow i, for $i = 1, 2, 3, 4, 5$. Of these five properties, there are $C(5, k)$ subsets of k different properties. The number of arrangements that satisfy these k properties is $(6 - k)!$. Therefore, by the principle of Inclusion-Exclusion, we conclude that the number of arrangements that satisfy none of the 5 properties is $6! - 5 \times 5! + C(5, 2)4! - C(5, 3)3! + C(5, 4)2! - C(5, 5)1!$. □

Combinations with Limited Repetition

In finding integer solutions of the linear equation $x_1 + x_2 + \cdots + x_n = k$, where each x_i is bounded above, say $x_i \leq d$, we often use the Principle of Inclusion-Exclusion. First we consider all nonnegative integer solutions of this equation and for $i = 1, 2, \ldots, n$, suppose p_i denotes the property that variable x_i exceeds its upper bound, that is, $x_i \geq d + 1$. We wish to count precisely those solutions that satisfy none of the properties p_i.

Example 4 How many positive integers less than 10,000 will have digits that sum to 25?

Solution
We can think of each integer as consisting of four digits $d_1 d_2 d_3 d_4$ (leading zeros are added for integers with fewer than four digits) that sum to 25. Our problem is equivalent to finding the number of nonnegative integer solutions of $d_1 + d_2 + d_3 + d_4 = 25$ that satisfy $d_i \leq 9$. Let p_i be the property that $d_i \geq 10$. We wish to count the solutions that satisfy none of the properties p_i. We start by including the total number of nonnegative integer solutions, which is $C(28, 3)$. We first exclude those solutions that satisfy property p_i, for $i = 1, 2, 3, 4$. When property p_i is satisfied, we count the solutions satisfying $d_i \geq 10$, which is $C(18, 3)$. This first step results in a total of $4C(18, 3)$ solutions being excluded.

Next we include those solutions that satisfy a pair of properties i and j. If two specific properties p_i and p_j are satisfied, we count the solutions that satisfy $d_i \geq 10$ and $d_j \geq 10$, which is $C(8, 3)$. Since there are $C(4, 2)$ different pairs of properties, the total number of solutions included in this step will be $6C(8, 3)$.

No solutions will satisfy three or more of the properties since the total sum of the four integers is only 25. Therefore, by the Principle of Inclusion-Exclusion, the total number of allowable solutions is $C(28, 3) - 4C(18, 3) + 6C(8, 3)$. □

Example 5 (Optional) Euler's Phi Function
Suppose we are given a positive integer whose prime factorization is $n = p_1^{e_1} p_2^{e_2} \cdots p_k^{e_k}$. The number of integers from 1 to n (inclusive) that are relatively prime to n is denoted by $\phi(n)$ and was first studied by Euler. Show that $\phi(n) = n(1 - 1/p_1)(1 - 1/p_2) \cdots (1 - 1/p_k)$.

Solution
The only integers that are not relatively prime to n are divisible by one of the prime factors $p_1, p_2, \ldots, p_k$. Let $X = \{1, 2, \ldots, n\}$ and $A_i = \{x \mid x \in X$ and p_i divides $x\}$. By the Principle of Inclusion-Exclusion $\phi(n) = |X| - S_1 + S_2 + \cdots + (-1)^k S_k$, where $S_m = \sum |A_{i_1} \cap A_{i_2} \cap \cdots \cap A_{i_m}|$. The set $A_{i_1} \cap A_{i_2} \cap \cdots \cap A_{i_m}$ consists of precisely those elements of X that are multiples of $p_{i_1} p_{i_2} \cdots p_{i_m}$, so $|A_{i_1} \cap A_{i_2} \cap \cdots \cap A_{i_m}| = |X|/(p_{i_1} p_{i_2} \cdots p_{i_m})$. Therefore we see that

$$\phi(n) = |X| - |X|\sum \frac{1}{p_i} + |X|\sum \frac{1}{p_i p_j} + \cdots + \frac{(-1)^k |X|}{p_1 p_2 \cdots p_k}$$
$$= |X|(1 - 1/p_1)(1 - 1/p_2) \cdots (1 - 1/p_k)$$
$$= n(1 - 1/p_1)(1 - 1/p_2) \cdots (1 - 1/p_k).$$ □

3.2
PROBLEMS

1. On a standard chessboard consider arrangements of rooks such that no two are in the same row or column.
   a) In how many ways can we arrange two rooks?

b) In how many ways can we arrange eight rooks?

c) In how many ways can we arrange eight rooks such that none is on the main diagonal (going from the upper left corner to the lower right corner)?

2. a) In how many ways can n married couples form n male-female pairs to dance simultaneously?

b) Repeat part (a) if no wife dances with her own husband.

3. In the game of rencontres, balls numbered $1, 2, 3, \ldots, n$ are drawn from an urn. A rencontre occurs when the ball numbered i is the ith ball drawn.

a) In how many ways can all n balls be drawn with exactly one rencontre occurring?

b) In how many ways with exactly m rencontres occurring?

4. How many secret codes can be made by assigning to each letter of the English alphabet a unique letter that is different from itself?

5. How many arrangements are there of the integers $\{1, 2, 3, \ldots, 12\}$ where $1, 2, 3, 4, 5$, and 6 are not in their natural positions?

6. How many 12-letter strings constructed from the English alphabet contain each of the vowels $\{a, e, i, o, u\}$ at least once?

7. Find the number of 6-digit positive integers whose digits sum to 30.

8. Find the probability of rolling ten different dice and obtaining a sum of 30?

9. A bag of coins contains nine pennies, six nickels, four dimes, and three quarters. Assuming that coins of any one denomination are identical, in how many ways can ten coins be selected?

10. An exam contains 12 questions. In how many ways can the points be assigned if each question must be worth 3, 4, 5, or 6 points and the total number of points assigned is 50 points?

11. Eight gentlemen check their hats at a restaurant. In how many ways can the hats be returned at random? What is the probability that no one receives his own hat? Determine the same probability for nine and ten gentlemen. For eight, nine, or ten gentlemen when is the probability greatest that no one receives his own hat?

12. The squares of a regular 8×8 chessboard are colored eight different colors, one color per square, so that every row receives one square of each color.

a) How many ways are there to color the first two rows if no two adjacent squares in the same column receive the same color?

b) How many ways are there to color all eight rows if no two adjacent squares in the same column receive the same color?

13. Find the number of different solutions of $x_1 + x_2 + x_3 + \cdots + x_{10} = 30$ if each x_i is a nonnegative integer no greater than 5.

14. Find the number of solutions of $x_1 + x_2 + x_3 + x_4 = 0$ in integers between -4 and 4, inclusive.

15. In how many ways can 100 identical chairs be distributed to three different classrooms if no more than half go in any one classroom?

16. Compute
a) $\phi(999)$ b) $\phi(1000)$ c) $\phi(1001)$

ADVANCED
PROBLEMS

17. For which values of n are the following formulas valid?
a) $D(n) = nD(n-1) + (-1)^n$
b) $D(n) = (n-1)(D(n-2) + D(n-1))$
c) $D(n) = n! - \sum_{k=1}^{n} C(n,k)D(n-k)$
d) $D(n) = [n!e^{-1}]$, where $[t]$ represents the largest integer less than or equal to t.
e) $D(n) = [n!e^{-1} + .5]$

18. In a small elementary school there are six teachers, one for each grade 1–6. At the end of a year, the teachers may switch grades as long as all the students get a new teacher when they move up to the next grade the following year. How many different teacher assignments are possible for the next year?

19. How many permutations of the integers $\{1,2,3,\ldots,n\}$ have i directly to the right of $i+1$ for at least one of $i = 1,2,\ldots,n-1$?

20. How many ways are there to arrange the digits $\{1,2,\ldots,9\}$ so that 1 is somewhere to the right of 2 (not necessarily adjacent), or 2 is somewhere to the right of 3, or 3 is somewhere to the right of 4?

*21. Five married couples stand in a row so that no wife stands next to her own husband. In how many different ways can they stand?

22. A team of nine bicycle racers travels single file to reduce wind resistance. At the halfway point of a race they change positions so that a new rider is in the lead. In how many ways can they change positions so that each racer is also preceded by a different racer?

*23. a) Find the number of ways n married couples can form n pairs to shake hands simultaneously.
b) Repeat part (a) if no wife shakes hands with her own husband.

24. How many positive integers less than one million have their digits arranged in nondecreasing order?

25. How many nonnegative integer solutions of $x_1 + x_2 + x_3 + x_4 = 25$ satisfy $x_1 > x_4$?

26. If n letters are placed at random into n envelopes, what is the average number of letters that get into the correct envelope?

27. Show that $D(n)$ is even if and only if n is odd.

28. Show that $\binom{n}{0}D(0) + \binom{n}{1}D(1) + \binom{n}{2}D(2) + \cdots + \binom{n}{n}D(n) = n!$, where $D(0)$ is defined to be 1.

29. For any positive integer n, show that $\phi(n^m) = n^{m-1}\phi(n)$.

30. If $n = p_1^{e_1}p_2^{e_2}p_3^{e_3} \cdots p_k^{e_k}$ is a prime factorization of the positive integer n, show that the sum of all the divisors of n is

$$\frac{(1 - p_1^{e_1+1})}{(1 - p_1)} \frac{(1 - p_2^{e_2+1})}{(1 - p_2)} \cdots \frac{(1 - p_k^{e_k+1})}{(1 - p_k)}$$

DISTRIBUTIONS

Sometimes the basic steps in a counting procedure can be thought of naturally as a **distribution**. In the distribution model we have a group of objects that are distributed to a group of (possible) recipients. In a distribution each object is assigned to exactly one recipient, and usually the order of distribution is immaterial. We will consider several variations of the basic model.

Distributions of Distinct Objects to Distinct Recipients

In the case where we have a set of n distinct objects and a set of k distinct recipients, a distribution can be thought of as a procedure whose outcome is equivalent to the assignments of some function. If an arbitrary assignment of recipients is allowed, we have a *function*. If no objects are assigned to the same recipient, we have an *injection*. If each recipient is assigned at least one object, we have a *surjection*. In Example 1, Section 2.4, we saw that it was possible to count the number of functions or the number of injections from one set to another using the Multiplication Principle. The number of surjections can now also be counted, using the Principle of Inclusion-Exclusion.

Example 1   Let $|A| = 4$ and $|B| = 7$. Find the number of surjections from B to A.

Solution
First consider arbitrary assignments of images from B to A. We know that there are 4^7 different functions from B to A. If we let p_i be the property that no element of B is assigned to the ith element of A, we wish to count the functions that satisfy none of the properties p_1, p_2, p_3, and p_4. Consider functions that do not assign any object to the ith element of A. The images must be selected from the other three objects in A, so there are 3^7 functions that satisfy property i, for $i = 1, 2, 3, 4$. Functions that do not assign images to two of the elements in A must assign objects to the remaining two elements, so there are 2^7 functions satisfying p_i and p_j. Similarly there are 1^7 functions that satisfy three of the properties and no functions that satisfy all four of the properties. By the Principle of Inclusion-Exclusion, we have the following formula for the number of surjections from B to A, $4^7 - 4(3^7) + C(4, 2)(2^7) - C(4, 3)(1^7) = 8400$. $\qquad\square$

THEOREM 3.4

Consider distributions of n different objects to k different recipients.
a) The number of arbitrary distributions (functions) is k^n.
b) The number of distributions with no objects assigned to the same recipient (injections) is $P(k, n)$.
c) The number of distributions with no recipient left empty (surjections) is given by $T(n, k) = k^n - k(k-1)^n + C(k, 2)(k-2)^n - \cdots + (-1)^{k-1} C(k, k-1) 1^n$.

Proof

The number of surjections can also be counted in general using the Principle of Inclusion-Exclusion. Suppose that the set of possible recipients consists of k different elements $x_1, x_2, x_3, \ldots, x_n$. Let property p_i be the property that a particular function does not assign any objects to x_i. As in Example 1, we wish to count the number of functions that do not satisfy any of the properties p_i. For each of the $C(k, i)$ subsets of i recipients, the number of functions that do not assign any objects to the elements of that subset is $(k - i)^n$ since each object must be assigned to the other $k - i$ recipients. Thus the Principle of Inclusion-Exclusion shows that the number of surjections $T(n, k)$ is given by the formula $T(n, k) = k^n - k(k-1)^n + C(k, 2)(k-2)^n - \cdots + (-1)^{k-1} C(k, k-1) 1^n$.

Distributions of Identical Objects to Distinct Recipients

In Chapter 2 we saw that distributions of identical objects and selections were sometimes equivalent, so we also have the following theorem.

THEOREM 3.5

Consider distributions of n identical objects to k distinct recipients.
a) The number of unlimited distributions is $C(n + k - 1, n)$.
b) The number of distributions with no more than one object assigned to any recipient is $C(k, n)$.
c) The number of distributions with no recipient left empty is $C(n - 1, n - k)$.

Proof

We can think of selecting n recipients from k different types. Arbitrary distributions correspond to combinations with unlimited repetition, and there are a total of $C(n + k - 1, n)$ different distributions. If no repetition of assignments is allowed, we can just pick a subset of n distinct recipients to receive one of the objects and there are $C(k, n)$ selections of this kind. If each recipient must be assigned at least one object, each type of recipient must be selected at least once so we have $C(n - 1, n - k)$ different distributions.

Example 2

Suppose 30 identical juggling balls are distributed to five different jugglers.
a) In how many ways can the balls be distributed so that each juggler receives at least three balls?
b) In how many ways can the balls be distributed so that each juggler receives between three and seven juggling balls?

Solution

Let x_i be the number of balls distributed to juggler i. As in Section 2.4, the distribution of identical objects can be represented by a 5-tuple of integers. In this case, each 5-tuple is a solution of the linear equation $x_1 + x_2 + x_3 + x_4 + x_5 = 30$, with each $x_i \geq 3$. We can first distribute three balls to each of the five jugglers and then randomly distribute the remaining 15 balls to the five jugglers. Since the balls are identical, there is only one way to complete the first step and $C(15 + 5 - 1, 5 - 1) = C(19, 4)$ ways to complete the second. Therefore the number of distributions possible in part (a) is $C(19, 4) = 3876$.

The number of distributions in part (b) can again be represented by solutions of the linear equation $x_1 + x_2 + x_3 + x_4 + x_5 = 30$. In this case, each x_i satisfies $3 \leq x_i \leq 7$. We proceed with the help of the Principle of Inclusion-Exclusion. First, consider all $C(19, 4)$ distributions with $x_i \geq 3$. If p_i is the property that $x_i \geq 8$, we count only those distributions that satisfy none of the properties p_i. The total count is thus $C(19, 4) - 5C(14, 4) + C(5, 2)C(9, 4) - C(5, 3)C(4, 4) = 121$ distributions. ☐

Distributions of Distinct Objects to Similar Recipients

When the objects of a set X are distributed to identical subsets, the result is a **partition** of X, that is, a subdivision of the objects of X into mutually disjoint subsets whose union is all of X. In Chapter 9 we shall see how equivalence relations can be used to partition the objects of a set into subsets of similar objects, and we shall study the problem of counting these subsets, which are called equivalence classes. For now we consider a simpler problem. The partitions of X into k nonempty, unordered subsets correspond exactly to distributions of the n different elements of X into k identical subsets, where each subset is assigned at least one element.

Partitions of a Set

The number of partitions of the n objects of X into k nonempty subsets is denoted by $S(n, k)$. The numbers $S(n, k)$ are also known as the Stirling numbers of the second kind.

$S(4, 1) = 1$	$S(4, 2) = 7$	$S(4, 3) = 6$	$S(4, 4) = 1$
$\{1, 2, 3, 4\}$	$\{1, 2\}, \{3, 4\}$	$\{1, 2\}, \{3\}, \{4\}$	$\{1\}, \{2\}, \{3\}, \{4\}$
	$\{1, 3\}, \{2, 4\}$	$\{1, 3\}, \{2\}, \{4\}$	
	$\{1, 4\}, \{2, 3\}$	$\{1, 4\}, \{2\}, \{3\}$	
	$\{1, 2, 3\}, \{4\}$	$\{2, 3\}, \{1\}, \{4\}$	
	$\{1, 2, 4\}, \{3\}$	$\{2, 4\}, \{1\}, \{3\}$	
	$\{1, 3, 4\}, \{2\}$	$\{3, 4\}, \{1\}, \{2\}$	
	$\{2, 3, 4\}, \{1\}$		

There is a simple relationship between $T(n, k)$, the number of distributions of n different objects to k different recipients with no recipient left empty, and $S(n, k)$. The relationship is similar to that between $P(n, k)$ and $C(n, k)$, which we used in Section 2.3.

THEOREM 3.6 $S(n, k) = T(n, k)/k!$

Proof
To count the distributions of n different objects to k different recipients, where each recipient is assigned at least one object, we could first distribute the n different objects to k nonempty identical subsets and then distribute one subset to each recipient. Thus we obtain $T(n, k) = S(n, k)k!$. We deduce that $S(n, k) = T(n, k)/k!$ is equal to the number of unordered partitions of n different objects into k nonempty subsets. Note that $T(n, k)$ can also be interpreted as the number of ordered partitions of n different objects into k nonempty subsets, whereas $S(n, k)$ is the number of unordered partitions of n different objects into k nonempty subsets.

We have already computed $T(n, k)$ using the Principle of Inclusion-Exclusion. This method of computing $T(n, k)$ is somewhat complicated, and we do have another method of computing $S(n, k)$, which uses a recurrence relation, similar to the one for $C(n, k)$.

THEOREM 3.7 $S(n, 1) = 1 = S(n, n)$ and for $1 < k < n$, $S(n, k) = S(n - 1, k - 1) + kS(n - 1, k)$.

Proof
There is precisely one way to partition a set X with n different elements into one subset, namely, X itself, and one way to partition X into n identical nonempty subsets with one element in each subset. Thus $S(n, 1) = S(n, n) = 1$. To obtain the recurrence, note that a partition of n objects into k nonempty subsets can be obtained either

1. From a partition of the first $n - 1$ objects into $k - 1$ nonempty subsets and a singleton subset containing the nth object.
2. By starting with a partition of the first $n - 1$ objects into k nonempty subsets and adding the nth object to any of these k subsets.

Adding the number of partitions obtained by either method 1 or 2, we obtain the recurrence relation $S(n, k) = S(n - 1, k - 1) + kS(n - 1, k)$.

In the following triangular arrangement we list the numbers $S(n, k)$ for $1 \le n \le 6$.

```
              1
           1     1
        1     3     1
     1     7     6     1
  1    15    25    10     1
1    31    90    65    15     1
```

Example 3   a) In how many ways can six toys be distributed to four similar boxes so that each box receives at least one toy?

b) In how many ways can the six toys be distributed to four different orphans if each orphan receives at least one toy?

Solution
a) The number of distributions to four similar recipients is $S(6,4) = 65$.
b) The number of distributions to four different recipients is $S(6,4)4! = 1560$. ☐

Example 4   In how many ways can $t \geq 2$ travelers share two identical cabs with no cab empty?

Solution
The number of partitions of a set of t distinct objects into two nonempty subsets is equal to $S(t,2) = (2^t - 2)/2! = 2^{t-1} - 1$. ☐

Example 5   In how many ways can we factor the integer 30,030 into three positive integers if the order of the factors is unimportant and each factor is greater than 1?

Solution
The number 30,030 can be factored into six distinct primes $2 \times 3 \times 5 \times 7 \times 11 \times 13$. Any factor greater than 1 is a product of some nonempty subset of the six prime factors. The factorizations under consideration correspond to partitions of the six prime factors into three nonempty subsets. Thus the number of factorizations is $S(6,3) = 90$. ☐

We summarize the results on distributions in the following table.

A Table of Distributions
(n objects distributed to k recipients)

	Arbitrary distributions	No recipient left empty
n different objects k different recipients	k^n	$S(n,k)k! = T(n,k)$
n identical objects k different recipients	$\binom{n+k-1}{k-1}$	$\binom{n-1}{k-1}$
n different objects k identical recipients	$\sum_{i=1}^{k} S(n,i)$	$S(n,k)$
n identical objects k identical recipients	(See Example 4, Section 7.3.)	

3.3
PROBLEMS

1. a) In how many ways can 40 identical cans be distributed to five poor families?
   b) In how many ways if each family receives at least one can?
   c) At least five cans?

2. a) In how many ways can a professor distribute seven different books to 12 students if no student gets more than one book?

b) In how many ways can the 12 students each be assigned to read one of the seven books so that every book is assigned to at least one student?

3. How many ways are there to distribute 18 toys to six children if each child receives a toy and
   a) The toys are identical?
   b) The toys are all different?

4. A juggler colors 12 identical juggling balls red, white, and blue.
   a) In how many ways can this be done if each color is used at least once?
   b) In how many ways if each color is used at least three times?

5. Let B^n be the set consisting of all binary sequences of length n.
   a) Compute the number of injections from B^2 to B^3.
   b) Compute the number of surjections from B^4 to B^2.

6. a) In how many ways can 30 identical balls be distributed to six different jugglers?
   b) In how many ways can 10 white, 10 blue, and 10 red balls be distributed to six different jugglers?

7. How many unordered partitions are there of the nine letters in the set $\{a, b, c, d, e, f, g, h, i\}$ consisting of
   a) Three nonempty subsets?
   b) Three subsets of three letters?

8. a) In how many ways can 12 identical coins be distributed to four different persons if each person receives at least one coin?
   b) In how many ways can 12 different books be distributed to four identical boxes if each box receives exactly three books?
   c) Compute the number of ways to partition a set of 12 different objects into four nonempty subsets.

ADVANCED
PROBLEMS

9. a) Find a compact formula for $S(n, 3)$ (avoid long summations).
   b) Show that $S(n, 3)$ is a multiple of 3 for any positive even integer n.
   c) Show that $S(n, 3)$ is a multiple of 5 for infinitely many values of n.

10. Explain the following formulas:
    a) $S(n, n - 1) = C(n, 2)$
    b) $S(n, n - 2) = C(n, 3) + 3C(n, 4)$

11. At the end of the day, a bakery has seven oatmeal cookies, eight sugar cookies, and nine chocolate chip cookies.
    a) In how many ways can the cookies be distributed to two different employees so that each employee receives at least one cookie?
    b) In how many ways in part (a) will both employees receive 12 cookies?

12. Let $X = \{1, 2, 3, \ldots, 8\}$ and $Y = \{a, b, c, d, e\}$.
    a) Count the number of surjections from X to Y.

b) Count the number of functions from X to Y whose image consists of exactly three elements of Y.

13. How many ways are there to distribute n identical balls to k different boxes with exactly j boxes empty?

14. a) In how many ways can 25 identical books be assigned to five different book shelves?

   b) In how many ways can 25 different books be assigned to five different bookshelves if the order of the books on each shelf is considered important?

15. Show that the number of ways to partition a set of n distinct elements into k nonempty ordered lists equals $n!C(n - 1, k - 1)$.

16. a) In how many ways can n identical objects be distributed to five different boxes if the first two boxes receive no more than two balls each?

   b) Repeat part (a) for n different objects.

17. Suppose the prime factorization of an integer n has exactly m primes, all distinct. How many ways are there to factor n into k factors where k is some integer less than or equal to m

   a) If each factor must be greater than 1?

   b) If 1 is allowed as a factor?

18. On a ship, signals are transmitted by putting flags on flagpoles (the order of the flags on each pole is important). There are 10 different flags and three different poles and all 10 flags are used. How many different signals can be sent if each pole must contain at least one flag?

19. In how many ways can five pennies, five nickels, five dimes, and five quarters be distributed to four different pockets so that each pocket receives at least one coin?

20. Let X be an n-element set and Y be a k-element subset.

   a) Show that the number of surjections from X to Y is equal to $k!S(n, k)$.

   b) Compute the number of functions from X to Y whose image consists of precisely i elements.

   c) Show that $k^n = \sum_{i=1}^{n} S(n, i)P(k, i)$.

3.3
SUPPLEMENTARY COMPUTER PROJECTS

1. Bell Numbers

   a) Write a program that computes $S(n, k)$, the number of partitions of a set of n objects into k nonempty subsets, for a given pair of integers k and n with $0 \le k \le n$.

   b) The nth Bell number B_n is equal to the total number of partitions of a set of n objects. Write a program that computes B_n for a given positive integer n.

   c) Show that B_n is also equal to the total number of different equivalence relations on a set X with n elements. *Hint:* See Section 1.4, Problem 18.

CHAPTER

3   REVIEW PROBLEMS

1. Among all n-digit integers, how many of them contain the digits 0 and 1 but not the digits 8 and 9?

2. If the letters of the word COMBINATORICS are arranged in a sequence, how many arrangements
   a) Will have two consecutive letters the same?
   b) Will either begin with a C or end with an S?

3. If five dice are rolled, what is the probability that the sum of the five dice is less than 20?

4. How many ways are there to distribute 30 identical balls to six distinct boxes if box 1 and box 2 each receive fewer than 10 balls?

5. A bridge hand is a subset of 13 cards chosen from the standard deck. How many bridge hands contain four cards of the same rank?

6. How many positive integers smaller than one million have digits that sum to 25?

7. A pair of different dice are rolled n successive times. How many sequences of outcomes will contain all possible doubles (a pair of 1's, a pair of 2's, and so on)?

8. Nine different objects are distributed to four different jugglers.
   a) How many distributions are possible if each juggler receives at least one object?
   b) How many distributions are possible if each juggler receives at least two objects?

9. Given a set X with 12 different elements, how many ways are there to partition X into
   a) Two nonempty subsets.
   b) Three subsets of size 3, 4, and 5, respectively.
   c) Two subsets of size 6.
   d) Three nonempty subsets.

10. The 52 cards of the standard deck are arranged in a sequence.
    a) For how many sequences will the King and Queen of spades not be adjacent?
    b) For how many sequences will the King and Queen of the same suit (all four suits) never be adjacent?

11. How many eight-digit integers formed from two 0's, two 1's, two 2's, and two 3's have no pair of consecutive digits the same?

12. A bakery has on display eight chocolate chip cookies, six peanut butter cookies, and seven oatmeal cookies. In how many ways can a dozen cookies be selected if at least one of each kind is selected?

CHAPTER

3

SUMMARY

In this chapter we studied the Principle of Inclusion-Exclusion, which can be expressed in terms of overlapping sets or properties. We were able to count objects that satisfy none of a certain set of properties, at least one property, or at least m properties. In Section 3.2, this principle was used to count derangements, combinations with limited repetition, and other restricted arrangements. Finally, we encountered a variety of distribution models in Section 3.3. In particular we were able to count the number of different surjections from one set to another. A distribution problem is often related to a corresponding partition problem. The Stirling numbers, which were introduced in Section 3.3, were used to count the number of partitions of a set of n different objects into k nonempty subsets. Partitions of an integer or, equivalently, partitions of a collection of identical objects will be discussed in Chapter 7. See any of the combinatorics books listed at the end of Chapter 2 or either of the books [1, 2] for more details.

BIBLIOGRAPHY

1. Hall, M. *Combinatorial Theory*. New York: Wiley and Sons, 1967.
2. Ryser, H. *Combinatorial Mathematics*. Washington, D.C.: MAA, 1963.

CHAPTER

4

COMBINATORIAL ALGORITHMS

4.1 ALGORITHMS

An algorithm is a procedure for solving a problem or a whole set of similar problems. The steps of an algorithm can be performed by a computer or by a human problem solver. In either case, an algorithm must be a finite process that eventually terminates, giving an answer to the problem. Each step should be precisely defined and take a finite amount of time to complete. After one step is performed, it should always be clear which step is to be performed next.

Algorithms come in various types and forms, like the problems they solve. Algorithms fall into three broad categories:

1. *Direct computation* algorithms consist of a fixed number of steps that are always performed in the same sequential order.

2. *Enumeration* algorithms try every possible answer to a problem until they find one that works. Normally a human problem solver would not attempt such a solution on any large problem, but computers often will because of their speed.

3. *Iterative and recursive* algorithms solve a problem by looking at a sequence of smaller problems. These algorithms are usually more complex than enumeration algorithms, though they may be considerably more efficient.

Example 1   Let $f(x) = a_n x^n + a_{n-1} x^{n-1} + \cdots + a_1 x + a_0$. Explain how to evaluate $f(x)$ on a simple calculator that can add, subtract, multiply, and divide any two numbers.

Solution

Any individual term $a_k x^k$ can be evaluated using k successive multiplications. A straightforward method of evaluating $f(x)$ would be to multiply out and store all the individual terms and finally add them together. On some hand calculators storing intermediate values may be difficult, so we present the following algorithm (Horner's method), which can compute $f(x)$ more efficiently and without storing any intermediate values. To compute $f(x) = a_n x^n + a_{n-1} x^{n-1} + \cdots + a_1 x + a_0$, the coefficient a_n is multiplied by x, the coefficient a_{n-1} is added, the result is multiplied by x, the coefficient a_{n-2} is added, the result is multiplied by x, and so on. In this way $f(x) = ((\ldots(a_n x) + a_{n-1})x + \cdots + a_1)x + a_0$ can be computed using a total of n multiplications and n additions, and without having to store any intermediate values. See Problem 10, Section 4.2, for an efficient algorithm that computes powers of x. □

Circular Arrangements

Thus far we have considered permutations of n different objects in a line or a row. There are $n!$ different permutations of this kind. Now we consider arrangements of n different objects in a circle. In particular, how many different circular permutations of n different objects are there? Two circular arrangements are considered to be the same if they differ by just a rotation that shifts each object uniformly the same number of positions around the circle. This is typical of what happens in counting highly symmetrical arrangements. We discuss general techniques for counting such highly symmetrical arrangements in Chapter 9.

THEOREM 4.1   The number of distinct circular permutations of n different objects is $(n-1)!$.

Proof

To count the number of circular permutations, we can fix the place of one object by a rotation, and then we can think of arranging the other objects with reference to it around the circle. Any one of the other $n-1$ objects can be placed to its right; any one of the $n-2$ remaining objects can be placed to the right of that, and so on. Thus the total number of circular permutations of n different objects is $(n-1)(n-2)\cdots 2 \times 1 = (n-1)!$.

The circular permutations of $\{1, 2, 3, 4\}$ are listed in Fig. 4.1.

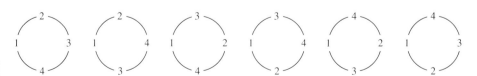

Figure 4.1

Example 2   The Traveling Salesperson Problem

A traveling salesperson, starting at a home city, must visit each of $n - 1$ other cities and return home. The cost of traveling from city i to city j is given by c_{ij}, and the total cost of the trip is the sum of the costs for each individual segment of the trip. If the order in which the cities are visited is unimportant, except that the overall cost of the trip should be minimized, which route should be taken?

Solution

The traveling salesperson problem is a well-known difficult problem in computer science, and indeed many people feel it is unlikely that an efficient algorithm for solving it will ever be found.

Consider an enumeration algorithm for solving the traveling salesperson problem. That is, suppose we check all possible routes and calculate the cost of each route to find the one with the smallest overall cost. A traveling salesperson's route can be thought of as a circular arrangement of the n cities. As we have just seen, there are $(n - 1)!$ different circular permutations of the n cities to check.

Obviously $(n - 1)!$ grows very quickly as n gets large. Even for a relatively small number of cities like $n = 25$, $24! = 6.2 \times 10^{23}$ routes would be impossible to check on a computer in any reasonable amount of time. Even with a very fast computer that could check one million possibilities per second, it would still take about 20 billion years.   □

Many interesting and important algorithms involve integers. There are algorithms to determine whether or not an integer n is a prime and also algorithms for factoring an integer n into prime factors.

The greatest common divisor of two positive integers n and k, denoted by (n, k), is the largest integer that divides both n and k. We see that $(n, k) = k$ if and only if k divides n. One of the most well-known basic algorithms is the Euclidean algorithm, which is used to find the greatest common divisor of two integers.

Example 3   The Euclidean Algorithm

Consider the problem of finding (n, k) for two positive integers n and k.

Solution

Many computers have an operation called integer division that divides an integer k into an integer n. This operation returns the quotient q and the remainder r, which satisfy $qk + r = n$ and $0 \le r < k$. The following Euclidean algorithm makes repeated use of this operation:

1. Input n and k.
2. Divide k into n.
3. If $r = 0$, output k (since $(n, k) = k$) and stop.
4. Replace n by k, replace k by r, and return to Step 2.

This algorithm always stops after a finite number of steps since k always decreases after each division. In computer science, when an algorithm has been constructed to perform a specific task, we still have to convince ourself that it really does work. This process is sometimes called verification. The Principle of Induction is often useful in this process. An inductive proof can be used to verify that the Euclidean algorithm will always output (n, k) since $(n, k) = (k, r)$ (see Problem 3). For $n = 560$ and $k = 154$, we obtain $(560, 154) = (154, 98) = (98, 56) = (56, 42) = (42, 14) = 14$.   □

Analysis of Algorithms

When comparing algorithms for efficiency or determining which algorithms are feasible for use on a certain problem, we often ask how many steps the algorithm will take to solve the problem in question.

Usually an algorithm is designed to solve a whole set of similar problems of different sizes. To each algorithm for solving a combinatorial problem we associate a complexity function $c(n)$ that depends on the size n of the input problem. The function $c(n)$ is roughly the number of operations needed to solve an input problem of size n using the algorithm in question. The length of a solution may grow with the size of the problem, but the speed with which a computer performs operations will often make the solution feasible even for relatively large values of n. However, in Example 2, we have already seen that an inefficient algorithm like enumeration is not always feasible for some problems.

Example 4   A Coin-Weighing Puzzle

In a set of six coins, we know that there is exactly one counterfeit coin that is lighter than the others. We have at our disposal an equal arm balance which can compare the weights of any two sets of coins. Any weighing has three possible outcomes: the right and left sides can be equal in weight, the right side can be lighter than the left, or the left side can be lighter than the right. Give an algorithm that will find the counterfeit coin in two weighings.

Solution
One general technique that can be used is to divide the group of coins into two groups, equal in number, when the total number of coins under consideration is even. When the number of coins is odd, leave out one coin and divide the rest into two equal groups. (For six coins, we have the following algorithm:

1. If six coins $\{c_1, c_2, \ldots, c_6\}$ are under consideration, compare $\{c_1, c_2, c_3\}$ and $\{c_4, c_5, c_6\}$. Remove the heavier group from consideration.
2. If three coins $\{d_1, d_2, d_3\}$ are under consideration, compare $\{d_1\}$ and $\{d_2\}$. If $\{d_1\}$ and $\{d_2\}$ are equal in weight, d_3 is counterfeit. Otherwise, the lightweight coin is counterfeit.   □

This same technique also works for seven coins, finding the counterfeit coin in two weighings, but two weighings will not suffice for eight or more coins using this technique. Can you find other algorithms for eight, nine, or more coins that always find the counterfeit coin in two weighings? (See Problem 14.)

Sorting a List

Suppose we wish to store a list of n different numbers in a computer. For various reasons it is often desirable to store them in order. For example, it is much easier to search the list for a particular number if the numbers are listed in increasing order. A set of names or numbers listed in their correct order is usually called a **sorted list**. If we wish to arrange a list of n different integers in increasing order, it is obviously not desirable to check all $n!$ different arrangements. However, we can arrange the integers in order by repeatedly finding the largest integer as in the next two examples.

Example 5   Consider the problem of finding the largest of n integers $\{x_1, x_2, \ldots, x_n\}$ on a computer. Assuming a computer can only compare two integers at a time, find a sequence of steps that will eventually find the largest integer in the set, which we denote by $\max\{x_1, x_2, \ldots, x_n\}$.

Solution
The sequence of steps is as follows:

    1. Compare x_1 and x_2 to obtain $\max\{x_1, x_2\}$.
    2. Compare $\max\{x_1, x_2\}$ and x_3 to obtain $\max\{x_1, x_2, x_3\}$.
    3. Compare $\max\{x_1, x_2, x_3\}$ and x_4 to obtain $\max\{x_1, x_2, x_3, x_4\}$.
       $\vdots$
$n-$**1.** Compare $\max\{x_1, x_2, \ldots, x_{n-1}\}$ and x_n to obtain $\max\{x_1, x_2, \ldots, x_n\}$.

A total of $n - 1$ comparisons are used. At each intermediate step, we compute $\max\{x_1, x_2, x_3, \ldots, x_i\}$ by comparing $\max\{x_1, x_2, \ldots, x_{i-1}\}$ and x_i. In a similar manner we can find the smallest of n integers in a total of $n - 1$ comparisons. □

Example 6   Selection Sort
Consider the problem of sorting a list of n different numbers $\{x_1, x_2, \ldots, x_n\}$.

Solution
The following method for sorting a list is called a **selection sort**. Using the algorithm in Example 5, we can find the largest number of the set in $n - 1$ comparisons. Similarly, the second largest number can be found by obtaining the largest of the remaining $n - 1$ numbers in $n - 2$ comparisons. The third largest number can be found in $n - 3$ comparisons by looking at the remaining $n - 2$ numbers, and so on. Thus the total number of comparisons needed by this method to sort a set of n integers is $(n - 1) + (n - 2) + \cdots + 2 + 1 = n(n - 1)/2$. □

Next we look at a slightly more sophisticated method of sorting known as quicksort, which makes use of recursion. It was developed in 1960 by C. A. R. Hoare.

Recursion

Mathematicians have long known that induction is a powerful tool for proving theorems. In a similar way, computer scientists are finding that recursion is an important programming tool. The basic idea of a recursive procedure is that it calls itself to solve a problem by solving similar problems that are somehow smaller than the original problem. Thus the concept of working backward is an important characteristic of recursion. As with induction, it is essential that a recursive program be able to solve some trivial cases, because this is the only thing that stops the execution of the program.

Quicksort

Suppose we wish to sort a list of n names $A_1, A_2, \ldots, A_n$ so that the names appear in alphabetical order. Quicksort partitions the list of names into two parts, and then sorts the two parts independently. Consider the following list of names:

Joseph, Michael, Anthony, Joel, David, Derek, Neal, Peter, Thomas, Patrick

Note that the seventh name, Neal, is in its correct position in the list. Not only that, but the first six names come before Neal alphabetically, and the last three names come after Neal alphabetically. We say that an element of this kind is a splitter.

Quicksort creates a splitter in the list. To do this, an element is chosen at random from the list and it is compared with every other element in the list. The names that come before the chosen element are put before it in the order that they are discovered, and the elements that come after the chosen element are put after it in the order that they are discovered. If the newly created splitter is in the ith position, quicksort calls upon itself to sort the list $A_1, A_2, \ldots, A_{i-1}$ and again to sort the list $A_{i+1}, A_{i+2}, \ldots, A_n$.

This method works most efficiently when the list is divided into two nearly equal parts. Roughly speaking, the lists are then successively divided in half $\log_2 n$ times until (sorted) lists with a single name result. More precisely we can say that, on the average, quicksort requires about $2n \log_2 n$ comparisons to sort a list of n names, but we omit the details. Note that in the worst case, when the first splitter is the last element in alphabetical order, the second splitter is the next-to-last element in alphabetical order, and so on, quicksort takes the same number of comparisons as selection sort.

4.1
PROBLEMS

1. Find the greatest common divisor of 1722 and 462 using the Euclidean algorithm.

2. Show that $(6n + 5, 4n + 2) = 1$ for any positive integer n.

3. a) For two positive integers a and b, $a \geq b$, suppose that b divides a with quotient q and remainder r. Show that $(a, b) = (b, r)$.
   b) Use part (a) to show that, given any two positive integers n and k, the Euclidean algorithm will always output their greatest common divisor.

4. The sequence of Fibonacci numbers F_n is defined as $F_1 = 1$, $F_2 = 1$, and for $n > 2$, $F_n = F_{n-1} + F_{n-2}$. Write an algorithm for obtaining F_{100}.

5. Suppose we have two n-digit decimal numbers. If a computer can compare corresponding digits of the two numbers, describe an algorithm for determining which of the two numbers is larger.

6. Suppose we have two words of arbitrary length. If a computer can compare any two letters, describe an algorithm for determining which word comes first in alphabetical order.

7. In the game of roulette, the numbers $0, 1, 2, \ldots, 36$ are placed on the outside of a spinning wheel. In how many different ways can the numbers be arranged if two arrangements are considered to be the same if they differ by just a rotation of the wheel?

8. In how many ways can we choose k different objects out of n different objects and arrange them in a circle?

9. Describe an algorithm that, given n integers, $x_1, x_2, \ldots, x_n$, will output 1 when the integers are all distinct and will output 0, otherwise.

10. Describe an algorithm that inputs a positive integer N and outputs its binary representation. *Hint:* Repeated division by 2.

11. a) Describe an algorithm that inputs two n-digit binary numbers and outputs their sum (in binary).
    b) Describe an algorithm that inputs two n-digit binary numbers and outputs their product (in binary).

ADVANCED PROBLEMS

12. There are n gossips, each of whom knows some information that the others do not. Whenever two gossips call each other, they always tell each other all the information that they know.
    a) Describe a sequence of calls that will result in each gossip hearing all the information.
    b) Show that for $n \geq 4$, everyone can learn all the gossip in $2n - 4$ calls.

13. Suppose we start with a sorted list containing m elements and another containing n elements. Describe an algorithm for merging two sorted lists into a single sorted list of $m + n$ elements using at most $m + n - 1$ comparisons.

14. In a group of nine coins there is one counterfeit coin that is lighter than the others. Describe an algorithm for finding the counterfeit coin in two weighings on an equal arm balance.

15. In a group of nine coins there is one counterfeit coin that can be lighter or heavier than the others. Describe an algorithm for finding the counterfeit coin in three weighings on an equal arm balance.

16. Five married couples are sitting around a circular table with men and women alternating. How many different seating arrangements are possible?

17. A mathematician picks a number from the set $\{1, 2, 3, \ldots, 2^n\}$. A computer scientist tries to guess the chosen number by asking questions with a yes-no answer. Describe an algorithm that allows the computer scientist to guess the number in n questions.

*18. Imagine a square table that rotates about its center. At each corner is a deep well, and hidden from view at the bottom of each well is a drinking glass that is either upright or inverted. To begin with, the glasses are in a random mixed state. If they ever happen to be all turned in the same direction, a bell rings. A person attempts to ring the bell through a sequence of moves. During a move, the table is spun at random, and when it stops, the person reaches each hand into a different well. Since there is no way to distinguish its corners, the person has two choices: reach into two adjacent wells, or reach into diagonally opposite wells. The orientation of the two glasses may be adjusted in any way. Describe a finite sequence of moves that will always ring the bell eventually.

19. At a certain party there are $k + 1$ truthtellers (who never lie) and k normal persons (who may or may not lie). Assuming that the persons know all about each other and must answer any yes-no questions that are asked, describe an algorithm that would allow an outside observer to find all the normal persons.

20. Multiplying two complex numbers $(a + bi)$ and $(c + di)$ results in the expression $ac - bd + (ad + bc)i$, which appears to have taken four multiplications of pairs of real numbers. Show that it can be done using only three multiplications (an unlimited number of additions and subtractions are allowed). ***Hint:*** Look at $a(c)$, $b(d)$, and $(a + b)(c + d)$.

*21. Multiplying two 2×2 matrices $\begin{bmatrix} a & b \\ c & d \end{bmatrix}$ and $\begin{bmatrix} w & x \\ y & z \end{bmatrix}$ results in the matrix $\begin{bmatrix} aw+by & ax+bz \\ cw+dy & cx+dz \end{bmatrix}$, which appears to have taken eight multiplications and four additions. Show that the calculation can be done using only seven multiplications.

22. Suppose a set X contains 2^n different integers. Let a_n be the minimum number of comparisons needed to find the largest and smallest integers in X. Show that $a_1 = 1$, $a_2 = 4$, and $a_n \leq 2a_{n-1} + 2$. Deduce that $a_n \leq 3(2^{n-1}) - 2$.

23. Show that it is possible to sort 2^n different numbers using no more than $n2^n$ comparisons. ***Hint:*** If a_n is the number of comparisons needed to sort 2^n numbers, use Problem 13 to show that $a_n \leq 2a_{n-1} + 2(2^{n-1})$.

24. Eight knights are seated at a round table. In how many ways can they change seats so that each knight has a different knight directly across from him? As usual, circular arrangements that differ by just a rotation are considered to be the same.

4.1
SUPPLEMENTARY
COMPUTER
PROJECTS

1. Mystery Algorithm
   Given two relatively prime positive integers a and b, let $A = (a_1, a_2, a_3)$ and $B = (b_1, b_2, b_3)$ denote 3-tuples. Consider the following procedure:

   1. Set $A = (a, 1, 0)$ and $B = (b, 0, 1)$.

   2. If $a_1 = 1$, output A and stop; if $b_1 = 1$, output B and stop; otherwise, go to Step 3.

   3. If $a_1 > b_1$, replace A by $A - B$ and return to Step 2; otherwise, replace B by $B - A$ and return to Step 2.

   For example, for $a = 12$ and $b = 41$, we get

A	B
$(12, 1, 0)$	$(41, 0, 1)$
$(7, 4, -1)$	$(29, -1, 1)$
$(2, 7, -2)$	$(17, -2, 1)$
	$(5, -3, 1)$
	$(3, -10, 3)$
	$(1, -17, 5) \leftarrow$ Output

   Precisely what problem does this procedure solve? **Hint:** $12(-17) + 41(5) = 1$.

2. Evaluating a Polynomial
   a) Given a polynomial $f(x)$ and a real number x, write a program that will find $f(x)$ using Horner's method in Example 1.
   b) Given a polynomial $f(x)$ and a positive integer n, write a program that will compute $f(1) + f(2) + \cdots f(n)$.

SECTION 4.2   ASYMPTOTIC ANALYSIS OF ALGORITHMS

For a small problem, almost any algorithm will suffice. Mainly we will compare algorithms for efficiency when the size of the problem is relatively large. To study the growth of a complexity function $c(n)$, let us first look at some numerical data for some common complexity functions.

Table of Values

n	1	$\log_2 n$	n	n^2	2^n	$n!$
2	1	1	2	4	4	2
4	1	2	4	16	16	24
8	1	3	8	64	256	40,320
16	1	4	16	256	65,536	2.1×10^{13}
32	1	5	32	1024	4.3×10^9	2.6×10^{35}

Obviously an algorithm that takes a (small) constant number of steps to solve any problem would be highly desirable. Typically, however, we have a complexity function $c(n)$ that grows as n gets large. The smallest of the common complexity functions is $\log n$, which grows only slowly as n gets large. A logarithmic complexity function often arises for an algorithm that solves a problem by transforming it into a smaller problem whose size is reduced by a constant fraction. (See Problems 10 & 12.)

Next in terms of size come the polynomial functions. A *linear* complexity function is one that is proportional to n. A linear complexity function often arises for an algorithm that does a small amount of processing on each of n inputs. A complexity function that is proportional to n^2 is said to be *quadratic*. When n is one thousand, n^2 is one million. Thus an algorithm with a quadratic complexity function is less useful on large problems than an algorithm with a linear complexity function.

For a complexity function $c(n)$, consider the ratio $c(n+1)/c(n)$, which we call the **rate of growth**. From this point of view, a complexity function $c(n)$, which is a polynomial, is seen to be good since the rate of growth $c(n+1)/c(n)$ can be shown to approach 1 for sufficiently large values of n by using l'Hôpital's rule.

When $c(n) = b^n (b > 1)$ is an exponential function, the rate of growth is always b. For the factorial function $c(n) = n!$, the rate of growth gets arbitrarily large as n goes to infinity. These complexity functions often arise in algorithms that solve a problem by enumerating every possible answer. Algorithms with exponential complexity functions are likely to be appropriate only for small values of n. Thus an algorithm is said to be a good algorithm or a polynomial algorithm if its complexity function is bounded by a polynomial in n. A complexity function, like the exponential function $c(n) = b^n$ or the factorial function $c(n) = n!$, is not as desirable for large values of n since it grows quite quickly.

In determining computational complexity, we do not always know exactly how many steps a computation will take for a problem of size n. If the complexity of an algorithm can vary for problems of the same size, we often use the number of steps in the worst possible case as a measure of computational complexity. On the other hand, it is often appropriate to take the average number of steps needed to solve a problem as the complexity of the algorithm. We note that these two measures occasionally will differ greatly. One widely used algorithm for solving linear programming problems is known as the *simplex method*, which on the average is a highly efficient polynomial algorithm, but in the worst case can require an exponential number of steps.

Example 1   Compare the complexity functions $c(n) = 100^n$ and $d(n) = n^{100}$.

Solution
It is easy to check that $c(1) > d(1)$, $d(2) > c(2)$, and $c(100) = d(100)$. To finish, we use the fact that $y^x > x^y$, for real numbers satisfying $x > y \geq e$ (Problem 13). Thus, for $2 < n \leq 99$, $d(n) > c(n)$, but for $n > 100$, $c(n) > d(n)$.   □

Example 2   Compare the complexity functions $c(n) = 100^n$ and $d(n) = n!$.

Solution

Obviously for small values of n, $c(n) > d(n)$, but since the growth rate for $c(n)$ remains constant and the growth rate for $d(n)$ increases to infinity, eventually the values of $d(n)$ will overtake those of $c(n)$. It suffices to find the first n for which $d(n) > c(n)$. Since the numbers involved will be quite large, it is helpful to use logarithms (base 10). Since $\log n$ is an increasing function, it suffices to find the first n for which $\log n! = \log 1 + \log 2 + \cdots + \log n$ is greater than $\log 100^n = 2n$. Using a hand calculator, we find that $n = 269$ is the smallest n for which $n! > 100^n$. Therefore, $c(n) > d(n)$ for $n < 269$ and $d(n) > c(n)$ for $n \geq 269$. $\square$

In some calculations involving $n!$, we can use Stirling's formula to obtain an easily computed approximation for $n!$. Stirling's formula is as follows:

$$n! \cong s(n) = \sqrt{2\pi n}(n/e)^n$$

The approximation $s(n)$ is close to $n!$ for large values of n in the sense that $s(n)/n!$ approaches 1 as n goes to infinity. In Example 2, note that $n = 269$ is also the smallest value of n for which $s(n) > 100^n$ (see the table that follows) and that $s(n)$ is far easier to compute than $n!$.

n	$2n$	$\log n!$	$\log s(n)$
268	536	535.962	535.962
269	538	538.392	538.392
270	540	540.824	540.823

Big-O Notation

In comparing two complexity functions for large values of n, it is often more important to know approximately how fast the two functions grow rather than their exact values. We introduce a standard notation for comparing the growth of two functions. We say that $f(n)$ is $O(g(n))$ [pronounced big-O of $g(n)$] if there exist constants $k_1, k_2 > 0$ such that $|f(n)| \leq k_1|g(n)|$ for all integers $n \geq k_2$. Roughly speaking, to say that $f(n)$ is $O(g(n))$, means that the rate of growth for the function f does not exceed the rate of growth for the function g, at least when n is relatively large. In more practical terms, when $f(n)$ is $O(g(n))$, any advantage of using an algorithm with complexity function f could be neutralized by using an algorithm with complexity function g on a computer that runs a constant times faster. If $f(n)$ is $O(g(n))$ and $g(n)$ is $O(f(n))$, we see that $f(n)$ and $g(n)$ grow at approximately the same rate.

Example 3   a) Show that $1 + 2 + 3 + \cdots + n$ is $O(n^2)$.

Solution

Since $1 + 2 + 3 + \cdots + n \leq n + n + n + \cdots + n = 1(n^2)$, then $1 + 2 + 3 + \cdots + n$ is $O(n^2)$.

b) Show that n^2 is $O(1 + 2 + 3 + \cdots + n)$.

Solution

Since $n^2 \leq 2(1 + 2 + 3 + \cdots + n) = n(n + 1)$, then n^2 is $O(1 + 2 + 3 + \cdots + n)$. $\quad\square$

Example 4   Show that n^2 is not $O(n)$.

Solution

Since $\lim\limits_{n \to \infty} n^2/n = \infty$, there are no constants k and N such that $n^2 \leq kn$ for all $n \geq N$. $\quad\square$

We have the following properties of polynomial functions.

THEOREM 4.2

a) The polynomial complexity function $p(n) = a_k n^k + a_{k-1} n^{k-1} + \cdots + a_0 [a_k \neq 0]$ is $O(n^k)$.

b) For $m > k > 0$, n^k is $O(n^m)$, but n^m is not $O(n^k)$.

Proof

a) If $p(n) = a_k n^k + \cdots + a_1 n + a_0$, then $|p(n)| < (|a_k| + \cdots + |a_1| + |a_0|)n^k$ for all $n \geq 1$. Thus $p(n)$ is $O(n^k)$.

b) Since $n^k \leq n^m$ for all $n \geq 1$, then n^k is $O(n^m)$. On the other hand, $\lim\limits_{n \to \infty} n^m/n^k = \infty$, so for any constant c, $n^m \geq cn^k$ as long as n is sufficiently large and it follows that n^m is not $O(n^k)$.

An algorithm often consists of several steps, so it is usually helpful to calculate the complexity of each step and combine these to obtain the overall complexity (see Problem 2). The following theorem contains several other useful properties of the big-O notation.

THEOREM 4.3

a) If $k > 0$, then $f(n)$ is $O(kf(n))$.

b) If $f(n)$ is $O(g(n))$ and $g(n)$ is $O(h(n))$, then $f(n)$ is $O(h(n))$. [Transitive Property]

Proof

a) If $k_1 = 1/|k|$ and $k_2 = 1$, then $|f(n)| \leq k_1|kf(n)|$ for all $n \geq k_2$. Thus $f(n)$ is $O(kf(n))$.

b) If $|f(n)| \leq k_1|g(n)|$ for all $n \geq k_2$ and $|g(n)| \leq k_3|h(n)|$ for all $n \geq k_4$, then $|f(n)| \leq k_1 k_3 |h(n)|$ for all $n \geq \max\{k_2, k_4\}$. Therefore $f(n)$ is $O(h(n))$.

Example 5   Show that $2^n + n!$ is $O(n!)$.

Solution

For $n \geq 4$, $2^n \leq n!$ (see Example 4, Section 1.2). Since $2^n + n! \leq 2(n!)$, then $2^n + n!$ is $O(2(n!))$, which is $O(n!)$. Therefore $2^n + n!$ is $O(n!)$. $\quad\square$

THEOREM 4.4

a) If $k > 0$ and $b > 1$, then n^k is $O(b^n)$.
b) If $b > 1$, then b^n is $O(n!)$.

Proof

a) Using l'Hôpital's rule, we deduce that $\lim_{n \to \infty} n^k/b^n = 0$. Thus, for sufficiently large n, $n^k \le b^n$, and hence n^k is $O(b^n)$.

b) As in part (a) $\lim_{n \to \infty} b^n/n! = 0$ (see Example 2), so $b^n \le n!$, for sufficiently large n. Therefore b^n is $O(n!)$.

4.2

PROBLEMS

1. Show that $f(x) = x^{1000}$ is $O(g(x) = 2^{(\log_2 x)^2})$. Find the smallest value for which $f(x) < g(x)$.

2. Prove the following properties.
   a) If $f(n)$ is $O(g(n))$ and $c(n)$ is $O(d(n))$, then $f(n)c(n)$ is $O(g(n)d(n))$.
   b) If $c(n)$ is $O(f(n))$ and $d(n)$ is $O(f(n))$, then $c(n) + d(n)$ is $O(f(n))$.

3. If $m > 0$, show that $\log n$ is $O(n^m)$, but that n^m is not $O(\log n)$.

4. If $0 < b_1 < b_2$, show that b_1^n is $O(b_2^n)$, but that b_2^n is not $O(b_1^n)$.

5. If $\lim_{n \to \infty} f(n)/g(n) = k < \infty$, show that $f(n)$ is $O(g(n))$.

6. For each of the following pairs of functions, prove that $f(n)$ is $O(g(n))$.
   a) $f(n) = n^2 + 2^n$ $g(n) = n!$
   b) $f(n) = 3^n - n^3 - 1000$ $g(n) = 3^n$
   c) $f(n) = n^{\log n}$ $g(n) = 2^n$
   d) $f(n) = 100 \log(\log n)$ $g(n) = n \log n$

7. If $\lim_{n \to \infty} f(n)/g(n) = \infty$, show that $f(n)$ is not $O(g(n))$.

8. For each of the following pairs of functions, prove that $f(n)$ is not $O(g(n))$.
   a) $f(n) = n^{m+1}$ $g(n) = n^m$
   b) $f(n) = n^{3/2}$ $g(n) = n \log n$
   c) $f(n) = 2^n$ $g(n) = n^{\log n}$
   d) $f(n) = 3^n$ $g(n) = n^3$

9. For any integers $b, c > 1$, show that $\log_b n$ is $O(\log_c n)$ and that $\log_c n$ is $O(\log_b n)$. Thus, when we say that an expression is $O(\log n)$, it is unnecessary to specify the base of the logarithm.

ADVANCED
PROBLEMS

10. a) Show that x^{2^k} can be computed using k multiplications.
    b) Describe an $O(\log n)$ algorithm for computing x^n. **Hint:** Use the binary representation of n.

11. Show that the sum $1^k + 2^k + 3^k + \cdots + n^k$ is $O(n^{k+1})$, but not $O(n^k)$.

12. Let the sequence f_r be defined by $f_1 = 1$, $f_2 = 1$, and $f_r = f_{r-1} + f_{r-2}$, for $r \geq 2$. Show that if $m \leq n \leq f_k$, the Euclidean algorithm requires at most k steps to compute the greatest common divisor of m and n. Deduce that the number of steps required by the Euclidean algorithm is $O(\log n)$.

*13. Let x and y be real numbers such that $x > y \geq e$. Prove that $y^x > x^y$.

14. Show that $n(\log n)$ is $O(\log n!)$.

15. Show that $(2x + 1)(\log(x^3 + 1)) + 5x^2$ is $O(x^2)$.

16. Suppose that $f(x)$ is $O(g(x))$ and $\lim_{x \to \infty} f(x) = \lim_{x \to \infty} g(x) = \infty$.
   a) Show that $\log|f(x)|$ is $O(\log|g(x)|)$.
   b) Does it follow that $2^{f(x)}$ is $O(2^{g(x)})$?

SECTION 4.3 ENUMERATING PERMUTATIONS AND COMBINATIONS (Optional)

In the last two sections we studied many kinds of algorithms. If there is no efficient algorithm for solving a combinatorial problem, we can always resort to enumeration, though it may not always be feasible for a large problem. To do this, we need a systematic method of searching the possible solutions for the desired answer. In this section we present algorithms for enumerating all permutations and all combinations of a set since they occur naturally in many combinatorial problems. There are several algorithms for enumerating permutations and combinations, but we will present algorithms that enumerate them in lexicographic order. For example, on a sequence of letters forming a word, lexicographic order is the same as our usual alphabetical order.

Sometimes a finite collection of objects like the set of integers $\{1, 2, 3, \ldots, n\}$ or the set of letters $\{a, b, c, \ldots, z\}$ has a natural order. For every pair of different elements I and J in such an ordered set, we know which element comes first. If I comes before J in the natural order, we write $I < J$ and say that I is smaller than J. If $X = \{x_1, x_2, \ldots, x_n\}$ is an ordered set, there is a unique way of listing the elements $x_1 < x_2 < \cdots < x_n$ in order. A very simple way of enumerating such a set is to start with the smallest object and work up to the largest. Sequences of these objects can also be ordered in a natural way using lexicographic order.

DEFINITION   Lexicographic Order

Suppose $a_1 a_2 \cdots a_n$ and $b_1 b_2 \cdots b_n$ are two different n-digit sequences. We say that $a_1 a_2 \cdots a_n < b_1 b_2 \cdots b_n$ if and only if $a_1 < b_1$ or for some $i \leq n$, $a_1 = b_1$, $a_2 = b_2, \ldots, a_{i-1} = b_{i-1}$, and $a_i < b_i$.

Enumerating Permutations

An ordered selection or a permutation can naturally be thought of as a sequence. An unordered selection or a combination can also be represented by a single sequence if we always list the elements selected in increasing order. Thus if the answers to a combinatorial problem can be expressed in terms of combinations or permutations, we can enumerate them in lexicographic order. The following simple examples illustrate the use of lexicographic order in enumeration.

Example 1   Suppose a computer operator has n programs, labeled $1, 2, \ldots, n$, which are to be run on a single computer in some order. Each program requires the operator to set up the computer system in some particular way, using a certain compiler, disk drives, and so on. Not every program will require the same setup, so it makes sense to have programs that need a similar setup to run consecutively, in order to reduce the cost of converting from one setup to another. In general, the computer operator would like to minimize the overall cost of running the n different programs. It is natural to assume that the cost of converting from setup to setup will depend on the schedule that is chosen. Suppose we estimate for every pair $i \neq j$ that the cost of converting from the setup for program i to the setup for program j is c_{ij}. Thus we wish to find the schedule for running the programs that minimizes the total conversion costs.

Solution
Let $n = 4$ and suppose the conversion costs are given in the following matrix. For any value of n, there are $n!$ possible orders for the programs to run in. Thus for $n = 4$, we can list the 24 possible schedules in lexicographic order and compute the conversion costs for each schedule. We find that the schedule that minimizes conversion costs at 8 units is 4312.

$$
\begin{array}{cc}
 & \text{To setup} \\
\text{From setup} \quad
\begin{array}{c} 1 \\ 2 \\ 3 \\ 4 \end{array}
&
\begin{array}{cccc}
1 & 2 & 3 & 4 \\
\left[\begin{array}{cccc}
- & 3 & 5 & 5 \\
4 & - & 3 & 7 \\
2 & 6 & - & 6 \\
7 & 4 & 3 & -
\end{array}\right]
\end{array}
\end{array}
$$

Permutation	Cost	Permutation	Cost	Permutation	Cost
1234	12	2314	10	3412	16
1243	13	2341	16	3421	14
1324	18	2413	19	4123	13
1342	15	2431	12	4132	18
1423	12	3124	12	4213	13
1432	14	3142	11	4231	9
2134	15	3214	15	4312	8
2143	12	3241	20	4321	13

For larger values of n, it will be convenient to have an algorithm for listing the permutations of X in lexicographic order. When all the permutations of X are listed in lexicographic order, the first permutation in the list will have all the numbers arranged in increasing order, and the last number in the list will have all the numbers arranged in decreasing order. The main step in the algorithm is a rule that starts with an arbitrary permutation p and outputs the next permutation q in lexicographic order.

The Next Permutation

Intuitively it seems obvious that of all the permutations larger than p, the first digits of q must coincide with the first digits of p for the maximum possible number of digits. Suppose that the first $j - 1$ digits of p and q are equal, but the jth digit of q is greater than the jth digit of p. Since digit j in q must be one of the last $n - j$ digits of p, the jth digit in p must be smaller than some digit that follows it. Since q is as small as possible, the jth digit of p is the last digit that is smaller than some digit that follows it. Thus the last $n - j$ digits of p are in decreasing order. Also the jth digit of q is the last digit of p that is smaller than the jth digit of p, and the last $n - j$ digits in q must be in increasing order. Thus we have the following algorithm for enumerating all permutations of $\{1, 2, 3, \ldots, n\}$:

0. Input n.

1. Let $i = 1$ and $p_1 = 123 \cdots n$.

2. Output p_i and stop if $i = n!$.

3. If $p_i = X_1 X_2 X_3 \cdots X_n$, find the largest j so that $X_j < X_{j+1}$. (Thus X_j is the last digit that is smaller than some digit after it, and the digits after X_j are arranged in decreasing order.)

4. Find the largest k so that $X_k > X_j$.

5. Increase i by 1. The new permutation p_i is obtained by interchanging X_k and X_j and arranging the digits after the jth digit in increasing order. (Thus $p_i = X_1 X_2 \cdots X_{j-1} X_k X_n X_{n-1} \cdots X_{k+1} X_j X_{k-1} \cdots X_{j+1}$.) Return to Step 2.

Example 2 Suppose $X = \{1, 2, 3, 4, 5, 6, 7\}$ and $p = 3415762$. What is the next permutation q in lexicographic order?

Solution
The last digit in p that is smaller than some following digit is the fourth digit, 5. The smallest digit after the fourth that is larger than 5 is the sixth digit, 6. To find the next permutation in lexicographic order, we interchange 5 and 6, and we arrange the last three digits in increasing order to obtain 3416257.   □

Enumerating k-Combinations

Next we describe an algorithm for listing all the k-combinations of the set $1, 2, 3, \ldots, n$ in lexicographic order. Every k-combination is represented by a unique strictly increasing sequence of length k.

Example 3   A small computer company wants to hire three programmers. The company has a pool of five job applicants from which to choose. Each job applicant knows several programming languages. The company would like to select three applicants so that, for each of the programming languages BASIC, COBOL, FORTRAN, LISP, and Pascal, at least one applicant knows each language.

Solution

To find a subset of three applicants who know all five languages, we list all possible 3-combinations in lexicographic order and write YES if the three applicants know all five languages and NO if not. In the following matrix, we let the entry in row i and column j be 1 if applicant i knows language j and 0 if not.

				Language				
123	NO							
124	YES			B	C	F	L	P
125	YES							
134	NO		1	1	1	0	0	0	1
135	YES							
145	NO		2	0	0	1	1	0
234	YES							
235	NO	Applicant	3	1	0	0	1	0
245	YES							
345	YES		4	0	1	0	0	1
			5	1	1	1	0	0

The Next k-Combination

The first k-combination in lexicographic order is $123\ldots k$ and the last is $(n-k+1)(n-k+2)\cdots(n-1)n$. If p is an arbitrary k-combination, let q denote the next k-combination in lexicographic order. Obviously q must have the maximum possible number of first digits in common with p of any k-combination greater than p. If the jth digits of p and q are the first unequal pair, j is the largest integer for which the jth digit is not equal to $n-k+j$ and the jth digit of q must be 1 greater than the jth digit of p since q is as small as possible. Also the last $k-j$ digits following the jth digit of q are the next $k-j$ smallest numbers arranged in increasing order. Thus we have the following algorithm for enumerating all k-combinations of $\{1, 2, 3, \ldots, n\}$ in lexicographic order:

0. Input n and k.
1. Let $i = 1$ and $c_1 = 123\cdots k$.
2. Output c_i and stop if $i = C(n, k)$.
3. If $c_i = y_1 y_2 y_3 \cdots y_k$, find the largest j such that $y_j < n - k + j$.
4. Increase i by 1. The next k-combination is $c_i = y_1 y_2 \cdots y_{j-1}(y_j + 1)(y_j + 2) \cdots (y_j + k - j + 1)$. Return to Step 2.

Example 4   Let $X = \{1, 2, 3, \ldots, 9\}$ and $p = 134789$. What is the next 6-combination in lexicographic order?

Solution

The largest j for which the jth digit is not equal to $n - k + j$ is $j = 3$. Therefore the next 6-combination in lexicographic order is $q = 135678$.   ☐

Enumerating All Subsets

Finally we consider an algorithm that may be used to generate all the subsets of a given set $X = \{x_1, x_2, \ldots, x_n\}$. We will use the previously discussed one-to-one correspondence between the subsets of X and the binary sequences of length n (see Example 2, Section 1.4). These binary sequences can also be thought of as the numbers $0, 1, 2, \ldots, 2^n - 1$ in binary notation. We list the binary numbers in order, starting with 0 and ending with $2^n - 1$, by essentially simulating the odometer of a car. In other words, the binary representation of $k + 1$ is obtained from the binary representation of k as follows:

1. If k ends in a 0 change it to a 1.
2. If k ends in one or more 1's, starting at the right (and moving to the left) change each 1 to a 0 until you reach the first 0, which is changed to a 1.

The algorithm for enumerating all subsets is as follows:

1. Start with $v = 000\cdots 0$ and output v.
2. Stop if you reach $v = 111\cdots 1$.
3. Start at the right-hand digit of v.
4. If the bit you are looking at is a 0, change it to a 1, output this new vector, and return to Step 2. Otherwise, change this digit to a 0, move left one position, and repeat Step 4.

Example 5   The Knapsack Problem

Another famous problem that is not known to have an efficient solution is sometimes referred to as the knapsack problem. Suppose an airplane (or a large knapsack) can carry up to C pounds of cargo. There are n different items that could be transported, with item i weighing a_i pounds and providing a profit of c_i dollars if transported. The goal is to find a cargo that maximizes the profit among all cargos whose weight does not exceed the capacity of the airplane.

Solution

A simple, but inefficient, method of solving the knapsack problem involves enumerating the subsets in lexicographic order as shown earlier. A subset of the items is an acceptable cargo if its total weight does not exceed C pounds. For each such cargo we compute the total profit obtained when this subset is transported. By checking each of the 2^n subsets, we would eventually find the acceptable cargo for which the total profit is maximized.   ☐

4.3
PROBLEMS

1. Suppose the permutations of the set $X = \{1, 2, 3, \ldots, 9\}$ are listed in lexicographic order. Find the permutation that comes directly before and directly after, each of the following permutations.
   a) 374125689   b) 453192876

2. Suppose the 5-combinations of the set $X = \{1, 2, 3, \ldots, 9\}$ are listed in lexicographic order. Find the 5-combination that comes directly before and directly after each of the following 5-combinations.
   a) 34689   b) 13567

3. Enumerate all 4-combinations of $\{1, 2, 3, 4, 5, 6\}$ in lexicographic order.

4. Give a rule that when given an arbitrary permutation of $\{1, 2, 3, \ldots, n\}$ determines the permutation directly before it in lexicographic order.

5. Give a rule that when given an arbitrary k-combination of $\{1, 2, 3, \ldots, n\}$ determines the k-combination that comes right before it in lexicographic order.

6. A company has several aging factories that it plans to remodel. If the cost of remodeling factory i to manufacture product j is given by the following matrix, find by enumeration the most efficient way to remodel the four factories so that the company can manufacture all four products, each at a different factory.

Product

	1	2	3	4
1	11	5	7	3
2	6	9	4	10
3	2	8	6	7
4	5	6	7	8

Factory

7. A computer center has enough funds to hire three student assistants out of six applicants. Together the three tutors should know each of the six languages, ALGOL, BASIC, COBOL, FORTRAN, LISP, and Pascal. In the following matrix, there is a 1 in row i and column j if and only if student i knows language j. Find by enumeration all subsets of three tutors that can be hired.

Language

	A	B	C	F	L	P
1	1	1	0	0	0	0
2	0	1	0	1	0	1
3	0	1	0	0	1	1
4	1	1	1	0	0	0
5	0	0	1	1	0	1
6	0	1	0	0	1	0

Student

8. A traveling salesperson plans to travel through five cities starting and ending at city 1, her home city. If the cost of traveling from city i to city j is given by the following matrix, find the least costly route that goes through each city exactly once.

$$
\begin{array}{c}
\text{To} \\
\begin{array}{cccccc}
 & 1 & 2 & 3 & 4 & 5 \\
1 & - & 5 & 7 & 6 & 5 \\
2 & 6 & - & 5 & 9 & 6 \\
\text{From } 3 & 6 & 4 & - & 5 & 10 \\
4 & 5 & 8 & 6 & - & 6 \\
5 & 7 & 5 & 11 & 4 & - \\
\end{array}
\end{array}
$$

9. Consider the k-permutations of $\{1, 2, 3, \ldots, n\}$. Which k-permutation comes first and which comes last? Give a rule that starts with an arbitrary k-permutation and outputs the next k-permutation in lexicographic order.

10. Define lexicographic order for sequences of arbitrary length modeled after our usual definition of alphabetical order. Consider the set of sequences consisting of one to five distinct digits from the set $\{1, 2, 3, 4, 5\}$.
a) What is the sequence immediately following 124?
b) What is the sequence immediately preceding 124?
c) Give a rule that when given a sequence of one to five distinct digits outputs the next such sequence in lexicographic order.

11. Give an algorithm that lists the ternary sequences of length n in lexicographic order.

ADVANCED PROBLEMS

12. a) When the permutations of X are listed in lexicographic order, show that the position of an arbitrary permutation $x_1 x_2 \cdots x_n$ in the list is given by the formula $a_1(n-1)! + a_2(n-2)! + \cdots + a_{n-1}1! + 1$, where a_i equals the number of digits following x_i in the permutation $x_1 x_2 \cdots x_n$, which are smaller than x_i.
b) Deduce that $n! = (n-1)(n-1)! + (n-2)(n-2)! + \cdots + 1(1!) + 1$.

13. a) When the k-combinations of X are listed in lexicographic order, show that the position of an arbitrary k-combination $i_1 i_2 \cdots i_k$ is given by the formula $C(n, k) - C(n - i_1, k) - C(n - i_2, k - 1) - \cdots - C(n - i_k, 1)$.
b) Deduce that $C(n, k) = C(n-1, k) + C(n-2, k-1) + \cdots + C(n-k, 1) + 1$.

14. Give an algorithm that lists the k-permutations with repetition of $\{1, 2, 3, \ldots, n\}$ in lexicographic order. Find a formula for the position of an arbitrary sequence $x_1 x_2 \cdots x_k$ in the list.

15. Consider the set of all sequences of digits $\{1, 2, \ldots, 9\}$ containing k digits or less.

a) Give an algorithm for listing the preceding sequences in lexicographic order.

b) For a given sequence of digits $d_1 d_2 \cdots d_m$, $m \leq k$, in what position does the sequence appear in the entire list?

4.3

SUPPLEMENTARY COMPUTER PROJECTS

1. Integer Solutions in Lexicographic Order

a) Write a program that will list in lexicographic order the nonnegative integer solutions of $x_1 + x_2 + \cdots + x_k = n$, for a given pair of positive integers k and n.

b) Write a program to list in lexicographic order the positive integer solutions of $x_1 + x_2 + \cdots + x_k = n$, for given positive integers k and n.

2. A Postage Problem

In how many ways can you select one-cent, two-cent, three-cent stamps so that their total value is n cents? Equivalently we would like to find a_n, the number of nonnegative integer solutions of the equation $3x_1 + 2x_2 + x_3 = n$.

a) Write a program that will generate all the solutions in lexicographic order. Thus, for $n = 8$, we get the 10 solutions $(0, 0, 8)$, $(0, 1, 6)$, $(0, 2, 4)$, $(0, 3, 2)$, $(0, 4, 0)$, $(1, 0, 5)$, $(1, 1, 3)$, $(1, 2, 1)$, $(2, 0, 2)$, $(2, 1, 0)$. Note that only two (nested) loops are needed since $x_3 = n - 2x_1 - 3x_2$. It may be helpful to use the greatest integer function.

b) In part (a), delete your PRINT statement and insert a counter. You now have a program for computing a_n. Check that $a_{50} = 234$.

c) Run your program for part (a) with $n = 20$. Carefully note how many solutions have $x_1 = 0$, $x_1 = 1, \ldots, x_1 = 6$. Express a_n as a summation. Check that this works for all values of n.

4   REVIEW PROBLEMS

1. a) Eight knights sit in a row. How many different seating arrangements are possible if two of the knights, Galahad and Lancelot, refuse to sit next to each other?

b) Repeat part (a) if instead they sit at a round table and seating arrangements that differ by just a rotation are considered to be the same.

2. Given that $X = \{1, 2, \ldots, n\}$, describe an algorithm that lists its k-combinations with unlimited repetition in lexicographic order.

3. a) In how many ways can nine men and five women stand in a line so that no two women stand next to each other?

b) Repeat part (a) if instead they stand in a circle.

4. Consider the following method for arranging n distinct numbers $x_1, x_2, \ldots, x_n$ into a single sorted list. Compare x_i and x_{i+1} for $i = 1, 2, \ldots, n-1$. If $x_i > x_{i+1}$,

switch the two numbers before moving on to the next comparison. As a result of these comparisons, the largest number will always be in the nth position. Continuing in this same manner, now arrange the first $n - 1$ numbers and so on. Find the total number of comparisons needed to sort n distinct numbers using this method, which is known as the bubble sort.

5. Show that $(\log(\log n))^2$ is $O(\log n)$.

6. Arrange the following functions in increasing order of their rates of growth, for large n. That is, list them so that each one is big-O of its successor; n^2, $\log n^5$, $\sqrt{n!}$, $n^{\log n}$.

7. a) Given a list of n numbers, $a_1, a_2, \ldots, a_n$, describe an algorithm for determining whether or not a given number x is in the list using at most $O(n)$ comparisons.
   b) If the preceding list is sorted, describe an algorithm that uses at most $O(\log n)$ comparisons.

8. If $\lim_{n \to \infty} f(n)/g(n) = L$, where $0 < L < \infty$, show that $f(n)$ is $O(g(n))$ and $g(n)$ is $O(f(n))$.

9. a) Show that $1 + 1/2 + 1/3 + \cdots + 1/n = S_n$ is $O(\log n)$.
   b) Show that $\log n$ is $O(S_n)$.

10. Describe an algorithm that finds the largest and second largest integers in a set of 2^m integers using at most $m + 2^m - 2$ comparisons.

CHAPTER 4

SUMMARY

In this chapter we used combinatorial counting techniques to analyze algorithms. To compare two algorithms for efficiency, it is often important to count how many steps each would take on a problem of a certain size. We say that an algorithm is good if it is a polynomial algorithm. For a large class of problems, referred to as NP-complete problems, it is not known whether or not it is possible to find a good solution. See [2] for more details. In Section 4.2 we studied limiting techniques for comparing algorithms using the big-O notation. In addition we studied methods for enumerating permutations and combinations in Section 4.3. Many important algorithms in computer science can be represented as graph algorithms. Graphs and graph algorithms will be discussed in the next two chapters. Many of the combinatorics books listed at the end of Chapter 2 can be used as references for these topics also.

Many new books about computer science and algorithms are being written, but we especially recommend the book by Garey and Johnson [2] and any of the books by Knuth [3]. The derivation of Stirling's formula is a standard topic in most advanced calculus texts, including [7].

BIBLIOGRAPHY

1. Riordan, J. *Combinatorial Identities.* New York: Wiley and Sons, 1968.

Algorithms

2. Garey, M., and D. Johnson. *Computers and Intractibility.* San Francisco: W. H. Freeman, 1979.

3. Knuth, D. *The Art of Computer Programming*, Vol. 1: Fundamental Algorithms, Vol. 2: Seminumerical Algorithms, Vol. 3: Searching and Sorting. Reading, Mass.: Addison-Wesley, 1973.

4. Reingold, E., J. Nievergelt, and N. Deo. *Combinatorial Algorithms: Theory and Practice.* Englewood Cliffs, N.J.: Prentice-Hall, 1977.

5. Sedgewick, R. *Algorithms.* Reading, Mass.: Addison-Wesley, 1983.

6. Aho, A., J. Hopcroft, and J. Ullman. *The Design and Analysis of Computer Algorithms.* Reading, Mass.: Addison-Wesley, 1974.

Advanced Calculus

7. Buck, R. *Advanced Calculus,* 2nd edition. New York: McGraw-Hill, 1965.

CHAPTER

5

GRAPHS

SECTION 5.1 GRAPH MODELS

A graph is a simple geometrical object that is a useful model in mathematics and computer science. Since the solutions of many interesting computer science problems can be expressed most easily in terms of graph algorithms, graph theory has come to be recognized as one of the most useful mathematical subjects for a computer scientist to study. Historically many problems involving games and puzzles were solved using graphs, so we will see a wide variety of graph theory applications. Figure 5.1 represents a map of the area near Santa Cruz, California.

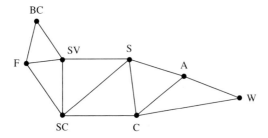

Figure 5.1

134

Graph Theory Terminology

Geometrically an undirected graph G consists of a finite set of vertices $V(G)$ and a finite set of edges $E(G)$ joining these vertices. We usually let $p = |V(G)|$ represent the number of vertices of G and $q = |E(G)|$ represent the number of edges of G. Each edge in $E(G)$ has two endpoints in $V(G)$. An edge with two identical endpoints is called a **loop**.

To gain the insight necessary to solve a problem, it is sometimes helpful to draw a figure. In combinatorial problems, the appropriate figure is often a graph. In such cases we usually represent a graph by a drawing in the plane, with one point for each vertex and one line segment, joining the appropriate endpoints, for each edge. Any graph can be properly drawn so that every edge is a line segment (not necessarily straight) that joins its endpoints but contains no other vertices in its interior. A proper drawing may have edges that intersect in their interiors, but a graph that can be drawn without intersecting edges is said to be a planar graph (see Section 5.4).

The basic geometrical relationships between edges and vertices are described in the following way.

DEFINITION   Incidence

An edge e joining two vertices x and y is said to be incident to its endpoints x and y.

Since it is equally appropriate to say that e joins x to y or joins y to x, we sometimes refer to e as an undirected edge. In Fig. 5.2 edge a is incident to vertex 1 and to vertex 2, but not to vertex 3 or to vertex 4.

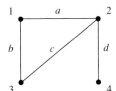

Figure 5.2

DEFINITION   Adjacency

Two vertices that are endpoints of the same edge are said to be adjacent vertices, and two edges that are incident to the same vertex are said to be adjacent edges.

In Fig. 5.2, vertex 1 is adjacent to vertex 2 and to vertex 3, but not to vertex 4, whereas edge b is adjacent to edge a and edge c, but not to edge d. Sometimes we refer to the vertices adjacent to a vertex v as the neighbors of v.

A pair of vertices x and y may be joined by more than one edge.

DEFINITION   Simple Graphs

Two edges that have the same endpoints are called parallel edges. A graph with no parallel edges and no loops is said to be a simple graph.

Figure 5.2 is a simple graph, whereas Fig. 5.3 is not because it has a loop at vertex *a* and two parallel edges joining vertex *c* and vertex *d*.

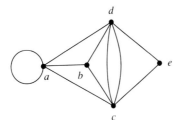

Figure 5.3

We sometimes need to know when two graphs are the same. Mathematically two structures that are essentially the same are said to be isomorphic.

DEFINITION   Isomorphic Graphs

Two graphs are isomorphic if there is a one-to-one correspondence between their vertices and another between their edges that together preserve incidence and adjacency.

Figure 5.4

The reader can easily show that the two graphs in Fig. 5.4 are isomorphic.

The two graphs in Fig. 5.5 are not isomorphic since in one graph all the vertices incident to three edges are adjacent, but in the other they are not. The graph isomorphism problem, which is to find a simple set of properties to check that will determine whether or not two arbitrary graphs G and G' are isomorphic, is a famous unsolved problem in computer science that is thought to be difficult.

In certain applications, graphs can be used to represent chemical compounds or electrical networks. In these cases, two isomorphic graphs usually represent the

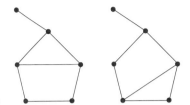

Figure 5.5

same compound or electrical network. Therefore it is important to be able to tell when two graphs are isomorphic in order to reduce the inventory of objects that are to be studied (see Chapter 9). The graphs in Fig. 5.6 represent two different chemical compounds, both containing 4 carbon and 10 hydrogen atoms.

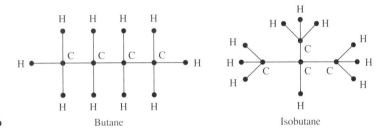

Figure 5.6   Butane   Isobutane

DEFINITION   Complete Graphs

A simple graph in which each pair of distinct vertices is joined by an edge is called a complete graph. The complete graph with n vertices is denoted by K_n.

Two drawings of K_4 are given in Fig. 5.4, but it is easy to see that any two complete graphs with the same number of vertices are isomorphic. The graph K_n has n vertices and $\binom{n}{2}$ edges since there is exactly one edge for each pair of distinct vertices.

A bipartite graph is a graph whose vertices can be partitioned into two subsets X and Y such that each edge has one end in X and one end in Y. The bipartite graph shown in Fig. 5.7 represents the applicants who have applied for a job at a firm and the available positions for which each is qualified. We leave it to the reader to find a set of applicants who can be hired to fill all the empty positions (see Chapter 10).

DEFINITION   Complete Bipartite Graph

A complete bipartite graph with bipartition (X, Y) is a simple bipartite graph in which each vertex of X is joined to each vertex of Y. If X has n vertices and Y has m vertices, this graph is denoted by $K_{n,m}$.

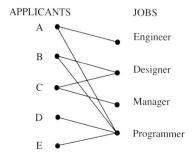

APPLICANTS   JOBS

A

Engineer

B

Designer

C

Manager

D

Programmer

E

Figure 5.7

In $K_{n,m}$ each of the n vertices of X is joined to m vertices in Y, so we see that there are a total of $n + m$ vertices and nm edges. The bipartite graph $K_{3,3}$ is pictured in Fig. 5.8.

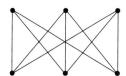

Figure 5.8

The cube in Fig. 5.9 is also a bipartite graph. Note that a bipartite graph is often drawn with all the vertices in X on one side and all the vertices in Y on the other, but this is not necessarily so. Can you find a bipartition of the cube (see Problem 22)?

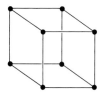

Figure 5.9

Graph Models

Several types of graphs can be used to model a variety of different situations. The type of graph we have been considering so far is called an **undirected graph**. Two other kinds of graphs that we will encounter are directed graphs and weighted graphs. In a **directed graph**, each edge is assigned a specific direction. A **directed edge** may join a vertex x to a vertex y, whereas an **undirected edge** between vertices x and y is considered to join x to y and to join y to x. In a **weighted graph**, each edge is assigned a weight $w(e)$ that generally corresponds somehow to its length, whereas each edge in an undirected graph is automatically assumed to have length 1. We illustrate the differences between these models by looking at the following four different kinds of maps:

1. *A communications network.* Consider a collection of cities. Suppose that certain pairs of cities can communicate with each other directly and that other pairs cannot. An undirected graph would be the appropriate model for this situation. The cities would be the vertices of the graph, and cities that can communicate with each other directly would be joined by an undirected edge.

2. *A city map.* Since a city may have one-way streets, a directed graph would be the appropriate model for this map. Take the vertices of the graph to be the points where two or more streets intersect. Two intersections are joined by an edge directed from x to y if there is a street going directly between x and y and if it is legal to travel on this street from x to y.

3. *A driving time map.* In a collection of cities, some pairs of cities are joined directly by a highway. A highway between two cities can be traveled in either direction, but not all highways are equally long. A weighted graph is the appropriate model for this situation. There will be one vertex for each city and one weighted edge for each highway traveling directly between a pair of cities, with the weight of an edge equal to the amount of time it takes to traverse the corresponding highway.

4. *A transportation network.* Consider a network of shipping routes for transporting a commodity from its source to a large processing plant. The source, the destination, and any intermediate points are represented by vertices. A network, which is a directed graph with weighted edges, is the appropriate graph model in this situation. Each individual route is represented by a directed edge with an associated weight that corresponds to the maximum rate at which the commodity can be transported along this route. Later (in Chapter 10) we shall see how to determine the maximum amount of material that can be shipped through a given transportation network.

Graphs of Relations

Another way of explaining some of our graph models is by using the mathematical concept of a relation. A relation on a set of objects V can be thought of as a subset R of the ordered pairs in $V \times V$. An arbitrary relation R can be represented by a directed graph, with one vertex for each object in V and one directed edge for each ordered pair in R. For example, the flow chart of a computer program can be represented by a directed graph. The instructions will be the vertices and directed edges will be used to indicate the logical flow between the instructions.

A relation R is said to be symmetric if for every x and y in V, either both (x, y) and (y, x) are in R or neither is in R, and R is said to be irreflexive if none of the ordered pairs (x, x) is contained in R. A symmetric irreflexive relation R can be represented by an undirected simple graph with one vertex for each object in V and one undirected edge joining x and y for each pair (x, y) and (y, x) contained in R. In representing the friendships in a group of people we usually assume that friendship is a symmetrical relationship. Thus we can use an undirected graph to display the friendships.

Puzzle 1   The Friendship Puzzle

In any group of two or more people, show that there are always two people with exactly the same number of friends inside the group. *Hint:* The friendships can be represented by a simple graph. (See Problem 15.)   □

Example 1   Tournaments

Let V be the set of teams in a tournament, say, $t_1, t_2, \ldots, t_n$. Suppose that a number of games, each involving a pair of teams, are played. Assuming that no team plays itself or another team more than once, t_i played t_j describes a symmetric irreflexive relation. Thus we can represent the games played in the tournament by an undirected graph. In addition, suppose that every game results in one winning team and one losing team. If we wish to record the winner of each game, a directed graph should be used to represent the results. There is one vertex for each team and one directed edge for each game that starts at the winning team and ends at the losing team. Note that in fact a certain kind of directed graph is called a tournament. A tournament in which every pair of different teams plays exactly one game is called a round-robin tournament. The word "tournament" in graph theory is reserved for precisely those directed graphs that can be thought of as representing the results of a round-robin tournament. Tournaments are discussed more fully in Chapter 10.   □

A Basic Counting Formula

A simple numerical quantity that is useful in the study of graphs is the degree of a vertex.

DEFINITION   Degree

The degree of a vertex v in the graph G is the number of edges in G which are incident to v (with loops counted twice), and is denoted by $\deg v$.

In Fig. 5.10 $\deg v_1 = 1$, $\deg v_2 = 4$, $\deg v_3 = 2$, and $\deg v_4 = 5$.

$$\sum_{i=1}^{4} \deg v_i = 1 + 4 + 2 + 5 = 12 = 2q$$

Figure 5.10

Let G be a graph with p vertices and q edges.

DEFINITION   Degree Sequence

If the vertices of a graph G are $v_1, v_2, \ldots, v_p$, $(\deg v_1, \deg v_2, \ldots, \deg v_p)$ is said to be a degree sequence of G.

Sometimes we will just need to know either the largest of these degrees, $\max\{\deg v_1, \deg v_2, \ldots, \deg v_p\}$, or the smallest, $\min\{\deg v_1, \deg v_2, \ldots, \deg v_p\}$. This maximum degree will be denoted by δ^+ and this minimum degree by δ^-. If every vertex of a graph G has the same degree, we say that G is regular. If every vertex of G has degree r, we say that G is r-regular.

Note that two isomorphic graphs will have the same graphical properties. In particular, they will have the same number of vertices, the same number of edges, and since corresponding vertices will have the same degree, they will also have the same degree sequence. However, the converse is not true (see Problem 8).

For an arbitrary graph G, we have the following basic result about the degrees of G.

THEOREM 5.1   If G is a graph with p vertices, $v_1, v_2, \ldots, v_p$ and q edges, then $\sum_{i=1}^{p} \deg v_i = 2q$.

Proof
Break up the sum of the degrees in two different ways. The sum added up vertex by vertex is what we have on the left. On the other hand, every edge is counted in the sum twice, once for each of its endpoints, so the sum added up edge by edge is what we obtain on the right. Thus we obtain the preceding formula (see Fig. 5.10).

Suppose we say that a vertex is even or odd depending on whether its degree is even or odd. As we have just seen, the sum of the degrees of a graph G is always even; consequently we have the following result.

COROLLARY 1   Every graph has an even number of odd vertices.

Conversely one can show (Problem 23) that every finite sequence of nonnegative integers whose sum is even is the degree sequence of some graph. However, not all these sequences will correspond to the degree sequence of a simple graph. In a simple graph no degree exceeds $p - 1$, so $\delta^+ \leq p - 1$. Also Puzzle 1 states that every degree sequence of a simple graph has at least one pair of matching degrees. The following puzzle involves a simple graph with exactly one pair of matching degrees.

Puzzle 2   **The Handshake Puzzle**
There are four married couples who attend a party including the host and hostess. Several handshakes take place, but no one shakes hands with himself (herself), with his (her) spouse, or with anyone else more than once. Suppose the hostess asks each individual (except herself) how many hands they shook, and each person gives a different answer.
a) How many hands did the hostess shake (explain why the answer is unique)?
b) How many hands did the host shake?
Hint: The handshakes can be represented by a simple graph. (See Problem 16.)   □

Our basic theorem on the degrees of a graph G has special interpretations for certain kinds of graphs.

COROLLARY 2   If G is an r-regular graph with p vertices and q edges, then $q = rp/2$.

COROLLARY 3   For a bipartite graph G with bipartition (X, Y) each edge has one end in X and one end in Y so we obtain $\sum_{x_i \in X} \deg x_i = q = \sum_{y_j \in Y} \deg y_j$.

This idea can be used in the following puzzle.

Puzzle 3   The Marriage Puzzle

In a small village each single man knows k single women and each single woman knows k single men, $k \geq 1$. *Hint:* This situation can be represented by a bipartite graph with an edge joining each man and woman who know each other.

a) Show that the number of single men must equal the number of single women. (See Problem 17.)

b) A more difficult version of this puzzle would ask you to show that in fact every single man and every single woman can get married simultaneously to someone whom they know (see Section 10.3).   ☐

We have seen that counting can be useful in analyzing certain graph theory problems, but other combinatorial ideas can be used, too. The pigeonhole principle is helpful in analyzing the following puzzle.

Puzzle 4   Chromatic Triangles

Six points are placed in the plane such that no three lie on the same line. A line segment is drawn between each pair of distinct points. Each line segment is colored one of two colors: red or white. We say that three points form a chromatic triangle if the three line segments joining pairs of these points are either all red or all white.

a) Show that no matter how the edges are colored there will always be at least one chromatic triangle.

b) Show that in fact there will always be at least two chromatic triangles.

Hint: Any point is incident to at least three edges of the same color. (See Problem 18.)   ☐

5.1

PROBLEMS

1. Suppose we use a graph to model the friendships in this combinatorics class by assigning a vertex to each student and by drawing an edge between vertices if the corresponding students are friends.

a) What can we say about the vertex representing the most popular student in the class?

b) What can we say about the vertex representing a new student?

2. Suppose that a math department has the same number of students as professors. They plan to assign a different professor to advise each student, so each student is asked to indicate a nonempty set of professors he or she would like to have as an advisor. These advisor requests can be modeled by a bipartite graph G where each student and each professor are represented by a vertex and each advisor request is represented by an edge between the corresponding vertices. If the department is able to assign each student an advisor that he/she requested, what does this say about the graph?

3. Several police officers are deployed on a stakeout. Two officers who are sufficiently close to each other can communicate directly using portable radios. If the setup is modeled by a graph with officers as vertices and edges drawn between pairs of vertices representing officers who can communicate directly,

a) How can we describe the graph of a setup where every pair of officers can communicate directly?

b) How can we describe the graph of a setup where every pair of officers can communicate at least indirectly through other officers?

4. Consider the graphs where the vertices correspond to students at a university and two vertices are joined by an edge if and only if they correspond to two students having the same major. Describe the graphs that can occur (assuming each student has just one major).

5. If G is simple, then explain why

a) $q \leq \binom{p}{2}$ b) $\delta^+ \leq p - 1$

6. If G and H are isomorphic, explain why
   a) G and H have the same number of vertices.
   b) G and H have the same number of edges.
   c) G and H have the same degree sequences.

7. Find the eleven nonisomorphic simple graphs on four vertices.

8. Find three nonisomorphic graphs with the same degree sequence $(1, 1, 1, 2, 2, 3)$.

9. Show that the following graphs are not isomorphic.

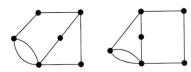

10. Show that the following graphs are isomorphic.

11. a) The complement G^c of a simple graph G is the simple graph with vertex set $V(G)$, two vertices being adjacent in G^c if and only if they are not adjacent in G. Describe the graphs K_n^c and $K_{m,n}^c$.

   b) A simple graph G is said to be self-complementary if G and G^c are isomorphic. Exhibit a self-complementary graph G with five vertices, but explain why there is no such graph with six vertices.

   c) Show that if G is a self-complementary graph with p vertices, then $p \equiv 0$ or 1 (mod 4).

12. Suppose G is a graph with p vertices and q edges whose smallest degree is δ^- and whose largest degree is δ^+. Show that $\delta^- \le 2q/p \le \delta^+$.

13. At the beginning of a math department meeting, there are 10 persons and a total of 26 handshakes.

   a) Explain why there must be a person who shakes hands at least six times.

   b) Explain why there are not exactly three people who shake an odd number of hands.

14. If possible, give an example of a graph G such that G has

   a) No odd vertices   b) No even vertices

   c) Exactly one odd vertex   d) Exactly one even vertex

15. Show that in any simple graph there are always two vertices with exactly the same degree.

16. Solve Puzzle 2.

17. Solve Puzzle 3(a).

18. Solve Puzzle 4.

19. a) If G is a graph with 25 edges and each degree is at least four, what is the maximum number of vertices that G can have?

   b) If G is a simple graph with 50 edges, what is the least number of vertices that G can have?

20. During a summer vacation nine students promise to keep in touch by writing letters, so each student promises to write letters to three of the others.

   a) Is it possible to arrange for each student to write three letters and also to receive three letters?

   b) Is it possible to arrange for each student to write letters to three other students and also to receive letters from the same three students?

21. Suppose that G is a simple graph with p vertices and minimum degree $\delta^- = 3$.
   a) What is the smallest number of edges that G can have?
   b) Explain why there is no 3-regular graph with p vertices if p is odd.
   c) Give a method for constructing a 3-regular simple graph with $p \geq 4$ vertices for any even p.

22. Define the n-cube to be the graph with exactly one vertex for every n-digit binary sequence, two vertices being adjacent if the corresponding sequences differ in exactly one digit.
   a) Draw the 3-cube including its three-digit vertex labels.
   b) How many vertices does the n-cube have?
   c) What is the degree of each vertex in the n-cube?
   d) How many edges does the n-cube have?
   e) Explain why the n-cube is bipartite.

23. Show that any sequence of nonnegative integers $(d_1, d_2, \ldots, d_p)$ whose sum is even must be the degree sequence of some graph (not necessarily a simple graph).

24. A sequence $(d_1, d_2, \ldots, d_p)$ is graphic if and only if it is the degree sequence of some simple graph.
   a) Show that the sequences $(7, 5, 5, 5, 3, 2, 1)$ and $(6, 6, 5, 4, 2, 2, 1)$ are not graphic.
   *b) If $(d_1, d_2, \ldots, d_p)$ is graphic and $d_1 \geq d_2 \geq \cdots \geq d_p$, then $\sum_{i=1}^{p} d_i$ is even and
   $$\sum_{i=1}^{k} d_i \leq k(k-1) + \sum_{i=k+1}^{p} \min\{k, d_i\} \text{ for } 1 \leq k \leq n.$$

***25.** Show that a sequence $(d_1, d_2, \ldots, d_p)$ with $d_1 \geq d_2 \geq \cdots \geq d_p, p \geq 2$, and $d_1 \geq 1$ is graphic, if and only if $(d_2 - 1, d_3 - 1, \ldots, d_{d_1+1} - 1, d_{d_1+2}, \ldots, d_p)$ is graphic.

26. Show that in any group of 10 people there are either four mutual friends or three mutual strangers.

5.1

1. Given an adjacency matrix A of a graph G, (page 148) write a program that will compute the degrees of its vertices and the number of edges it contains.

SECTION
5.2 PATHS AND CONNECTEDNESS

On many occasions when a graph occurs in a problem, it is convenient to think of traveling from vertex to vertex. Obviously one can travel along an edge from one vertex to an adjacent one, but it is also appropriate to think of traveling along a sequence of edges. More precisely we define a walk, a trail, and a path in a graph.

DEFINITION **Walk**

A walk in a graph G is a nonempty finite sequence $W = v_0 e_1 v_1 e_2 v_2 \cdots e_k v_k$ whose terms are alternately vertices and edges, such that every edge is incident to its neighboring vertices. The length of a walk is the number of edges it contains.

If v_0 is the initial vertex and v_k is the terminal vertex of the walk, we say that W is a (v_0, v_k)-walk. In a simple graph, a walk is uniquely determined by its vertices $v_0, v_1, v_2 \cdots v_k$, so we often represent a walk by its sequence of vertices alone.

DEFINITION **Trail and Path**

A trail is a walk in a graph with no repeated edges. If in addition the vertices $v_0, v_1, v_2, \ldots, v_k$ of W are distinct, we say that W is a path from v_0 to v_k.

In Fig. 5.11 note that *acefecgh* is a walk but not a path, whereas the walk *acdefgh* is also a path.

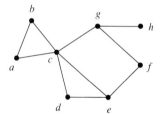

Figure 5.11

Two vertices u and v of G are said to be connected if there is a walk from u to v in G. Sometimes, if a problem can be represented by a graph, a solution to the problem will correspond to a walk or a path from one vertex to another.

Subgraphs

In many situations it will be useful to consider a graph H that is contained in a larger graph G.

DEFINITION **Subgraph**

We say that a graph H is a subgraph of G if and only if $V(H) \subseteq V(G)$ and $E(H) \subseteq E(G)$.

We denote by $G - e$ the subgraph obtained from G by removing the edge e. We also denote by $G - v$ the subgraph obtained from G by removing the vertex v

together with the edges incident to v. A spanning subgraph of G is a subgraph H with $V(H) = V(G)$. (See Fig. 5.12.)

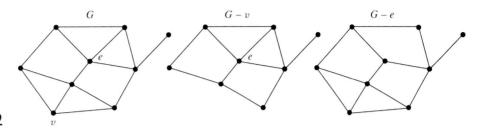

Figure 5.12

Connectedness

For a graph G we have just defined the relation "connected to" for pairs of vertices in $V(G)$. Two vertices are connected if there is a walk from u to v or equivalently if there is a path from u to v (see Problem 1). This relation is reflexive since any vertex is trivially connected to itself by a walk of length 0. It is also symmetric since an (x, y)-walk can be traversed in the opposite direction to give a (y, x)-walk. Finally it is a transitive relation since an (x, y)-walk and a (y, z)-walk can always be combined to give an (x, z)-walk. Thus "connected to" is an equivalence relation on the set of vertices $V(G)$. This means that there is a partition of $V(G)$ into nonempty subsets $V_1, V_2, \ldots, V_w$ such that u and v are connected if and only if both u and v belong to the same subset V_i. For each subset V_i we define a subgraph G_i whose vertex set is V_i and whose edge set consists of precisely those edges with both endpoints in V_i. The subgraphs $G_1, G_2, \ldots, G_w$ are called the **components** of G. Note that each vertex of G is contained in exactly one component of G, as is each edge of G.

DEFINITION   Connected Graph

In a graph G which has exactly one component every pair of vertices are connected by a walk and we say that G is a connected graph. Otherwise G is said to be disconnected and we denote by $w(G)$ the number of components of G.

In Fig. 5.13(a) we have a connected graph and in Fig. 5.13(b), a disconnected graph with four components.

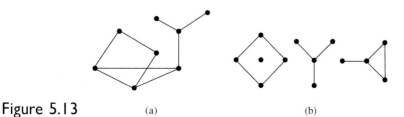

Figure 5.13   (a)   (b)

Graphs are sometimes used to analyze certain properties of a telecommunications network. A network of this type can be represented by an undirected graph with vertices representing locations in the network and edges representing direct communication links between various pairs of these locations. If two vertices in the graph are connected, a message can be relayed between the corresponding locations in the telecommunications network through a sequence of communication links. A more difficult problem concerns the reliability of a communications network: How many links must be disrupted before the network becomes disconnected (see Chapter 10)?

Graphs and Matrices

Especially when a graph theory problem is being analyzed on a computer, a drawing might not be a useful way to represent the graph. A matrix is another way to represent a graph that is very convenient for computer analysis. Since a graph is completely determined by its adjacencies, an adjacency matrix can be used to store the structural properties of the graph. Suppose a graph G has p vertices $v_1, v_2, \ldots, v_p$. Then the **adjacency matrix** of G, denoted by $A(G)$, is the $p \times p$ matrix $A(G) = [a_{ij}]$, where a_{ij} is the number of edges joining v_i and v_j. Note that the adjacency matrix of a graph G gives the number of walks of length 1 between any pair of vertices. For a generalization of this fact see Problems 14 and 15. A graph G and its adjacency matrix are shown in Fig. 5.14.

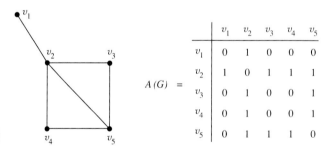

Figure 5.14

A matrix is not the only way to represent a graph on a computer. Although an adjacency matrix is easy to construct, this representation requires that p^2 entries be stored. This can be quite inefficient, especially when most of the entries are zeros. In this case, it may be better to represent the graph using a set of **adjacency lists**. To form the adjacency lists of G, we list its vertices in a vertical column, and after each vertex we write the vertices to which it is adjacent.

$$
\begin{aligned}
v_1 &: \quad v_2 \\
v_2 &: \quad v_1, v_3, v_4, v_5 \\
v_3 &: \quad v_2, v_5 \\
v_4 &: \quad v_2, v_5 \\
v_5 &: \quad v_2, v_3, v_4
\end{aligned}
$$

5.2

PROBLEMS

1. Show that if there is a walk from u to v in G, there is also a path from u to v in G.

2. For any vertex v of a simple graph G with $\delta^- \geq k$, show that G has a path of length k with initial vertex v.

3. Show that G is connected if and only if, for every partition of V into nonempty subsets V_1 and V_2, there is an edge with one end in V_1 and one end in V_2.

4. If a graph G has exactly two components that are both complete graphs with k and $p - k$ vertices respectively ($1 \leq k \leq p - 1$) then
   a) for which values of k is the number of edges a minimum?
   b) for which values of k is the number of edges a maximum?

5. a) Show that if $\delta^- \geq p/2$, then G is connected.
   b) For each even p, describe a disconnected graph with $\delta^- = p/2 - 1$.

6. Let G be a disconnected graph. Show that the vertices of G can be labeled such that the adjacency matrix of G has the following form:

$$\left[\begin{array}{c|c} A_{11} & 0 \\ \hline 0 & A_{22} \end{array}\right]$$

where 0 represents a matrix whose entries are all 0.

7. Let G be a bipartite graph. Show that the vertices of G can be listed such that the adjacency matrix of G has the following form:

$$\left[\begin{array}{c|c} 0 & A_{12} \\ \hline A_{21} & 0 \end{array}\right]$$

where 0 represents a matrix whose entries are all 0 and A_{21} is the transpose of A_{12}.

8. Let A be the adjacency matrix of a simple graph G. What can you say about the column sums of A?

ADVANCED PROBLEMS

9. Show that in any graph G, a vertex of odd degree must always be connected by a walk to another vertex of odd degree.

10. Show that any two longest paths in a connected graph have at least one vertex in common.

11. Show that if G is simple and connected, but not complete, G has three vertices u, v, and w such that uv and vw are in $E(G)$ but uw is not in E.

12. Show that if G is disconnected, G^c is connected. [See Problem 11, Section 5.1]

13. If a simple graph G has two vertices that are not connected by a path of length 3 or less, then every pair of vertices in G^c are connected by a path of length 3 or less.

14. a) If $i \neq j$, show that the (i, j)th entry of A^2, where A is the adjacency matrix of a simple graph G, is the number of paths of length 2 from v_i to v_j.
    b) Show that the (i, i)th entry of A^2 is equal to $\deg v_i$.

15. Show by induction that the number of walks from v_i to v_j of length k in a simple graph G is the (i, j)th entry of A^k.

16. If the graph G becomes disconnected when the vertex v is removed, show that there is a pair of vertices a and b in G such that all paths from a to b pass through v.

17. If a graph G has p vertices and $q > \binom{p-1}{2}$ edges, show that G is connected.

18. For any connected graph G with p vertices, show that the vertices of G can be listed in order $v_1, v_2, \ldots, v_p$ so that for $i \geq 2$, vertex v_i is adjacent to at least one previous vertex on the list.

19. A cutedge in a connected graph G is an edge whose removal separates the graph into two components. Show that an edge e in G is a cutedge if and only if no cycle in G contains e.

SECTION 5.3 CIRCUITS AND CYCLES

A walk is closed if it has positive length and also begins and ends at the same vertex.

DEFINITION Circuit and Cycle

A circuit is a closed walk that has no repeated edges. A cycle is a circuit whose beginning vertex and internal vertices are distinct.

Many problems in graph theory can be resolved by finding a certain kind of circuit or cycle. A cycle of length k is called a k-cycle, and we denote by C_k the graph with k vertices and k edges consisting of a single cycle of length k. A k-cycle is odd or even according to whether k is odd or even. Later, in Section 6.2, we study an important class of connected graphs called **trees**, which are precisely those connected graphs with no cycles.

DEFINITION Eulerian Trails and Circuits

An Eulerian circuit of a graph G is a circuit that traverses each edge of G exactly once. We say that a graph G is Eulerian if and only if it has an Eulerian circuit. A trail that traverses every edge of a graph G exactly once is called an Eulerian trail of G if it begins and ends at distinct vertices.

The solutions to several puzzles depend on the existence of an Eulerian circuit or trail in some graph.

Puzzle 1   The Königsberg Bridge Puzzle

In the earliest known paper on graph theory, Euler (1736) showed that it was impossible to cross each of the seven bridges of Königsberg once and only once, during a walk through town. The seven bridges of Königsberg are pictured in the left side of Fig. 5.15. Also consider the graph to the right where each area in town is represented by a vertex and each bridge is represented by an edge joining two vertices. Obviously an Eulerian trail or an Eulerian circuit in the graph corresponds to a walk through the town that crosses each bridge exactly once and vice versa. (See Problem 7a.)

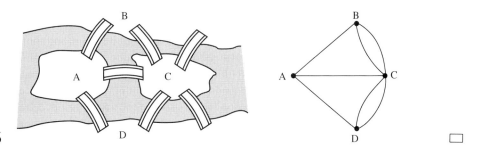

Figure 5.15

Puzzle 2   A Tracing Puzzle

Can we trace the figure in Fig. 5.16 without lifting our pen from the paper or covering a line more than once? (See Problem 5a.)

Figure 5.16

Puzzle 3   A Crossing Puzzle

Can one continuous line be drawn that passes through each edge of the figure in Fig. 5.17 exactly once without passing through any vertex? *Hint:* Draw a graph with one vertex for each region and one edge for each possible crossing. (See Problem 5b.)

Figure 5.17

The following results discovered by Euler can be used to find precisely those graphs that have an Eulerian trail or circuit.

THEOREM 5.2 | A connected graph G is Eulerian if and only if it has no vertices of odd degree.

Proof

Suppose that the graph G possesses an Eulerian circuit C that begins and ends at the vertex v. Each time a vertex u occurs as an internal vertex of C, two of the edges incident to u are used. Since an Eulerian circuit contains every edge of G, $d(u)$ is even for all $u \neq v$. Since C starts and ends at v, $d(v)$ is also even. Thus G has no vertices of odd degree.

Conversely let G be a connected graph G with no vertices of odd degree. We start at any vertex v and go through the edges of G such that no edge will be traced more than once. Starting at v, we choose an edge that is incident to it and travel along this edge to its other endpoint. Upon reaching a vertex, we search for an unused edge incident to it. When the trail enters a vertex $u \neq v$ through an edge, it can always leave the vertex through another edge that has not been used before since every vertex has even degree and an odd number of edges incident to u have been used in reaching u. Therefore the construction, when it ends, will result in a circuit that begins and ends at v. If all of the edges in G were traced in this way, we would have an Eulerian circuit. (See Fig. 5.18.)

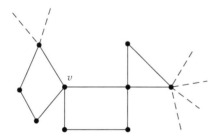

Figure 5.18

If unused edges remain, there must be at least one unused edge that is incident to one of the vertices u on the existing circuit since the graph G is connected. Starting with this edge, we can trace another circuit that consists of edges that were not used before because the number of unused edges incident to any vertex is still even. The two circuits can be combined into a single circuit by breaking apart the original circuit at u to include the new circuit. Continuing in this manner, the circuit can be enlarged until all the edges of G are used. Eventually an Eulerian circuit is constructed. Therefore G is Eulerian.

In a similar way we obtain the following result on graphs that have an Eulerian trail.

THEOREM 5.3

A connected graph G has an Eulerian trail if and only if it has exactly two vertices of odd degree.

Proof

If G has an Eulerian trail that begins at u and ends at v, $u \neq v$, then both u and v have odd degree and the remaining vertices have even degree.

Conversely, suppose that G has exactly two vertices u and v of odd degree. Let G' be the graph obtained from G by adding an extra edge e between u and v. The resulting graph G' has all even degrees, so it must have an Eulerian circuit, which we may assume starts with the edge e. When e is deleted, we obtain an Eulerian trail of G. (See Fig. 5.19.)

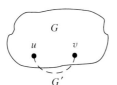

Figure 5.19

DEFINITION   **Hamiltonian Paths and Cycles**

A path that contains every vertex of G is called a Hamiltonian path of G, and a cycle that contains every vertex of G is called a Hamiltonian cycle of G.

Such paths and cycles are named after Sir Rowan Hamilton who invented a game that required a player to complete a Hamiltonian cycle on the dodecahedron. A graph G is said to be Hamiltonian if and only if it contains a Hamiltonian cycle. The graph on the left side of Fig. 5.20 represents the dodecahedron and it is Hamiltonian, whereas the graph on the right is non-Hamiltonian because it is a bipartite graph with an unequal number of vertices in its bipartite sets.

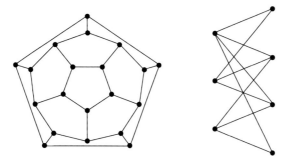

Figure 5.20

Puzzle 4   Touring a Chessboard

A mythical chess piece is allowed to move one square vertically or one square horizontally. Show that it is not possible to move from one corner of an 8×8 chessboard and to visit each square exactly once, ending at the diagonally opposite corner. *Hint:* Express as a problem involving a Hamiltonian path in a bipartite graph. (See Problem 10a.)   □

In contrast with the case of Eulerian graphs, no easy-to-check necessary and sufficient condition for a graph to be Hamiltonian is known. The problem of finding such a condition is one of the important unsolved problems in graph theory. However, the following theorems give simple conditions that imply that a graph G has a Hamiltonian path or a Hamiltonian cycle.

THEOREM 5.4

Suppose that G is a simple graph with p vertices. If $\deg x + \deg y \geq p - 1$ for each nonadjacent pair of vertices x and y in G, then G has a Hamiltonian path.

Proof

Either two vertices x and y of G are connected by an edge, or $\deg x + \deg y \geq p - 1$. In the latter case, x and y must have a common neighbor and are connected by a path of length 2. Therefore G is always connected.

We have the following algorithm that terminates with a Hamiltonian path in G.

0. Start with any path P.

1. If either endpoint of P is adjacent to a vertex that is not already on P, extend the path to include this vertex. Continue in this manner until we obtain a path P whose endpoints are only adjacent to other vertices in P.

2. Let n denote the number of vertices in P. If $n = p$, stop since P is a Hamiltonian path. If $n < p$, we construct a cycle containing the vertices of P in the following manner. Suppose that P consists of the sequences of vertices $v_1 v_2 \cdots v_n$.

    a) If v_n is adjacent to v_1, then $C = v_1 v_2 \cdots v_n v_1$ is a cycle containing the vertices of P.

    b) If v_n is not adjacent to v_1, denote by $v_{i_1}, v_{i_2}, \ldots, v_{i_k}$ the vertices of P that are adjacent to v_1. Since $d(v_1) + d(v_n) \geq p - 1 \geq n$ and $d(v_n) \geq n - k$, then v_n is adjacent to at least one of the vertices $v_{i_j - 1}$. In that case, $C = v_1 v_2 \cdots v_{i_j - 1} v_n v_{n-1} \cdots v_{i_j} v_1$ is a cycle containing the vertices of P. (See Fig. 5.21.)

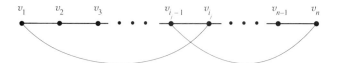

Figure 5.21

3. Since C does not contain all the vertices of G and G is connected, there is a path, and hence an edge, that has one endpoint in C and one endpoint not in C. If e is an edge that has one endpoint v_k in C and one endpoint x not in C, then by deleting one of the edges in C incident to v_k and adjoining e, we obtain a path P containing $n + 1$ vertices. Designate this new path by P and return to Step 1.

We also have a similar result for Hamiltonian cycles but its proof is left as an exercise (Problem 15).

THEOREM 5.5 | Suppose that G is a simple graph with $p \geq 3$ vertices. If $\deg x + \deg y \geq p$ for all pairs of nonadjacent vertices x and y in G, then G has a Hamiltonian cycle.

5.3
PROBLEMS

1. Show that if an edge e is contained in a circuit of a simple graph G, then e is also contained in a cycle of G.

2. Give an example of a graph G that has a circuit containing vertices u and v, but no cycle containing u and v.

3. Show that if $\delta^- \geq 2$, then G contains a cycle.

4. A policeman's beat is pictured by the following connected graph:

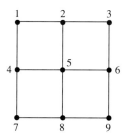

A policeman needs to walk the beat, covering both sides of every street.
a) Construct a closed walk in the graph that uses each edge exactly twice.
b) Explain why there is always a closed walk in any connected graph G that uses each edge exactly twice.

5. a) Solve Puzzle 2.
b) Solve Puzzle 3.

6. A domino is a 1×2 rectangular tile with $0, 1, 2, \ldots, 6$ dots on each half. In a complete set of 28 dominos, each combination of numbers appears exactly once on the two halves of some domino. Show that the dominos can be laid end to end with adjacent halves containing the same number of dots.

7. a) Solve Puzzle 1.
    b) In the city of Kalingrad (formerly Königsberg), two new bridges have been added. Is it now possible to design a route that crosses every bridge exactly once?

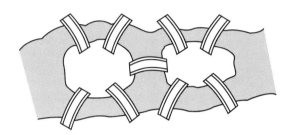

8. If G is a graph that has all vertices of even degree, show that any edge e of G is contained in a cycle.

9. If G is a 4-regular connected graph with no loops, show that the edges of G can be colored red and blue with two red and two blue edges incident to each vertex.

10. a) Solve Puzzle 4.
    b) A knight's move on a chessboard starts by first going two squares horizontally or vertically and ends by going one square perpendicularly. Is it possible to move a knight on an 8×8 chessboard in such a way that it completes every possible move exactly once, where a move between two squares is said to be completed when it is made in either direction?

11. A graph G is randomly Eulerian from a vertex v if every trail of G with initial vertex v can be extended to an Eulerian circuit by adding edges to the end of the trail. Give examples of Eulerian graphs with six vertices that are randomly Eulerian from
    a) None of its vertices   b) One vertex
    c) Two vertices   d) All of its vertices
    (In fact, these are the only possibilities.)

12. Two cycles in a graph are said to be the same if they consist of the same cyclic rotation of vertices, whether or not they start at the same vertex.
    a) Count the number of different Hamiltonian cycles in the complete graph K_n.
    b) Count the number of different Hamiltonian cycles in the complete bipartite graph $K_{n,n}$.

13. Draw a simple graph that has
    a) An Eulerian circuit and a Hamiltonian cycle.
    b) An Eulerian circuit but no Hamiltonian cycle.

   c) A Hamiltonian cycle but no Eulerian circuit.
   d) Neither a Hamiltonian cycle nor an Eulerian circuit.

14. Show that there is a Hamiltonian path but no Hamiltonian cycle in the
    following graph.

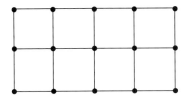

ADVANCED

PROBLEMS

15. Use the algorithm in Theorem 5.4 to prove Theorem 5.5.

16. Show that if G is simple graph with $\delta^- \geq 2$, then G contains a cycle of length at
    least $\delta^- + 1$.

17. The girth of G is the length of a shortest cycle in G, and if G has no cycles, we
    define the girth of G to be ∞. Show that
    a) An r-regular graph of girth 4 has at least $2r$ vertices, and (up to
       isomorphism) there is exactly one such graph with $2r$ vertices.
    b) An r-regular graph of girth 5 has at least $r^2 + 1$ vertices.

18. Show that if a graph G contains a closed walk of odd length, G contains a cycle
    of odd length.

19. Among the many rooms in an old mansion, there is a ghost in each room that
    has an even number of doors. If the mansion has only one entrance,
    a) Give an algorithm that will enable a person entering from the outside to
       reach a room with no ghost.
    b) Give an algorithm that will enable a person who gets lost inside to find her
       way back to the entrance. *Hint:* Use a marking device in these algorithms.

20. a) Let G be a connected graph with four vertices of odd degree. Show that we
       can find two trails that together contain each edge of G exactly once.
    b) Show that if a connected graph has $2k$ vertices of odd degree, there are k-
       edge disjoint trails in G that together contain each edge of G exactly once.

21. Prove that an Eulerian graph G is randomly Eulerian from a vertex v if and
    only if every cycle of G contains v.

22. Consider the n-cube Q_n, which has one vertex for every binary sequence of
    length n, two binary sequences being adjacent if and only if they differ in
    exactly one digit.
    a) Show that Q_n has a Hamiltonian cycle for every $n \geq 2$.
    b) For which values of n is Q_n Eulerian.

23. a) Find the maximum length of a trail in K_8.
b) Find the maximum length of a circuit in K_8.

24. Every day at a conference lasting five days, 11 professors eat lunch at a circular table. Find a seating schedule for the five days that allows every pair of professors to sit next to each other during one of the meals.

*25. A simple graph G has $2n$ vertices and contains no cycles of length 3. Show that G has at most n^2 edges.

26. Suppose that a graph G has $2m$ vertices of odd degree. Show that any circuit containing every edge of G must contain at least m edges more than once.

27. a) Let G be a simple graph with p vertices and $q \geq \binom{p-1}{2} + 2$ edges. Show that G has a Hamiltonian cycle.

b) Exhibit a graph with p vertices and $\binom{p-1}{2} + 1$ edges that has no Hamiltonian cycle.

5.3
SUPPLEMENTARY COMPUTER PROJECTS

1. Eulerian Graphs
Given an adjacency matrix A of a graph G
a) Write a program that determines if G is Eulerian.
b) Write a program that finds an Eulerian circuit if G is Eulerian.

2. The Traveling Salesperson Problem
A traveling salesperson wants to travel through each of n cities exactly once and then return to his or her starting point. We would like to find the route with the minimum overall distance. This can be expressed as a weighted graph problem. Start with a weighted complete graph on vertices $\{1, 2, \ldots, n\}$, where the weight on the edge between vertices i and j equals d_{ij}, the distance between city i and city j. We would like to find the minimum-weight Hamiltonian cycle in this graph. It is not known if there is a good algorithm that solves the traveling salesperson problem, and as we saw in Section 4.1 it is not possible to exhaustively search every solution for any problem with a large number of cities. This has led researchers to concentrate on developing a good algorithm that always finds a near optimal solution to the traveling salesperson problem. The nearest neighbor method described attempts to find a Hamiltonian cycle whose overall distance is close to the minimum.

1. Pick any city as a starting circuit with one vertex.

2. Given a k-vertex circuit C_k, find the vertex u, not on C_k, that is closest to a vertex on C_k.

3. If u is closest to vertex v on C_k, let C_{k+1} be the $k+1$-vertex circuit obtained by inserting u immediately in front of v.

4. Repeat this process until a circuit containing all the vertices is constructed.
   a) Given an $n \times n$ matrix D whose (i, j)th entry is d_{ij}, write a program that uses the nearest neighbor method to construct a circuit containing all n cities.
   b) Use the triangle inequality $(d_{ij} \leq d_{ik} + d_{kj})$ to show that the overall distance of a circuit obtained by this method is no more than twice as long as a minimum distance cycle.

SECTION

5.4 PLANAR GRAPHS

When a graph is drawn on the plane it may have pairs of edges that cross. Planar graphs were first introduced around 1880 in analyzing the four-color theorem. (See Section 5.5.)

DEFINITION   Planar Graph
A graph is said to be planar if it can be drawn in the plane in such a way that none of its edges cross.

An important application of planar graphs is in the design and construction of electrical circuits. In designing a circuit, it is sometimes important to minimize the amount of nonplanarity since the circuit on a silicon chip or a printed circuit board is usually planar. (See Fig. 5.22.)

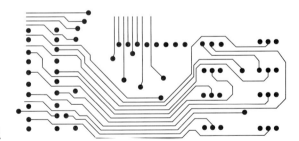

Figure 5.22

Before proceeding, we introduce the game of sprouts which was invented by the famous gamester and mathematician John H. Conway. (See Fig. 5.23.)

Figure 5.23
A Simple Game of
Sprouts

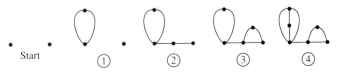

Start   ①   ②   ③   ④

Puzzle I   The Game of Sprouts

To start the game of sprouts, place $p \geq 2$ points on a piece of paper. Two players take turns drawing edges as follows. During a single turn in sprouts a player draws a curve, joining two points or a single point to itself, which does not intersect any other points or previously drawn edges. At no time is any point allowed to have degree greater than 3. After this curve is drawn, a new point is placed in its interior. The last person to draw an edge wins. Show that the game of sprouts will always end by finding a maximum for the number of moves that a game of sprouts starting with p points can last. (See Problem 9.) *Hint:* Concentrate on the number of unused adjacencies after each turn. (See the book *Winning Ways* by Berlekamp, Conway, and Guy for a discussion of this and many other mathematical games [3].)   ☐

A nonplanar graph cannot be drawn in the plane with no edges crossing. Note, however, that if a graph has been drawn with edges crossing, it could still be planar because there might be another way to draw the graph without edges crossing.

Puzzle 2   The Three Houses–Three Utilities Puzzle

Suppose we have three new houses H_1, H_2, H_3 and three utility outlets, electricity, gas, and water. Is it possible to connect every house with each of the three utilities by a utility line so that no two utility lines cross? Note that if we represent each house and each utility outlet by a vertex, the utility lines will form the complete bipartite graph $K_{3,3}$ shown in Fig. 5.24. Thus the three houses–three utilities puzzle asks whether or not $K_{3,3}$ is a planar graph. (See Problem 8b.)   ☐

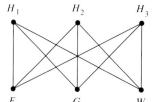

Figure 5.24

A planar graph drawn in the plane such that no two edges intersect is called a plane graph. Let G be a plane graph with p vertices and q edges. The parts of the plane that remain after we remove the edges and the vertices of G are called the regions of G. We let r represent the number of regions of G (including one unbounded region). Although many different plane graphs may represent a given planar graph, the following formula discovered by Euler shows that two such plane graphs will always form the same number of regions.

THEOREM 5.6   (Euler's Formula)

If G is a connected plane graph with p vertices, q edges, and r regions, then $p - q + r = 2$.

Proof

Any connected plane graph G can be constructed in the following manner:

1. Start with a single vertex. This part of the drawing has one vertex, zero edges, and one region, so $p - q + r = 2$.
2. If D is the set of vertices drawn so far and $V - D$ is nonempty, there will always be an edge from D to $V - D$ since G is connected (See Problem 3, Section 5.2). Adding an edge of this kind increases both p and q by one leaving $p - q + r$ unchanged.
3. Once all the vertices of G have been drawn, any new edges drawn will connect two vertices on the boundary of the same region. When an edge of this type is added, q will increase by 1, and since this edge divides the region in two, r will also increase by 1, leaving $p - q + r$ unchanged.

When the drawing of G (See Fig. 5.25) is finally completed we see that $p - q + r$ will still be equal to 2.

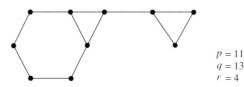

$p = 11$
$q = 13$
$r = 4$

Figure 5.25

COROLLARY   If G is a planar graph with p vertices and q edges, any plane drawing of G will contain $r = q - p + 2$ regions.

The boundary of each region of a plane graph can be thought of as a closed walk. In the plane graph in Fig. 5.26, the boundary of the region R_2 is $v_1 v_4 v_7 v_2 v_1 v_3 v_6 v_5 v_3 v_1$ and the boundary of region R_4 is $v_1 v_2 v_7 v_{11} v_8 v_{11} v_9 v_{11} v_{10} v_7 v_4 v_1$. We denote by $\deg R_i$ the number of edges in the closed walk surrounding region R_i. Thus $\deg R_2 = 9$ and $\deg R_4 = 11$.

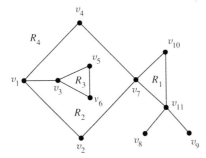

Figure 5.26

Sometimes it is convenient to apply Euler's formula in showing that a graph is nonplanar.

THEOREM 5.7 | If G is a simple connected plane graph with at least two edges, then $q \leq 3p - 6$.

Proof

When G forms one region, every edge of G is contained twice in the boundary of this region. When G separates the plane into more than one region, every edge is either counted twice in the boundary of one region or once each in the boundaries of two regions. Therefore $\sum_{i=1}^{r} \deg R_i = 2q$. In a simple graph, every cycle has at least three edges. The boundary of any region R_i will either contain a cycle or at least two edges that are traversed twice. Thus we see that $\deg R_i \geq 3$, and $\sum_{i=1}^{r} \deg R_i \geq 3r$. Comparing these two sums, we see that $2q \geq 3r$, which implies that $2q/3 \geq r$. For a connected plane graph, we know that $p - q + r = 2$, so $p - q + 2q/3 \geq 2$. Therefore $3p - 6 \geq q$.

Example 1   Show that the graph K_5 is nonplanar.

Solution

The graph K_5 has $p = 5$ and $q = \binom{5}{2} = 10$. Therefore K_5 is not planar because $3p - 6 = 9 < 10 = q$.   □

A variation of this argument can be used to show that $K_{3,3}$ is also nonplanar, thus solving the three houses–three utilities puzzle (see Problem 8).

Although Euler's formula can sometimes be used to show that a graph is nonplanar, we have no way of showing that a graph is planar except by actually drawing it on the plane with no edges crossing. However, the following theorem (Kuratowski's theorem) can be used to characterize those graphs that are planar. There are efficient linear algorithms for determining whether or not a graph is planar, but they are complicated and will not be discussed here.

A subdivision of a graph G is a graph obtained from G by inserting vertices of degree 2 into the edges of G. Clearly the planarity of a graph is not affected by these insertions.

THEOREM 5.8   (Kuratowski's Theorem)

| A graph G is planar if and only if G contains no subgraph isomorphic to K_5 or $K_{3,3}$ or any subdivision of K_5 or $K_{3,3}$.

Proof

The proof of this theorem is lengthy, but not difficult, and we shall not include it here.

5.4
PROBLEMS

1. a) Find the smallest simple graph that is 4-regular and planar.
    b) Find a simple graph that is 5-regular and planar.

2. Show that a simple planar graph with fewer than 30 edges has a vertex of degree 4 or less.

3. In a connected simple planar graph with p vertices and $3p - 6$ edges, show that the boundary of each region is a triangle.

4. Show that every simple planar graph with two or more vertices contains at least two vertices of degree 5 or less.

5. A plane graph is said to be a triangulation if the boundary of each of its regions is a triangle. Show that every simple plane graph is a spanning subgraph of some simple plane triangulation.

6. Show that if a graph G has fewer than 12 vertices of degree 5 and the remaining vertices of G have degree 6, then G is nonplanar.

7. For which values of m and n is $K_{m,n}$ nonplanar?

8. a) Show that if G is a simple bipartite plane graph with at least two edges, then $q \le 2p - 4$.
   b) Deduce that $K_{3,3}$ is nonplanar.

9. Solve Puzzle 1.

10. Suppose that a disconnected planar graph has $w > 1$ components. Find a suitable modification of Euler's formula that holds for planar graphs with w components.

11. Let G be a graph with 11 or more vertices. Show that either G or its complement G^c is nonplanar.

ADVANCED PROBLEMS

*12. Let $P = \{p_1, p_2, \ldots, p_n\}$ be a set of $n \ge 3$ points in the plane. If the distance between any two points is at least 1, show that there are at most $3n - 6$ pairs of points at distance exactly 1.

13. If G is a connected planar graph with girth k, show that the inequality $q \le 3p - 6$ can be strengthened to $q \le (p - 2)k/(k - 2)$.

14. Show that the following graph (known as the Petersen graph) is nonplanar.

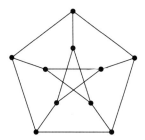

15. If a 4-regular connected plane graph with p vertices has 12 regions, compute p.

16. The union of two spanning subgraphs G_1, G_2 of G is the spanning subgraph with edge set $E(G_1) \cup E(G_2)$. The thickness $\theta(G)$ of G is the minimum number of planar spanning subgraphs of G whose union is G.
    a) Show that $\theta(K_p) \geq [(p + 7)/6]$, for all positive integers p.
    b) Show that $\theta(K_p) = [(p + 7)/6]$, for all $p \leq 8$.

17. Any graph can be drawn on the plane so that no three edges cross at a common point. The crossing number of a graph G, denoted by $cr(G)$, is the minimum number of pairs of crossing edges in a drawing of G on the plane.
    a) Show that $cr(K_5) = cr(K_{3,3}) = 1$.
    b) Find $cr(K_{4,3})$.
    c) Find $cr(K_6)$.

SECTION

5.5 | GRAPH COLORINGS

A proper coloring of a graph G is an assignment of colors to the vertices of G, one color to each vertex, so that adjacent vertices are assigned different colors. A proper coloring of G that uses n colors is called an n-coloring.

DEFINITION   Chromatic Number

The chromatic number of a graph G is the smallest n for which an n-coloring of G exists and is denoted by $X(G)$.

The Four-Color Problem

One of the oldest and most famous problems in mathematics involves map colorings. Suppose we start with a map that is divided into regions we call countries. We would like to color the countries so that any pair of countries that has a common boundary edge receives different colors. From about 1852 when this problem was first proposed, most mathematicians thought (without proof) that every map could be colored with four or fewer colors. This became known as the four-color problem. In 1976, Appel and Haken [1] finally proved that it was indeed true that every planar map could be colored with four or fewer colors. Their solution of this problem was quite unusual in that it required over 1200 hours of computer calculations.

The four-color problem is related to graph theory in the following way. To each map we associate a related planar graph called the dual graph. The vertices of the **dual graph** correspond to the countries of the map, and two vertices are adjacent if and only if the corresponding countries share a common boundary edge. Since a map can be colored with n colors if and only if its dual graph has an n-coloring, the four-color problem can be restated in terms of graphs as follows:

For every planar graph G, show that $X(G) \leq 4$.

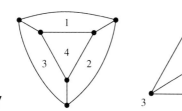

Figure 5.27

It is easy to see that some maps do require four colors. Obviously the map in Fig. 5.27 consisting of four mutually adjacent countries and its dual graph K_4 both require four colors. On the other hand, although we have seen that K_5 is not a planar graph, it is not obvious that some other more complicated planar graph might still require five colors. For example, the graph in Fig. 5.28 is known as the Grötzsch graph. It does not even have three mutually adjacent vertices, yet it has chromatic number 4 (see Problem 15).

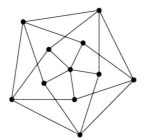

Figure 5.28
The Grötzsch Graph

Puzzle I   **The U.S.A. Puzzle**

It is easy to check that the map of the U.S. does not have four mutually adjacent states. However, can you explain why it is still not possible to color this map with fewer than four colors? *Hint:* Consider the region surrounding the state of Nevada. (See Problem 4.)   □

Although it is extremely difficult to prove the four-color theorem, it is not nearly as hard to show that any planar graph can be colored with five or fewer colors.

THEOREM 5.9   Any simple planar graph G has a vertex of degree 5 or less.

Proof
If we sum the degrees of the vertices of G, the result is $2q$. Since G is planar, $q \leq 3p - 6$, and $2q \leq 6p - 12$. Therefore the average degree of G is less than 6, and G must have a vertex of degree 5 or less.

THEOREM 5.10   (A Five-Color Theorem)
For every planar graph G, $X(G) \leq 5$.

Proof
Obviously this theorem is true for any graph G with five or fewer vertices. We proceed by induction. Suppose that the result is true for any graph with p vertices, and let G be a planar graph with $p + 1$ vertices. By the previous theorem, G has a vertex v of degree 5 or less. We denote by $G - v$ the graph obtained from G by removing the vertex v and all the edges incident to it. Since $G - v$ has p vertices, it follows from the induction hypothesis that $G - v$ can be colored with five colors. If one of these five colors is not used in coloring the vertices adjacent to v, we may assign that color to v, producing a 5-coloring of G also. The only remaining case to consider is when v is adjacent to five different vertices, each of which is assigned a different color in the 5-coloring of $G - v$. Without loss of generality, we assume that the neighbors of v are assigned colors 1, 2, 3, 4, and 5, respectively, in clockwise order around v, as pictured in Fig. 5.29.

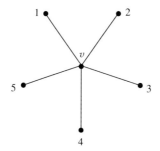

Figure 5.29

Denote by G_{13} the subgraph of $G - v$ consisting of vertices that are assigned either color 1 or color 3 in the 5-coloring of $G - v$, together with the edges that join pairs of these vertices. If the neighbors of v that receive colors 1 and 3 are in two different components of G_{13}, we may interchange colors 1 and 3 in one of these components to obtain a 5-coloring of $G - v$, where either color 1 or color 3 is not assigned to one of the neighbors of v.

If the neighbors of v that receive colors 1 and 3 are in the same component of G_{13}, we consider the subgraph G_{24}, which consists of vertices that are assigned either color 2 or color 4 in the 5-coloring of $G - v$. Since the neighbors of v that receive colors 2 and 4 are separated by a cycle passing through v and vertices in $G - v$ that receive either color 1 or color 3, they must be in two different components of G_{24}. Interchanging colors 2 and 4 in one of these components, we obtain a 5-coloring of $G - v$, where either color 2 or color 4 is not assigned to one of the neighbors of v. Thus we can always obtain a 5-coloring where one of the five colors is not used in coloring the vertices adjacent to v. As before, we assign the unused color to v, producing a 5-coloring of G.

The interested reader may wish to solve the following coloring problem, which is much simpler than the four-color problem.

Puzzle 2   The Penny Puzzle

Suppose that any number of pennies are placed flat on a plane with no pennies overlapping. The pennies are colored so that no two touching pennies receive the same color.

a) Exhibit an arrangement of pennies that requires four colors. (Note that four mutually touching pennies is not possible.)

b) Without using the four-color theorem, show that any arrangement of pennies can be colored with four or fewer colors. *Hint:* Show that in any arrangement, there is always a penny with three or fewer neighbors. (See Problem 16.)   ☐

Example 2

In a small computer science department, the professors each teach several courses. In setting up a final examination schedule, the department chairman must assign a final exam time to each course so that different sections of the same course receive the same final time and two courses receive different final exam times if they are taught by the same professor. Also it is convenient to set up a schedule requiring a small number of final exam times so that finals can be completed as early as possible. What is the smallest number of hours needed for the following schedule?

Professor	Course Number
A	CS 1, CS 3, CS 4
B	CS 3, CS 5, CS 9
C	CS 4, CS 7, CS 11
D	CS 1, CS 3, CS 11

Solution

We construct a graph G with one vertex for each course. Two vertices are joined by an edge if the corresponding courses are taught by the same professor. (See Fig. 5.30.) Clearly the minimum number of final exam times needed in this scheduling problem is $X(G)$. Since G has four mutually adjacent vertices (1, 3, 4, and 11), $X(G) \geq 4$. In fact it is easy to color the vertices of G with four colors. Thus four is the minimum number of final exam times needed.

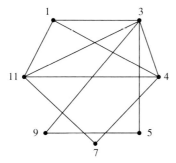

Figure 5.30   ☐

The Greedy Algorithm

In a typical scheduling problem, the associated graph may be quite large, so we describe the following simple algorithm for coloring the vertices of a graph. It is known as the greedy algorithm.

Suppose that G is a graph with vertices $v_1, v_2, \ldots, v_p$. Start with a set of colors $S = \{1, 2, \ldots, p\}$. Consider the following greedy algorithm for coloring the vertices of G.

1. We assign color 1 to v_1.

2. If vertices $v_1, v_2, \ldots, v_{i-1}$ have been colored, let C be the set of colors that have been assigned to some vertex that is adjacent to v_i. We assign to v_i the smallest color not in C. Repeat Step 2 until all of the vertices have been colored.

If the vertices of G are ordered so that no vertex v_i is adjacent to more than $n - 1$ previous vertices in the list, then the greedy algorithm will clearly color the vertices of G using at most n colors. (See Problems 10, 17, 18, 19.)

Chromatic Polynomials (Optional)

In determining the chromatic number of a graph G, some insight can be gained by considering the number of k-colorings of G. This idea was originally explored by Birkhoff as a possible means of attacking the four-color problem. We denote by $c_k(G)$ the number of different ways to color G using k colors. For certain special graphs G, $c_k(G)$ is easy to compute. In coloring the complete graph K_n, each vertex must receive a different color. Thus $c_k(K_n) = k(k - 1)(k - 2)\cdots(k - n + 1)$. Likewise, if G is an empty graph with n vertices and no edges, every vertex can be colored independently with any of the k available colors. Thus $c_k(G) = k^n$. In general, there is a simple recurrence for the number of k-colorings of a graph G. We denote by $G * e$ the graph obtained from G by removing the edge e and identifying its endpoints. (See Fig. 5.31.)

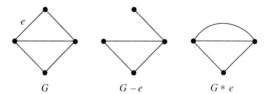

Figure 5.31 G $G - e$ $G * e$

THEOREM 5.11   If G is a simple graph and e is any edge of G, then $c_k(G) = c_k(G - e) - c_k(G * e)$.

Proof
Let x and y be the endpoints of the edge e. The k-colorings of $G - e$ can be divided into two types:

1. Consider a k-coloring of $G - e$ that assigns the same color to x and y.

Construct a coloring of $G * e$ by identifying x and y and assigning to this vertex the common color for x and y. This correspondence is obviously a bijection between the k-colorings of $G - e$ that assign the same color to x and y and the k-colorings of $G * e$.

2. Consider a k-coloring of $G - e$ that assigns different colors to x and y. In this case, the k-coloring of $G - e$ is also a k-coloring of G, so there is a bijection between the k-colorings of $G - e$ that assign different colors to x and y and the k-colorings of G.

Using Conditions 1 and 2, we see that $c_k(G - e) = c_k(G * e) + c_k(G)$, and the result follows.

By successively applying the preceding recurrence and removing any loops and multiple edges when they arise, we find that the chromatic number of any graph G can be computed using a collection of empty graphs and complete graphs. Thus we deduce that $c_k(G)$ is always a polynomial. For this reason, $c_k(G)$ is called the chromatic polynomial of G.

5.5

PROBLEMS

1. Show that $c_k(P_n) = k(k - 1)^{n-1}$, where P_n is the graph consisting of a single path containing n vertices and $n - 1$ edges.

2. Show that if $G_1, G_2, \ldots, G_w$ are the components of G, then
$c_k(G) = c_k(G_1)c_k(G_2)\cdots c_k(G_w)$.

3. a) Calculate $X(C_n)$, where C_n is the cycle with n vertices.
   b) The wheel W_n is obtained from C_n by adding a new vertex x and connecting it by an edge to each of the vertices in C_n. Calculate $X(W_n)$.
   c) If we denote by D_n, the graph of the regular $2n$-gon and all of its longest diagonals (n diagonals joining opposite vertices), compute $X(D_n)$.

4. Solve Puzzle 1.

5. When n circles are drawn in the plane, show that the regions formed can always be colored with two colors.

6. a) What is the smallest number of colors needed to color the faces of the cube so that no two adjacent faces receive the same color?
   b) What is the smallest number of colors needed to color the faces of the octahedron so that no two faces receive the same color?

7. Show that a graph G has chromatic number 2 if and only if it is bipartite.

8. Show that the Grötzsch graph has chromatic number 4.

9. A computer science department has eight committees and professors $\{A, B, C, D, E, F, G, H, I, J\}$ are assigned to these committees as follows.

Computing	{A, B, C, D}	Advising	{D, E}
Library	{A, E, F, G}	Curriculum	{C, A}
Recruitment	{G, H, I, J}	Fund Raising	{I, G}
RTP	{H, B, F}	Education	{J, C}

If each committee is scheduled to meet for one hour, what is the smallest number of hours required to schedule all eight committee meetings so that every professor is able to meet with all the committees to which he or she is assigned?

10. a) Show that no matter how the vertices of a graph G are ordered, the greedy algorithm will always color G in no more than $\delta^+(G) + 1$ colors.
    b) Show that for any graph G, there is an ordering of the vertices of G for which the greedy algorithm requires precisely $X(G)$ colors. **Hint:** Use a coloring with $X(G)$ colors.

ADVANCED PROBLEMS

11. For the p-cycle, C_p, show that $c_k(C_p) = (k-1)^p + (-1)^p(k-1)$.

12. If G is a connected graph with p vertices, show that $c_k(G) \leq k(k-1)^{p-1}$.

*13. If a plane graph G is Eulerian show that the regions of G are 2-colorable.

*14. Show that if G is a Hamiltonian plane graph, the regions of G are 4-colorable.

15. If a graph G has no cycles of odd length show that G is 2-colorable.

16. Solve Puzzle 2.

17. If G is a graph with $X(G) = k$, show that G has at least k vertices of degree $k - 1$ or greater.

18. Let G be a connected graph that is not regular. If G has maximum degree δ^+ and chromatic number $X(G)$, show that $X(G) \leq \delta^+(G)$.

19. Any number of lines are drawn in the plane so that no three lines meet at the same point. Consider the graph G whose vertices are the intersection points of these lines and whose edges are the line segments joining pairs of these intersection points. Show that $X(G) \leq 3$.

20. Show that if any two odd cycles of G have a vertex in common, then $X(G) \leq 5$.

21. Show that if every region in a plane graph G has an even number of edges in its boundary, then the vertices of G can be 2-colored.

22. Show that a graph with at most two odd length cycles can be 3-colored.

5.5
SUPPLEMENTARY COMPUTER PROJECT

1. The Greedy Algorithm
   Given an adjacency matrix A of a graph G, write a program that colors the vertices of G using the greedy algorithm.

CHAPTER

5

REVIEW PROBLEMS

1. For which values of m and n does the complete bipartite graph $K_{m,n}$ have
   a) A Hamiltonian cycle   b) An Eulerian circuit

2. Describe the graphs that have a walk that contains each edge
   a) Exactly two times   b) Exactly three times

3. Let G be a graph with 20 vertices.
   a) If every vertex of G has degree 5, compute the number of edges in G.
   b) If the maximum degree of G is 5 and the minimum degree of G is 3, what is the smallest number of edges that G can have?

4. Describe the graphs that have a walk containing every vertex at least once.

5. In the complete graph K_p, compute the number of
   a) Different paths of length n, for $1 \le n \le p - 1$.
   b) Different walks of length n, for $1 \le n \le p - 1$.

6. a) Give an example of a graph G with chromatic number 3 that does not have three mutually adjacent vertices.
   b) Give an example of a nonplanar graph with chromatic number 2.

7. Show that any planar graph with fewer than 12 vertices has a vertex of degree 4 or less.

8. A simple bipartite graph G has $2n$ vertices. Show that it has at most n^2 edges.

9. Let G be a simple graph with $2n$ vertices. In addition, suppose that every vertex of G has degree at least n.
   a) What is the smallest number of edges that G can have?
   b) Show that G is connected.

10. Let G be a 4-regular plane graph that is connected with p vertices. How many regions does G have?

11. Let G be a simple graph with p vertices. If G has three vertices of degree $p - 1$ and two vertices of degree $p - 2$, what is the smallest degree a vertex in G can have?

12. Give an example of a simple bipartite graph with six vertices and eight edges that is not isomorphic to $K_{2,4}$.

CHAPTER

5

SUMMARY

In this chapter we introduced graphs, concentrating on undirected graphs, and showed how they could be used to solve a wide variety of problems. Some of the results in graph theory we studied in this chapter were obtained by Euler over 200 years ago and mathematicians worked on the four color problem for over 120 years before a (correct) solution was found. For a solution of the four-color problem see [1, 2]. For an interesting book on the history of graph theory, see the book by Biggs, Lloyd, and Wilson [4]. In modern times, graph theory algorithms have become very useful in computer science. For a detailed discussion of graph algorithms related to planarity and colorings the reader is referred to Even [9]. Graph algorithms will be discussed in more detail in Chapter 6. To learn more about graphs and their applications consult either of the books by Bondy and Murty [5] or Deo [8]. Readers who would like a more formal treatment of graph theory as an interesting area of pure mathematics should see any of the books [5, 7, 8]. The book by Chartrand [6] is an excellent introductory text.

BIBLIOGRAPHY

1. Appel, K., W. Haken, and J. Koch. "Every planar map is 4-colorable." *Illinois J. Math.*, 21(1977) 429–567.
2. Barnette, D. *Map Coloring and the Four Color Problem.* Washington, D.C.: Mathematical Association of America, 1984.
3. Berlekamp, E., J. H. Conway, R. Guy. *Winning Ways*, Vols. I and II. New York: Academic Press, 1982.
4. Biggs, N., E. Lloyd, and R. Wilson. *Graph Theory* 1736–1936. London: Oxford University Press, 1976.
5. Bondy, A., and Murty, S. *Graph Theory with Applications.* New York: North-Holland, 1976.
6. Chartrand, G. *Introductory Graph Theory.* New York: Dover, 1985.
7. Chartrand, G., and Lesniak, L. *Graphs and Digraphs*, 2nd edition. Pacific Grove, Calif.: Wadsworth, 1986.
8. Deo, N. *Graph Theory with Applications to Engineering and Computer Science.* Englewood Cliffs, N.J.: Prentice-Hall, 1974.
9. Even, S. *Graph Algorithms.* Rockville, Md: Computer Science Press, 1979.
10. Harary, F. *Graph Theory.* Reading, Mass.: Addison-Wesley, 1960.

CHAPTER

6

GRAPH
ALGORITHMS
AND SEARCHING

6.1 BREADTH FIRST SEARCH

Many graph algorithms rely on various searching techniques for visiting each of the vertices in a graph. One such technique is known as a breadth first search. In this section we discuss algorithms for determining shortest paths in a graph as well as algorithms for determining whether or not a graph is bipartite, which both rely on the breadth first search technique. In Section 6.2 we discuss another widely used searching technique known as a depth first search.

Shortest Paths

In a graph theory problem, when we need to find a path between two vertices u and v in a graph G, we usually want to find the shortest such path. The length of a path in an undirected graph G is the number of edges in the path.

Since weighted graphs occur in many applications, it will be convenient to define the notion of length for a weighted graph also. If P is a path in a weighted graph and $w(e)$ represents the weight of an edge e, then

$$\text{Length of } P = \sum_{e \in E(P)} w(e)$$

DEFINITION   Distance

If vertices u and v are connected in the (weighted) graph G, the distance between u and v, denoted by $d(u,v)$, is the length of a shortest (u,v)-path in G. In case there is no path from u to v, we say that $d(u,v) = \infty$.

In the remainder of this section, we discuss efficient algorithms for computing distances in graphs. Given a pair of vertices u and v in a graph, we can find shortest (u,v)-paths in several different types of graphs.

First consider the case of an undirected graph G. We may as well assume that G is simple because loops and extra parallel edges do not affect distance. The following procedure, known as the breadth first search technique, can be used to find the distance from u to v. To start with, all vertices are unlabeled, but they will be successively assigned a label $l(x)$, which corresponds to the distance from u, in the following

Breadth First Search Algorithm

1. Label vertex u with 0.
2. Set $i = 0$ and $S = \{u\}$.
3. Find the set T of all unlabeled vertices that are adjacent to at least one vertex in S. If T is empty, stop. Otherwise, label all vertices in T with $i + 1$ and set $S = T$.
4. Increase i by 1 and return to Step 3.

If we let $l(x)$ denote the label of x assigned by this algorithm, we obtain the following result. If $l(x) = k$, then $d(u,x) = k$ and if x is unlabeled, $d(u,x) = \infty$. This algorithm finds $d(u,x)$ for each vertex x in the graph G. In case we only want to know the distance $d(u,v)$, we may as well terminate the algorithm as soon as v is labeled.

Example 1   The Wolf-Goat-Cabbage Puzzle

A wolf, a goat, and a cabbage are on one bank of a river. A boatman wants to take them across the river, but his boat is small, so he can only take one of them at a time. Assuming that neither the wolf and the goat nor the goat and the cabbage can be left alone unguarded, how is the boatman going to get them across the river?

Solution

We represent the puzzle by a graph. To start with, all four objects are on one side of the river, and we hope to end with none of the objects still there. Each time the boat crosses the river, some subset of the four objects wolf, goat, cabbage, and boat will remain on the original side of the river. A state of the puzzle will be represented by a vertex, which is labeled by the initials of the objects remaining on the original side of the river. We join two vertices if it is possible to go from one state to the other in one crossing. Starting with the vertex WGCB and applying the breadth first search algorithm, we obtain the graph in Fig. 6.1. We see that it takes seven crossings for the boatman to transport all three objects across the river ending at state *.

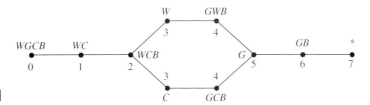

Figure 6.1

THEOREM 6.1 | For all $k \geq 1$ and for each vertex x in G, $l(x) = k$ if and only if $d(u, x) = k$.

Proof
Clearly $d(u, x) = 0$ if and only if $u = x$, and u is the only vertex whose label is 0. Assume that $d(u, w) = j$ if and only if $l(w) = j$, for all $j \leq k$. If $l(x) = k + 1$, then x is adjacent to a vertex x' satisfying $d(u, x') = k$. Any walk of length k from u to x' can be extended to a walk of length $k + 1$ from u to x, so $d(u, x) \leq k + 1$. Since $l(x) > k$, we know that $d(u, x) > k$ by our induction hypothesis. Therefore $d(u, x) = l(x) = k + 1$. By induction we see that $d(u, x) = k$ if and only if $l(x) = k$, for any nonnegative integer k. Therefore it is also true that $d(u, x) = \infty$ if and only if x remains unlabeled.

In Step 3 of the breadth first search algorithm, we will check each edge incident to a vertex in S to find the set T. Each edge will be encountered at most twice, once for each of its endpoints. Thus for a simple graph with p vertices and q edges, the breadth first search algorithm requires no more than $2q \leq p(p - 1)$ checks. Therefore it is a good algorithm for finding distances in an undirected graph since its complexity function is bounded by a polynomial. Note that a breadth first search can also be used to determine whether or not a given graph G is connected (see Problem 7).

As described earlier, the breadth first search algorithm determines the shortest distance from u to every vertex in the graph. To actually be able to determine shortest paths, we would need to keep track of the labeled vertex adjacent to each newly labeled vertex (Problem 8) and backtrack.

Finally we consider the case when G is a weighted graph. Suppose we have a collection of cities joined together by rail lines. We represent this by a weighted graph. The vertices are cities. The edges are rail lines traveling directly between two cities. The weight of an edge is the distance of the corresponding rail line. The problem of finding the shortest route between a pair of cities corresponds to that of finding a path of minimum weight connecting two specific vertices u and v. The indicated path in the weighted graph in Fig. 6.2 is a (u, v)-path of length 11 and it is a minimum-length path.

Since every weight $w(xy)$ represents a distance (the length of a railroad line from city x to city y), we assume that all weights are positive. If xy is not an edge of G, it is convenient to say that $w(xy) = \infty$, and we assume that $\infty + m = \infty$, for any number m. We present the following algorithm discovered by Dijkstra in 1959, which can be used to find the distance between u and v in any weighted graph G.

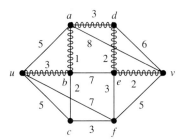

Figure 6.2

Dijkstra's Algorithm

1. To start with, each vertex x is given a label $l(x)$. Set $l(u) = 0$, and for each $x \neq u$, set $l(x) = \infty$.
2. Let $S = V(G)$, and set $i = 1$.
3. Compute $\min_{v \in S}\{l(v)\}$ and let x_i be a vertex for which this minimum is attained.
4. Let $S = S - \{x_i\}$.
5. If S is empty, stop.
6. For each $y \in S$ replace $l(y)$ by min $\{l(y), l(x_i) + w(x_i y)\}$.
7. Return to Step 3.

At each point in Dijkstra's algorithm, $l(x) \geq d(u, x)$, for every vertex x. When the algorithm terminates, the distance from u to x will equal $l(x)$.

THEOREM 6.2

For each vertex x in a weighted graph G, Dijkstra's algorithm terminates with $l(x) = d(u, x)$.

Proof
The proof is similar to that of the previous theorem so we omit it.

When Dijkstra's algorithm is applied to the graph in Fig. 6.2 the following labels are obtained:

Vertices	Labels		
u	0		
a	∞	$\not{8}$	4
b	∞	3	
c	∞	5	
d	∞	7	
e	∞	$\not{10}$	9
f	∞	7	
v	∞	$\not{12}$	11

We can also show that Dijkstra's algorithm is a good algorithm. In Step 3 the number of comparisons needed to find the minimum is $|S| - 1$, so overall the total number of comparisons will be $(p - 1) + (p - 2) + \cdots + 1 = p(p - 1)/2$, and essentially the same number of steps will be needed overall in Step 6. Thus approximately $p(p-1)$ comparisons are needed to complete Dijkstra's algorithm.

Cycles and Paths in Bipartite Graphs

Suppose that G is a bipartite graph with bipartition (X, Y), and let $W = v_0v_1v_2\cdots v_k$ be a walk in G. Since $v_{i-1}v_i$ is an edge of G, the vertices of W must alternate between X and Y. Using this idea we can describe precisely which graphs are bipartite.

THEOREM 6.3

A graph G is bipartite if and only if it contains no odd cycle.

Proof
Suppose that G is a bipartite graph with bipartition (X, Y), and let C be a cycle of G. Since the vertices of C alternate between X and Y, C must have an equal number of X and Y vertices, and therefore C must be an even cycle.

Conversely suppose that G is a graph that contains no odd cycles. Clearly it suffices to show that each component of G is bipartite, so we may as well assume that G is connected.

Let v be any vertex of G. Starting with v, perform a breadth first search. For $X = \{x \mid d(v, x) \text{ is even}\}$ and $Y = \{y \mid d(v, y) \text{ is odd}\}$, we will show that (X, Y) is a bipartition of G. To do so, we must show that no two vertices of X are adjacent and that no two vertices of Y are adjacent. We prove this by contradiction.

Assume that two vertices u and w of X are adjacent. Let P be a minimum-length path from v to u, and let Q be a minimum-length path from v to w. Denote by v' the last vertex that P and Q have in common. The section of P from v' to u together with the edge uw and the section of Q from w to v' form a cycle C. To begin with, both P and Q have even length. Also, the section of P from v to v' and the section of Q from v to v' must both be minimum-length paths (Problem 4), so they have the same length. Therefore the sections of P from v' to u and Q from v' to w either both have odd length or both have even length. In either case, the cycle C would have odd length overall, contradicting our original hypothesis. Thus no two vertices in X are adjacent and similarly no two vertices in Y are adjacent, showing that G is bipartite.

The proof of the preceding theorem suggests the following simple algorithm, which uses a breadth first search to determine whether or not an arbitrary graph G is bipartite.

1. Start with any vertex v and label it with an X. Set $S = \{v\}$.
2. If all the vertices of G are labeled, stop because G is bipartite, and a bipartition (X, Y) has been obtained.
3. Let T be the set of unlabeled vertices that are adjacent to a vertex in S. If two vertices of T are adjacent, stop because G is not bipartite. Otherwise, label each vertex in T with Y if they are adjacent to X-vertices, and with X if they are adjacent to Y-vertices.
4. Set $S = T$ and return to Step 2.

6.1

PROBLEMS

1. Three cannibals and three missionaries come to a river crossing where there is a small boat that holds at most two people. Assuming that both cannibals and missionaries can row, show how the river can be crossed so that at no time will the cannibals outnumber the missionaries on either side of the river (the boat must be rowed across the river in both directions).

2. a) Show that four cannibals and four missionaries could not cross at the river crossing described in Problem 1.
   b) Show that the eight people can cross if there is an island in the middle of the river.

3. For any three vertices u, v, and w in a graph G, explain why $d(u,v) + d(v,w) \geq d(u,w)$.

4. Let P be a path of shortest possible length joining vertices x and y in G. If w is in the interior of P, show that the initial segment of P from x to w is a path of shortest possible length from x to w.

5. Find the shortest driving time from Portland to Las Vegas.

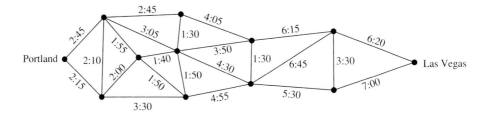

6. Each day a worker commutes from the suburbs to the city over a network of toll roads represented by the following weighted graph. The first number represents the mileage covered on the corresponding highway, and the second number represents the amount of tolls in cents to be paid on that highway.

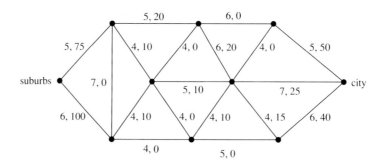

a) Find the minimum-mileage path from the suburbs to the city.
b) Find the minimum-cost (in tolls) path from the suburbs to the city.

7. Show how a breadth first search can be used to
a) Determine whether or not a graph G is connected.
b) Find the component of G containing a given vertex u.

8. a) What additional instructions do we need in order to use Dijkstra's algorithm to determine shortest paths as well as distance?
b) Find the shortest paths from v_0 to all other vertices in the following weighted graph using this algorithm.

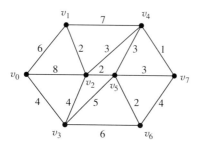

9. A company has offices in each of six cities. The fare of a direct flight from city i to city j is given by the (i, j)th entry in the following table where ∞ indicates that there is no direct flight. Prepare a table containing the fare of the least expensive route between each pair of different cities.

i \ j	1	2	3	4	5	6
1	—	99	∞	89	59	29
2	99	—	39	49	∞	59
3	∞	39	—	29	49	∞
4	89	49	29	—	29	59
5	59	∞	49	29	—	119
6	29	59	∞	59	119	—

10. Is the shortest path between two vertices u and v in a weighted graph G unique if the weights of all the edges are distinct?

ADVANCED
PROBLEMS

11. Count the number of different Hamiltonian paths in
a) $K_{5,5}$ b) $K_{5,4}$ c) $K_{5,3}$

12. Describe how to construct a circuit touching each square of an 8×8 chessboard exactly once using a mythical chess piece that can only move one square vertically or one square horizontally. What about an $n \times n$ chessboard for $n \geq 8$?

13. Show that if G is a simple graph with $2p$ vertices and p^2 edges, either G has a cycle of odd length or G is isomorphic to $K_{p,p}$.

14. Let A be the adjacency matrix of a connected simple graph G, and let v_i and v_j be distinct vertices of G. Prove that $d(v_i, v_j)$ is the smallest positive integer n for which the (i, j)th entry of A^n is not zero.

15. Let G be any undirected simple graph.
    a) Describe an algorithm that finds the length of the shortest cycle passing through a given vertex v in G.
    b) Describe an algorithm that finds the girth of G.

6.1
SUPPLEMENTARY COMPUTER PROJECTS

1. Matrix Arithmetic
   Given two $n \times n$ matrices A and B,
   a) Write a program to compute $A + B$.
   b) Write a program to compute $A \times B$.

2. Adjacency Matrices and Connectedness
   Given an adjacency matrix A of a graph G,
   a) Write a program to compute A^k.
   b) Use the program in part (a) to compute the shortest distance between a pair of vertices v_i and v_j in G. **Hint:** Look at Problem 14.
   c) Write a program to compute the sum $I + A + A^2 + \cdots + A^{p-1}$ (where I is the $n \times n$ identity matrix) and explain how it can be used to determine whether or not G is connected. **Hint:** In a connected graph, two vertices are always connected by a walk of length $p - 1$ or less.

SECTION 6.2 TREES

In this section we study an important class of graphs called trees. Trees can be used to model numerous real-life situations that involve connecting several locations as inexpensively as possible, and they show up in many computer science algorithms where it is desirable to solve a problem as efficiently as possible. Trees are also used in many computer programs as convenient structures for storing data.

Properties of Trees

DEFINITION **Tree**

A tree is a connected graph that has no cycles.

In general, a graph that has no cycles will have one or more components that are trees, so appropriately enough we refer to such a graph as a **forest**. (See Fig. 6.3.)

Figure 6.3

First we look at some properties of trees.

THEOREM 6.4

In a tree G, any two vertices x and y are connected by a unique path.

Proof
Since G is connected, x and y are joined by at least one path P. Suppose that x and y are also connected by a different path Q. Since $P \neq Q$, there is an edge e $= uv$ of P that is not an edge of Q. The remaining edges of P and Q form a walk from u to v that does not contain the edge e. By deleting edges if necessary, we can obtain a path from u to v that does not contain e (see Problem 1, Section 5.2). This path together with e forms a cycle, which contradicts the fact that G is a tree. Thus there is a unique path from P to Q.

A vertex of degree 1 in a tree is called an **end**. The fact that every tree has an end can be deduced from the following theorem.

THEOREM 6.5

If G is a graph with minimum degree $\delta^- \geq 2$, then G has a cycle.

Proof
Start with any vertex v_0. Since $\delta^- \geq 2$, we can always start at a vertex and leave on some edge. Also, after entering a vertex the first time, it is always possible to leave on an unused edge. Proceed through a sequence of vertices $v_0 v_1 v_2 \cdots v_k$ until the final vertex v_k first coincides with an earlier vertex. If $v_j = v_k$, then $v_j v_{j+1} v_{j+2} \cdots v_k$ forms a cycle in G.

Note that all the trees on five vertices (Fig. 6.3) have four edges. In general, it is true that all the trees on p vertices have the same number of edges.

THEOREM 6.6

If G is a tree with p vertices and q edges, $q = p - 1$.

Proof
The proof is by induction on p, the number of vertices of G. When $p = 1$, then $q = 1 - 1 = 0$. Suppose the theorem is true for all trees on p vertices, and let G be a tree on $p + 1$ vertices. If v is an end of G, and $\bar{G}$ is the graph obtained from G by removing v and the edge e incident to it, then $\bar{G}$ has no cycles and only a path beginning or ending at v would use the edge e. Therefore $\bar{G}$ is connected. Thus $\bar{G}$ is a tree with p vertices and by induction it has $p - 1$ edges. Therefore G has $p + 1$ vertices and p edges.

Using Theorem 6.6 we also obtain the following results.

COROLLARY 1   Let G be a tree with p vertices. If $(d_1, d_2, \ldots, d_p)$ is a degree sequence of G, then $\sum_{i=1}^{p} d_i = 2p - 2$.

See Problem 15 for a converse of this result.

COROLLARY 2   If G is a tree with $p \geq 2$ vertices, G has at least two ends.

The depth first search is a technique for scanning the vertices of a graph. Like the breadth first search, it is widely recognized as a powerful technique for solving various graph theory problems. Variations of the depth first search were already known in the nineteenth century and used in traversing mazes. Roughly speaking, a depth first search traverses the vertices of a graph G by moving on to a new vertex whenever one is available, whereas a breadth first search traverses the vertices by first checking all the vertices at each level before moving on to the next level. Thus the breadth first search was useful in finding the shortest path in a graph G because it could be used to check all paths and avoid any long dead ends, whereas the depth first search is more useful for finding a path when a large number of possible paths are available.

The depth first search starts at one vertex s and moves along the edges from vertex to vertex, discovering the structure of the graph as it is scanned. In order to visit all the vertices in the graph and halt with as little repetition as possible, we should clearly leave some markers as we go along. The vertices will be numbered in the order in which they are discovered. We denote the number of the vertex v by $\text{DFSI}(v)$ and refer to it as the depth first search index of v. In addition, we mark all the edges that are used in the search. Finally, for each vertex $v \neq s$, we remember the vertex $p(v)$ from which v was discovered. The vertex $p(v)$ is sometimes called the **parent** of v. The depth first search technique can now be described in the following way.

Depth First Search

1. For every vertex $v \in V(G)$, set $\text{DFSI}(v) = 0$. To start with, we let $i = 0, v = s$, and assume that all edges are unused.
2. Increase i by 1 and set $\text{DFSI}(v) = i$.
3. If there are no unused edges incident to v, go to Step 5.
4. Choose an unused edge e that joins v to another vertex u. Mark the edge e so we know that it is now used. If $\text{DFSI}(u) \neq 0$ (u has already been discovered), we return to Step 3. Otherwise, ($\text{DFSI}(v) = 0$), set $p(u) = v, v = u$, and return to Step 2 to number the newly discovered vertex.

5. If DFSI$(v) = 1$, stop because we have returned to the original starting vertex s.

6. When there are no unused edges incident to v, set $v = p(v)$ (backtrack to the parent of v) and return to Step 3.

DEFINITION **Spanning Tree**

A spanning tree of a graph G is a spanning subgraph of G that is a tree.

THEOREM 6.7 | Every connected graph contains a spanning tree.

Proof

We give the following "tree-growing procedure" for constructing a spanning tree in a connected graph G. Start with an initial tree T_1 that consists of a single vertex v_1 in G and no edges. If T_i is a partial tree with i vertices, $V = \{v_1, v_2, \ldots, v_i\}$, and $i - 1$ edges, $E = \{e_1, e_2, \ldots, e_{i-1}\}$, the construction proceeds as follows. Since G is connected, there is an edge $e_i = xv_{i+1}$ from a vertex x in V to a vertex v_{i+1} not in V. Let T_{i+1} be the subgraph of G with vertex set $V \cup \{v_{i+1}\}$ and edge set $E \cup \{e_i\}$. Since T_i is connected, then T_{i+1} is also connected because any path in T_i ending at x can be extended to a path ending at v_{i+1} in T_{i+1}. In addition T_i has no cycles, and T_{i+1} contains no cycle using e_i, so T_{i+1} has no cycles. Therefore T_{i+1} is a tree with $i + 1$ vertices and i edges. For a graph G with p vertices we continue until T_p is obtained. Since T_p is a tree with p vertices, it will be a spanning tree of G.

Since every connected graph G has a spanning tree we also obtain the following result.

COROLLARY 3 If G is a connected graph with p vertices then G has at least $p - 1$ edges.

In particular we have these two important methods of obtaining spanning trees. After applying the depth first search to a connected graph G with p vertices, consider the spanning subgraph T of G, which contains precisely those edges of the form $p(v)v$ through which new vertices were discovered by the depth first search. A depth first search starting from any initial vertex s in a connected graph will reach the other $p - 1$ vertices eventually (Problem 20), so T has p vertices. It follows from the proof of Theorem 6.7 that T is a spanning tree of G. We sometimes refer to the subgraph T as a depth first spanning tree of G.

Note that in a similar way one can define a breadth first spanning tree of G (see Fig. 6.4) using a breadth first search on G, but we leave the details to the reader.

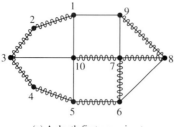 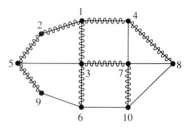

(a) A depth first spanning tree   (b) A breadth first spanning tree

Figure 6.4

Counting Spanning Trees (Optional)

There are several interesting combinatorial results concerning the number of labeled spanning trees in a graph G. In this situation, two spanning trees are considered to be distinct if they have different vertex labels even though they might be isomorphic. First we derive a simple recurrence for the number of spanning trees, which is similar to the recurrence for chromatic polynomials that was discovered in Section 5.5. We denote by $G * e$ the graph obtained from G by removing the edge e and identifying its endpoints. Let $t(G)$ represent the number of distinct labeled spanning trees of G.

THEOREM 6.8

If e is a link of G, then $t(G) = t(G * e) + t(G - e)$.

Proof
If we assume that G has p vertices, any spanning tree of G has $p - 1$ edges. Let T be a spanning tree of G that contains e. Clearly $T * e$ is a connected subgraph of $G * e$ without cycles. Since $G * e$ and $T * e$ both have $p - 1$ vertices, $T * e$ is a spanning tree of $G * e$. This correspondence gives a bijection between the spanning trees of $G * e$ and the spanning trees of G that contain e. (See Fig. 6.5.)

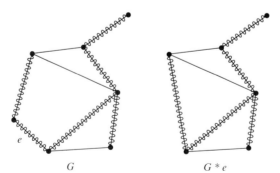

Figure 6.5

G $G * e$

Every spanning tree of G that does not contain e is also a spanning tree of $G - e$, and vice versa. Therefore $t(G - e)$ is the number of spanning trees of G that do not contain e. It follows that $t(G) = t(G * e) + t(G - e)$.

When G is a complete graph, we also have a closed formula for $t(G)$, which was first discovered by Cayley.

THEOREM 6.9   (Cayley's Theorem)

The number of labeled spanning trees of K_n is n^{n-2}.

Proof

To each labeled spanning tree of K_n we will associate a sequence of length $n-2$, whose entries are elements of V (not necessarily distinct). Since the number of sequences of this type is n^{n-2}, it suffices to show that this correspondence is a bijection.

To a spanning tree T of K_n we associate a sequence $(v_1, v_2, \ldots, v_{n-2})$, known as the Prüfer code, in the following way. Find the end l_1 of T with the smallest label, and let v_1 be the vertex that is adjacent to l_1. Continue by deleting l_1 and the edge incident to it, and proceed by finding the leaf l_2 with the smallest label in the resulting tree. At step i in this process, we let v_i be the vertex adjacent to the smallest remaining end l_i and proceed to the next step by removing l_i and the edge incident to it, until two vertices and a single edge remain. In this way a unique sequence of length $n-2$ is assigned to each spanning tree. (See Fig. 6.6.)

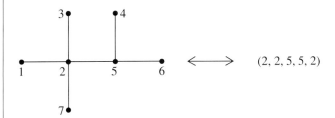

Figure 6.6

We also show that there is a unique labeled spanning tree for each Prüfer code. Note that a vertex is listed once in the Prüfer code for each vertex that it is adjacent to, except for the last remaining vertex. Thus each vertex v of T appears in the Prüfer code $\deg v - 1$ times, and in particular the ends of T are precisely those vertices that do not appear in the Prüfer code.

The edges of T are determined as follows. Let L_1 be the set consisting of the elements of V that are not in the sequence $(v_1, v_2, \ldots, v_{n-2})$. We see that l_1 must be the smallest element of L_1 and that the first edge of T removed was $l_1 v_1$. Next let L_2 be the elements of $V - \{l_1\}$ that are not in the sequence $(v_2, v_3, \ldots, v_{n-2})$. We see that l_2 is the smallest element of L_2 and that the second edge of T removed was $l_2 v_2$. In general, let L_i be the elements of $V - \{l_1, l_2, \ldots, l_{i-1}\}$ that are not in the sequence $(v_i, v_{i+1}, \ldots, v_{n-2})$. We see that the ith edge of T removed was $l_i v_i$. In this way we determine $n-2$ edges of T. We see that the remaining edge of T joins the two vertices of $V - \{l_1, l_2, \ldots, l_{n-2}\}$. Thus we have established the desired bijection.

6.2

PROBLEMS

1. a) List all nonisomorphic trees with exactly six vertices.
   b) Find two nonisomorphic trees with the same degree sequence.

2. If G is a connected graph with 10 edges, what is the maximum number of vertices in G?

3. Show that if G is connected but the removal of any edge from G makes it disconnected, G is a tree.

4. a) Which trees are regular graphs?
   b) Which trees have exactly two ends?

5. Given a graph with w components, what is the smallest number of edges that must be added to result in a connected graph?

6. Let G be a connected graph with p vertices and p edges. Show that G has exactly one cycle.

7. A carpenter plans to build a one-story house with nine rooms. Assuming that every door joins two rooms, what is the smallest number of doors that can be used so that every room can be reached from every other and from the outside.

8. A small apartment has a single wall outlet with room for exactly two electrical plugs. If the apartment dweller has five extension cords, each of which has room for three plug-ins, how many appliances can the apartment dweller use at one time?

9. Show that when a vertex v and the edges incident to it are removed from a tree G, the resulting graph has $\deg v = w$ components.

10. Show that if G is a tree with $\delta^+ \geq k$, then G has at least k vertices of degree 1.

11. Suppose that a tree has ten vertices of degree 2, ten vertices of degree 3, ten vertices of degree 4, one vertex of degree 5, and its remaining vertices have degree 1. How many vertices does T have?

12. Let G be a graph with p vertices and $p - 1$ edges. Show that the following three statements are equivalent.
    a) G is connected.
    b) G has no cycles.
    c) G is a tree.

13. Use the DFS method to determine whether or not the graph represented by the following set of adjacency lists is connected.

1	2	3	4	5	6	7	8	9	10	11	12
2	1	4	3	1	3	1	4	5	3	5	1
5	7	6	8	9	8	2	6	10	6	12	2
7	12	10		11				10	12		9
12											11

14. The following diagram represents a maze. Show how DFS can be used to find a path from the start to the finish in this maze.

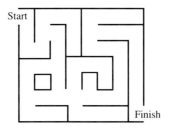

15. Let G be a graph with no cycles and let $(d_1, d_2, \ldots, d_p)$ be the degree sequence of G.

    a) If G is connected, find $\sum_{i=1}^{p} d_i$.

    b) If G has exactly k components, find $\sum_{i=1}^{p} d_i$.

ADVANCED PROBLEMS

16. If $(d_1, d_2, \ldots, d_p)$ is a sequence of positive integers satisfying $\sum_{i=1}^{p} d_i = 2p - 2$, describe an algorithm for constructing a tree with this degree sequence.

17. If G is a graph with p vertices, q edges, and w components, show that G has at least $q - p + w$ cycles.

∗18. A center of a graph G is a vertex u such that $\max_{v \in V} \{d(u, v)\}$ is as small as possible. Show that a tree has either exactly one center or two centers that are adjacent.

∗19. Show that the number of spanning trees of $K_n - e$, for any edge e, is $(n - 2)n^{n-3}$.

20. a) In a depth first search show that every edge of the form $p(v)v$ is traversed twice, once in each direction.
    b) Prove that the depth first search always reaches every vertex in a connected graph.

21. Use a depth first search to find a solution to the following puzzle. Three jealous husbands and their wives must get to town in a sports car that only holds two people. How can they do it so that no wife is ever left with one or more of the other husbands unless her own husband is also present?

22. a) Show that every tree is a planar graph.
    b) Show that every graph with a single cycle is a planar graph.
    c) Show that every graph with at most three cycles is a planar graph.

6.2

1. Determinants and Graphs

    Let T be an $n \times n$ matrix. Delete row i and column j to obtain an $(n-1) \times (n-1)$ matrix M_{ij}. This matrix is called the (i,j)th minor of T. The (i,j)th cofactor of T is defined to be $(-1)^{i+j} \det(M_{ij})$ (where det is short for determinant).

    a) Given a square matrix, write a program that will generate its (i,j)th minor. Test your program by printing the 16 minors of a 4×4 matrix (with distinct entries).

    b) Consider the following graph G.

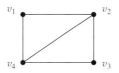

    Let A be its adjacency matrix. Form T by adding $\deg(v_i)$ to the ith diagonal entry of $-A$. Thus you should get the following matrix:

$$\begin{bmatrix} 2 & -1 & \cdots \\ -1 & 3 & \cdots \\ \vdots & \vdots & \end{bmatrix}$$

    i) Use a computer and your program in part (a) to evaluate all 16 cofactors of T.

    ii) List by hand all the spanning trees of G. What is amazing about the number of trees?

6.3 TREE ALGORITHMS

Rooted Trees and Searching

A directed graph T is said to be a **directed tree** if it becomes a tree when the arrows on the directed edges are removed. For any two vertices x and y of T, we say that y is **reachable** from x if and only if there is a **directed path** (sequence of directed edges) joining x to y. A directed tree is said to have a **root** r if every vertex of T is reachable from the vertex r. A directed tree with a root is called a **rooted tree** for short. In a rooted tree there is a unique directed path from r to any other vertex v.

For a rooted tree with root r, there are no directed edges ending at r, and for any other vertex $v \neq r$, there is exactly one directed edge ending at v. In a rooted tree, we say that a vertex v is a leaf if there are no directed edges starting at v, and the other vertices are sometimes referred to as **branches**.

A vertex y in a rooted tree is said to be a **descendant** of x if there is a directed path from x to y. A family tree is a special kind of rooted tree where the vertices represent people. In drawing a rooted tree, we always place the direct descendants of a branch below it, and in this way the arrows on the directed edges may be omitted because they will be understood to point downward.

An important type of rooted tree is known as a binary tree.

DEFINITION   **Binary Trees**

A binary tree is a rooted tree for which no more than two directed edges leave any vertex. A ternary tree will be a rooted tree for which no more than three directed edges leave any vertex. In general, an m-ary tree will be a rooted tree for which no more than m directed edges leave any vertex. (See Fig. 6.7.)

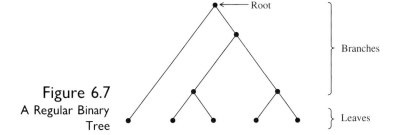

Figure 6.7
A Regular Binary Tree

An m-ary tree is said to be regular if each of its branches has exactly m directed edges leaving it.

An arithmetic expression can be represented by a regular binary tree because our usual arithmetic operations act on two numbers at a time. Normally, when an arithmetic expression is written sequentially, we use parentheses to keep track of the order in which the operations should be performed, as in the expression $((7 + 11 * (1 + 4)) + 6 * 8) - 5 * (71 + 23)$.

Another way of representing this expression is on a binary tree where each of the operands is represented by a leaf, and each of the operations is represented by a branch of the binary tree as in Fig. 6.8. Note that the parentheses are no longer necessary when the arithmetic expression is represented by a binary tree. We are able to perform an operation any time all of its descendants have been performed.

If we compute the value of an algebraic expression on a computer, some of the operations can be performed simultaneously (parallel processing). The **level** of a vertex in a rooted tree is defined to be the number of edges in the directed path from the root to that vertex. The **height** of a rooted tree is defined to be the largest level of any vertex in the tree. If an algebraic expression is represented by a binary tree of height h, we can compute the value of the expression in h steps by performing the operations at level $h - i$ in step i.

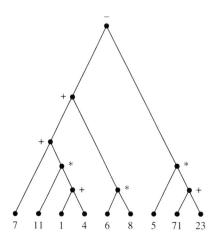

Figure 6.8   7   11   1   4   6   8   5   71   23

Rooted trees can also be used to represent many important decision processes in computer science. If each decision has at most m outcomes, the decision process can be represented by an m-ary tree. One fundamental fact about an m-ary decision tree of height h is that it has no more than m^h possible outcomes.

A Binary Search

Many searching problems can be solved and analyzed using rooted trees. Consider the following problem.

Suppose a mathematician picks an integer i from the set $\{1, 2, 3, \ldots, 16\}$, and a computer scientist tries to search for i by asking questions that can be answered with either a yes or a no. The computer scientist could certainly find i by asking the sequence of questions: Is $i = 1$? Is $i = 2$? Is $i = 3$? ... Is $i = 15$? But, in the worst case, we see that this search might take as many as 15 questions if the computer scientist were unlucky. Any searching strategy the computer scientist chooses can be represented by a binary tree, which must have at least 16 leaves, one for each possible outcome. The height of this binary tree represents the largest number of questions needed by the computer scientist to terminate the search. Thus any binary search strategy requires at least four questions. In fact, everyone is probably familiar with the standard halving strategy that would always find the unknown object i in exactly four ($\log_2 16$) questions. For example, we might first ask: Is $i > 8$? If the answer were yes, there would be eight remaining possibilities, namely, $\{9, 10, 11, \ldots, 16\}$, whereas after a no answer there would also be eight remaining possibilities, namely, $\{1, 2, 3, \ldots, 8\}$. Continuing to divide the remaining possibilities in half with each question, we would be left with one possibility for i after four questions. A binary search strategy using only comparison tests is pictured using the binary tree in Fig. 6.9.

The most elegant binary search can be obtained by using the binary representation of the numbers $\{1, 2, 3, \ldots, 16\}$. In that way we determine i by asking the following four questions:

Question j: Is the jth binary digit of $i = 1$?   ($j = 1, 2, 3, 4$)

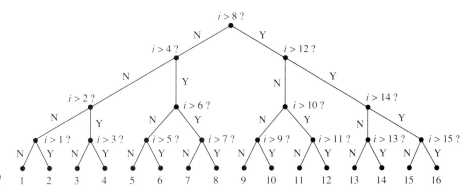

Figure 6.9

Puzzle 1   A Binary Search with One Lie Allowed

As before, a mathematician picks an integer i from the set $\{1, 2, 3, \ldots, 16\}$, and a computer scientist tries to search for i by asking yes-no questions. However, in this case, suppose that the mathematician is devious and can lie once (or not lie) to hinder the computer scientist.

a) Using a binary tree analysis show that at least seven questions are needed to find i (don't forget the possibilities for a lie).

b) Devise a searching strategy that will always find i in seven questions if no more than one lie is told. (See Problem 18.)

Minimum-Weight Trees

Trees can be used in analyzing many optimization problems. In particular, spanning trees are useful in analyzing the following minimal-connector problem.

Suppose that a rail network connecting several towns is being set up, and the cost of constructing a direct rail line between towns v_i and v_j is known to be c_{ij}. For economic reasons suppose that the rail system must be constructed as cheaply as possible, regardless of how inconvenient the system might be for its passengers. The problem of constructing a minimum-cost rail network that connects all the towns is referred to as the minimal-connector problem.

We represent the proposed rail lines by a weighted graph G with a vertex for each town and an edge $v_i v_j$ with weight c_{ij} for each pair of towns v_i and v_j. To solve the minimal-connector problem, we need to find a connected spanning subgraph of minimum weight. Since the weights represent costs, we may as well assume that they are positive and therefore the minimum-weight subgraph of G is a spanning tree of G. A minimum-weight spanning tree of a weighted graph G will be called an economy tree. The following algorithm was devised by Prim to find an economy tree in a weighted graph G. (See Fig. 6.10.)

Prim's Algorithm

Let G be a weighted graph with vertex set $V = \{v_1, v_2, \ldots, v_p\}$.

1. Let $i = 1$, $V_1 = \{v_1\}$, and $E_1 = \phi$.

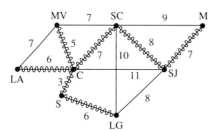

Figure 6.10

2. For $U_i = V - V_i$, compute $w_i = \min\limits_{x \in V_i, y \in U_i} \{w(x, y)\}$.

   Let $e_i = (x_i, y_i)$ be an edge for which this minimum w_i is attained.
3. Increase i by 1. Set $V_i = V_{i-1} \cup \{y_{i-1}\}$ and $E_i = E_{i-1} \cup \{e_{i-1}\}$.
4. If $i < p$, return to Step 2. Otherwise, stop because the subgraph T with vertex set $V = V_p$ and edge set E_p is a minimum-weight spanning tree.

THEOREM 6.10

The subgraph T determined by Prim's algorithm is a minimum-weight spanning tree.

Proof

Since Prim's algorithm uses the tree-growing procedure of Theorem 6.7 to construct T, then T will be a spanning tree of G. Suppose that the edges of T are $e_1, e_2, \ldots, e_{p-1}$ and let T^* be a minimum-weight spanning tree of G. If T and T^* have exactly the same edges, both are minimum-weight spanning trees. If not, then for some $q \le p - 1$, T and T^* have edges $e_1, e_2, \ldots, e_{q-1}$ in common but not e_q. The graph obtained by adding edge e_q to T^* has a cycle containing e_q. If e_q was the ith edge chosen by Prim's algorithm, it contains one endpoint in V_i and one in U_i. This cycle contains at least one other edge, say, e_q^*, which is incident to a vertex in V_i and another in U_i. The graph T' obtained from T^* by adding e_q and deleting e_q^* is a connected subgraph of G with $p - 1$ edges, so T' is another spanning tree of G (Problem 12, Section 6.2).

In Prim's algorithm, the edge e_q was chosen as an edge with smallest weight that was incident to both a vertex in V_i and a vertex in U_i. Thus $w(e_q) \le w(e_q^*)$ and $w(T') \le w(T^*)$. Since T^* is a minimum-weight spanning tree of G, so is T'. Furthermore, T and T' have edges $e_1, e_2, \ldots, e_q$ in common. By repeating this replacement process, we eventually see that the spanning tree T with edges $e_1, e_2, \ldots, e_{p-1}$ is also a minimum-weight spanning tree of G.

When Prim's algorithm is applied to the graph in Fig. 6.10 with $v_1 = $ SJ, the edge of weight 7 from SJ to M is chosen, followed by the edge of weight 8 from SJ to SC, the edge of weight 7 from SC to C, the edge of weight 3 from C to S, the edge of weight 5 from C to MV, the edge of weight 6 from C to LA, and the edge of weight 6 from S to LG.

In Prim's algorithm, we start with a subgraph that is a single vertex and we always choose a new edge that is incident to the previously chosen subgraph. Thus, in each step of this algorithm, the chosen subgraph is connected. We now describe a slight variation of this procedure that is known as Kruskal's algorithm. It can also be shown that Kruskal's algorithm always terminates with an economy tree (Problem 19) when applied to a connected weighted graph G.

Kruskal's Algorithm

Let G be a weighted graph with vertex set $V = \{v_1, v_2, \ldots, v_p\}$.

1. Let $i = 1$, and denote by T the subgraph of G consisting of a single vertex v_1.
2. Compute $w_i = \min \{w(e)\}$ over the set containing all edges (e) that do not form a cycle when added to T. Let e_i be an edge for which this minimum w_i is attained.
3. Increase i by 1. Replace T by $T + e_i$.
4. If $i < p$, return to Step 2. Otherwise, stop because the subgraph T is a minimum-weight spanning tree.

Optimal Trees and Sorting (Optional)

Suppose we have a set of numbers stored on a computer and we wish to list them in increasing order. Assuming that the numbers have already been organized into m existing sorted lists $L_1, L_2, \ldots, L_m$, we have the following procedure for arranging the numbers into a single sorted list.

First we show how to combine two of these lists into a single list. We compare the smallest numbers in each of the two lists to find the smallest number overall. We remove this number and place it first in the merged list. Next we compare the smallest numbers remaining in the two lists and place the smallest of these numbers in the second position of the merged list. We continue this step until one list becomes empty, at which point the remaining numbers in the nonempty list are placed in order at the end to complete the merged list. This procedure takes at most $n_1 + n_2 - 1$ comparisons to merge two sorted lists with n_1 and n_2 numbers.

Starting with m sorted lists, we select two of them and merge them into one list. We now select two lists from the remaining $m - 1$ sorted lists and merge them into one. Continuing in this way, we eventually obtain a single merged list.

In general, there are many different ways in which $m > 2$ lists can be merged. In each case, the merging process can be represented by a binary tree. The original lists $L_1, L_2, \ldots, L_m$ correspond to the leaves of the tree, and each of the $m - 1$ branches corresponds to a pair of lists being merged. Different orders of merging may not require the same number of comparisons overall (see Fig. 6.11).

Suppose that a given merging process is represented by a binary tree T. Let the size of list L_i be denoted by n_i and the height of the leaf representing L_i be given by h_i. We say that the size of T, denoted by $w(T)$, equals $\sum_{i=1}^{m} h_i n_i$. Among the trees with m leaves of size $n_1, n_2, \ldots, n_m$, the one with the smallest possible size is referred to as an **optimal tree**. For the merging process represented by T, the total number of comparisons needed is at most $\sum_{i=1}^{m} h_i n_i - (m - 1)$. This quantity can be minimized by finding an optimal tree T with m leaves of size $n_1, n_2, \ldots, n_m$. We describe the following procedure, due to Huffman, for constructing an optimal binary tree.

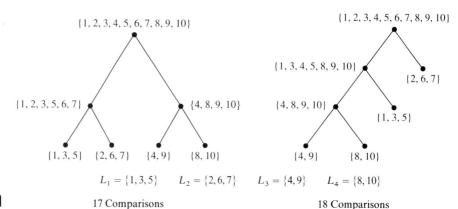

Figure 6.11

17 Comparisons   18 Comparisons

Huffman's Algorithm

1. Start with m rooted trees, each consisting of a single vertex, and label them $n_1, n_2, \ldots, n_m$, respectively. (These will end up being the leaves of the optimal tree.)
2. Arrange the roots according to size, so that $n_1 \leq n_2 \leq \cdots \leq n_m$.
3. Join the two roots n_1 and n_2 to a single vertex labeled $n_1 + n_2$. We now have $m - 1$ rooted trees with roots of size $n_1 + n_2, n_3, \ldots, n_m$.
4. Reduce m by 1. If $m = 1$, stop because an optimal binary tree has been constructed. Otherwise, return to Step 2 with the m rooted trees constructed so far.

An optimal tree with leaves of size 1, 2, 3, 4, 5, 6 is pictured in Fig. 6.12.

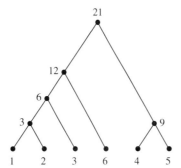

Figure 6.12

THEOREM 6.11

The binary tree constructed by Huffman's algorithm is an optimal binary tree with leaves of size $n_1, n_2, \ldots, n_m$.

Proof
The proof is not hard and we leave it as an exercise (Problem 16).

6.3
PROBLEMS

1. a) Find the shortest distance from Santa Cruz (SC) to each of the other cities in the following rail network.
    b) Find a minimum-weight spanning tree for the following rail network.

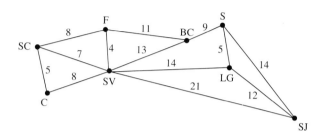

2. a) Find two different minimum-weight spanning trees in the following weighted graph.
    b) Show that in a weighted graph where each edge has a different weight there is a unique minimum-weight spanning tree.

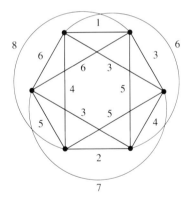

3. Find an optimal binary tree with weighted leaves 1, 4, 4, 7, 11, 17, 23, 43, 51.

4. a) How can the procedure for constructing an optimal binary tree be extended to m-ary trees?
    b) Construct an optimal ternary tree ($m = 3$) for the weights 1, 2, 3, 4, 5, 6, 7, 8, 9.
    c) Construct an optimal ternary tree for the weights 1, 2, 3, 4, 5, 6, 7, 8.

5. A mathematician picks an integer from 1 to 10, and a computer scientist tries to find the number by asking yes-no questions. From past experience, it is known that the mathematician picks the number 7 with probability $P(7) = 1/2$, and similarly $P(1) = P(3) = P(10) = 1/12$, and $P(2) = P(4) = P(5) = P(6) = P(8) = P(9) = 1/24$. Illustrate an optimal search using a binary tree.

6. A mathematician picks an integer i from the set $\{1, 2, \ldots, 15\}$ and a computer scientist tries to find the number by asking questions of the form: Is $i < x$, $i > x$, or $i = x$? Show that the number can always be found using three questions.

7. Suppose that among n coins there is exactly one counterfeit coin that is lighter than the others. Using an equal arm balance, show that one can always find the counterfeit coin in m weighings if $n = 3^m$ but not if $n = 3^m + 1$.

8. If T is a regular binary tree with p vertices, show that
    a) p is odd.
    b) The number of leaves is $(p + 1)/2$.

9. Twenty softball teams enter a tournament. In each round of the tournament, certain pairs of teams play a game (no ties are allowed) and the other teams do not play (they draw a bye). Any team that does not lose proceeds to the next round. The tournament ends when a single team remains.
    a) Explain why at least five rounds are needed to finish the tournament.
    b) Can the games be scheduled so that the byes only occur in the first round?

10. a) What is the smallest possible height for the decision tree of an algorithm that sorts four numbers using binary comparisons?
     b) Can you describe an algorithm that uses the minimum number of comparisons?

ADVANCED PROBLEMS

11. a) There are many ways of adding the numbers 1, 2, 3, ..., 100 together, though all these ways lead to the same answer. We can use parentheses to show a specific order of addition or such an algebraic expression can be represented by a binary tree. What is the number of branches in such a binary tree?
     b) What is the smallest height that a binary tree can have if it represents the addition of the numbers $\{1, 2, 3, \ldots, 100\}$?

12. Let $x_1, x_2, \ldots, x_{16}$ be a list of 16 different integers arranged in increasing order. What is the smallest number of comparisons needed to determine whether or not an integer x is in the list, and if so, what is its position in the list?

13. Suppose that among four coins, identical in appearance, it is suspected that there is one counterfeit coin that is either lighter or heavier than the others. Show that in two weighings it is not always possible to determine the counterfeit coin (if any) and whether it is lighter or heavier than the others.

14. Suppose that among 12 coins there is one counterfeit coin that can be either lighter or heavier than the others. Show that using an equal arm balance, we can always find the counterfeit coin in three weighings.

15. Suppose that among n coins there are exactly two counterfeit coins, both of which are lighter than the others. What is the highest value of n for which both counterfeit coins can be found in two weighings on an equal arm balance?

16. a) If T is an optimal binary tree with leaves of size $n_1, n_2, \ldots, n_m$, with $n_1 \le n_2 \le \cdots \le n_m$, show that there is an optimal tree T' where the leaves of size n_1 and n_2 are adjacent to the same branch.
 b) In T' replace the subtree containing leaves of size n_1 and n_2 by a single vertex of size $n_1 + n_2$. Show that the resulting tree T'' is an optimal binary tree with leaves of size $n_1 + n_2, n_3, \ldots, n_m$.
 c) Use parts (a) and (b) to prove Theorem 6.11.

17. Adapt Prim's algorithm to construct a minimum-cost rail network linking a number of towns, with the additional requirement that one selected pair of towns must be directly linked. Prove that this algorithm always works.

18. Solve Puzzle 1.

19. Show that Kruskal's algorithm always terminates with a minimum-weight spanning tree in a connected graph G.

20. Describe an algorithm that finds a maximum-weight spanning tree in a graph.

21. a) Use a binary decision tree to show that the efficiency of any algorithm that sorts a list of n numbers is at least $\log_2 n!$.
 b) Show that $\log_2 n!$ is $0(n \log_2 n)$. [See also Problem 14, Section 4.2.]

6.3

SUPPLEMENTARY COMPUTER PROJECTS

1. A Minimum Spanning Tree Algorithm
Suppose that G is a connected graph with N vertices and M (weighted) edges. Each edge will be represented by an ordered pair. Assume that the edges of G have been arranged so that their weights are in nondecreasing order. Also assume these two definitions:

1. An element of a pair is a *good* number if and only if it is not circled.
2. A pair is a *G-pair* if and only if it contains exactly one good number.
   Consider the following procedure:

1. Arbitrarily select a vertex v.
2. Find and output the first pair containing v. Circle all occurrences of its good numbers.
3. Output the first G-pair. Circle all of its good numbers. Repeat Step 3 until a total of $N - 1$ pairs have been generated.

Example   Figure 6.13 shows the estimated cost (in thousands of dollars) required to construct a road between any pair of the cities A, B, C, D, and E. The costs arranged in nondecreasing order are as follows:

40 BC, 45 CD, 50 ED, 55 CE, 60 BE, 65 BD, 100 AB, 110 AE, 120 AD, 125 AC

To apply the procedure to this graph,
  i) Pick any vertex, say, D.
  ii) Output CD.

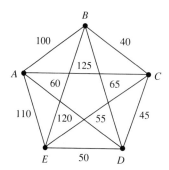

Figure 6.13

iii) Circle all occurrences of C and D.
iv) Output the first G-pair BC.
v) Circle all occurrences of its good number B.
vi) Output the next G-pair ED.
vii) Circle all occurrences of its good number E.
viii) Output the last G-pair AB.

a) Explain why this procedure always finds the least expensive network of roads connecting all the cities, A → B → C → D → E in this case.

b) Write a program that implements this algorithm. For convenience assume the vertices are numbered $1, 2, \ldots, N$ and that the edges have been ordered.

6 REVIEW PROBLEMS

1. Prove by induction that every tree with two or more vertices has chromatic number 2.

2. A tree with 100 vertices only has vertices of degree 3 and vertices of degree 1.
    a) How many edges does it have?
    b) How many vertices of degree 1 does it have?

3. Let T be a tree with 101 vertices. What is the largest number of vertices of degree 4 that T can have?

4. Describe an algorithm for determining a minimum-weight spanning forest in a weighted graph G (not necessarily connected).

5. To an isomer of a saturated hydrocarbon we associate a tree where vertices of degree 4 represent carbon atoms and vertices of degree 1 represent hydrogen atoms. If two isomorphic trees represent the same chemical compound, find the number of different isomers of
    a) C_3H_8 b) C_5H_{12}

6. A regular m-ary tree of height h is said to be balanced if all its leaves occur at level $h-1$ or level h. Show that any balanced regular m-ary tree of height h has at least m^{h-1} and at most m^h leaves.

7. Describe an algorithm that finds the shortest path in an undirected graph G going from vertex u to vertex v that passes through a given vertex w.

8. a) Describe an algorithm that always finds a spanning forest in an undirected graph G (not necessarily connected).
   b) What can you say about the number of trees in a spanning forest of G?

9. a) Describe an algorithm that finds a cycle in an undirected graph G or determines that no cycle exists.
   b) If G is a connected graph and e is an edge contained in a cycle of G, show that $G - e$ is connected.
   c) Use parts (a) and (b) to describe an algorithm that successively removes edges from a connected graph G until a spanning tree remains.

6 | SUMMARY

In this chapter we encountered many different problems that can be solved using graph algorithms. By using graph models we were able to determine whether or not two locations in a telecommunications network were connected by a communications link. Weighted graphs were used to solve the problem of finding the shortest path between two cities in a transportation network. Trees are the class of connected graphs that contain no cycles. Trees can be used to model certain simple algorithms that consist of a sequence of decisions. They were also used to find the least expensive way to link up several locations in a network. Algorithms involving directed graphs are discussed in Chapter 10. Any of the following books [1–4] can be used to obtain more information about graph algorithms. The book by Garey and Johnson [5] is a good source of information on the complexity of these algorithms.

BIBLIOGRAPHY

1. Even, S. *Graph Algorithms*. Rockville, Md.: Computer Science Press, 1979.
2. Minieka, E. *Optimization Algorithms for Networks and Graphs*. New York: Marcel Dekker, 1978.
3. Lawler, E. *Combinatorial Optimization: Networks and Matroids*. New York: Holt, Rinehart, and Winston, 1976.
4. Horowitz, E., and S. Sahni. *Fundamentals of Computer Algorithms*. Rockville, Md.: Computer Science Press, 1984.
5. Garey, M., and D. Johnson. *Computers and Intractibility: A Guide to NP—Completeness*. New York: W. H. Freeman, 1979.

7

GENERATING FUNCTIONS

In the next two chapters we consider the following situation. Suppose we are studying a set of similar counting problems that vary in size. It will often be appropriate to represent the size of a particular problem by a parameter i, where i can take any nonnegative integer value. If a_i is the number of outcomes when the parameter has value i, the solution of this collection of counting problems can be described by a sequence $A = (a_0, a_1, a_2, \ldots, a_i, \ldots)$. It is usually considered most desirable to have a simple function, like a polynomial, which can be evaluated at i to give the value of a_i. If f is such a function satisfying $f(i) = a_i$, we say that f is a closed formula for A.

Unfortunately it will sometimes be difficult or even impossible to find a closed formula for a sequence A representing the solution of a set of combinatorial problems. In this chapter we introduce the concept of a generating function for a sequence A. The generating function of a sequence is a generalization of the concept of a polynomial. The algebra of these generalized polynomials will be useful in solving many combinatorial problems. We will encounter selection problems, distribution problems, and later, problems involving partitions of integers that can be analyzed using generating functions.

7.1 GENERATING FUNCTION MODELS

Generating functions are important tools for analyzing various sets of combinatorial problems. In this section we introduce the ordinary generating function of a sequence and later, in Section 7.4, we introduce the exponential generating function.

DEFINITION   **(Ordinary) Generating Function**

To each sequence $A = (a_0, a_1, a_2, \ldots, a_i, \ldots)$ we associate the power series $A(z) = a_0 + a_1 z + a_2 z^2 + \cdots + a_i z^i + \cdots$. The expression $A(z)$ is called the generating function of the sequence A.

The term $a_i z^i$ is called the term of degree i, and a_i is called the coefficient of z^i. The coefficients are the important part. The symbol z^i is merely a convenient device for distinguishing a_i from the other terms of the sequence because, in this context, we usually do not evaluate this expression for any specific numerical values of z and thus we are not concerned with whether or not the series converges.

Consider the following example. Let X be a specific set with n elements. Of all the possible subsets that can be selected from X, we are sometimes interested only in those with precisely k elements. As we have seen before, the number of k-subsets of X is $C(n, k)$ for $0 \le k \le n$ and 0 for $k > n$. The solution of this set of problems can be represented by the generating function $A(z) = a_0 + a_1 z + a_2 z^2 + \cdots + a_n z^n$, where the coefficient of z^i is the number of different subsets whose size is i, namely, $C(n, i)$. Of course, the coefficients of this generating function were computed using other techniques. Shortly we shall describe a new method for obtaining this generating function.

If all the coefficients of a generating function $A(z)$ are 0 from some point on, it is just a polynomial. There is an algebra for manipulating generating functions that generalizes the normal algebraic operations on polynomials. Two generating functions can be added term by term. In other words, if a_i is the coefficient of z^i in A and b_i is the coefficient of z^i in B, then $a_i + b_i$ is the coefficient of z^i in the sum $A + B$. To multiply two generating functions A and B, we take all possible products containing one term from A and one term from B and combine like terms to obtain the appropriate term in the product $A \times B$. Thus the coefficient of z^i in $A \times B$ equals the sum $a_0 b_i + a_1 b_{i-1} + a_2 b_{i-2} + \cdots + a_i b_0$. Even if A and B have an infinite number of nonzero coefficients, the ith coefficient of $A \times B$ can be computed as usual by ignoring the terms of degree greater than i. This product is sometimes known as the *Cauchy product*.

Example 1   Let $A(z) = 1 + z^2 + 3z^5$ and $B(z) = 4 + z + 2z^3 + z^5$.
a) Compute $A(z) + B(z)$.

Solution
$A(z) + B(z) = 5 + z + z^2 + 2z^3 + 4z^5$.

b) Compute $A(z)B(z)$.

Solution
$A(z)B(z) = (1 \times 4) + (1 \times z) + (1 \times 2z^3) + (1 \times z^5) + (z^2 \times 4) + (z^2 \times z) +$

$$(z^2 \times 2z^3) + (z^2 \times z^5) + (3z^5 \times 4) + (3z^5 \times z) + (3z^5 \times 2z^3) + (3z^5 \times z^5) =$$
$$4 + z + 4z^2 + 3z^3 + 15z^5 + 3z^6 + z^7 + 6z^8 + 3z^{10}. \qquad \square$$

Example 2   Let $C(z) = 2 + 3z + 4z^2 + z^3 + z^4 + z^5 + z^6 + z^7 + z^8 + \cdots$ and $D(z) = 2z + z^2 + z^4 + z^6 + z^8 + \cdots$.

a) Compute the coefficient of z^8 in $C(z) + D(z)$.

Solution
$z^8 + z^8 = 2z^8$, so the coefficient is 2.

b) Compute the coefficient of z^8 in $C(z)D(z)$.

Solution
$2 \times z^8 + 4z^2 \times z^6 + z^4 \times z^4 + z^6 \times z^2 + z^7 \times 2z = 10z^8$, so the coefficient is 10.
$\qquad \square$

These operations can be used to build a generating function for a counting procedure in a manner reminiscent of the usual Multiplication and Addition Principles.

To illustrate this, let us return to the example involving the selection of a subset from a set $X = \{x_1, x_2, \dots, x_n\}$. To compute the total number of subsets of X, we first used the Multiplication Principle. In counting subsets, we use a counting procedure involving n steps. The two possible outcomes of step i are to include x_i, or not to include x_i in the subset, so the total number of subsets is 2^n. This is no help though if only subsets with exactly k elements are being considered. The problem with the usual Multiplication Principle is that it does not differentiate between the two outcomes, which after all have a different contribution to the size of the subset. Thus the steps in the preceding procedure would not be independent in the usual sense if only subsets containing a certain fixed number of objects are being counted.

On the other hand, suppose we differentiate between the choices that add an extra element to the subset, and those that do not, in the following way. We represent the outcome of not selecting x_i in step i by $z^0 = 1$ since this adds 0 to the size of the subset, and we represent the outcome of selecting x_i by $z^1 = z$ since this adds 1 to the size of the subset. Thus the outcome of each step in this counting procedure can be represented by the sum of these two terms, $(1 + z)$.

Now consider the product $(1 + z)^n$, with one factor for each step in the selection procedure. Each sequence in the expansion of $(1 + z)^n$ has n terms multiplied together. In each sequence of n terms, there is one term from each factor, either a 1 or a z. A 1 adds 0 and a z adds 1 to the overall exponent of the product of these terms. Therefore the size of a subset that corresponds to a certain sequence of n terms is also equal to the overall exponent of z in the product, and the number of sequences with overall exponent i will be the coefficient of z^i. Thus, as we first saw in the Binomial Theorem, the coefficient of z^i in $(1 + z)^n$ is $C(n, i)$, the number of ways to select a subset with i elements from the n-element set X. We shall see that composite generating functions for many counting procedures can be determined in a similar way, by multiplying.

In general, we have the following Multiplication Principle for computing the generating function of a counting procedure. The outcomes of a single step in a counting procedure will be represented by a generating function $a_0 + a_1 z + a_2 z^2 + \cdots + a_i z^i + \cdots$ if each outcome has an associated integer size and the number of outcomes that add i to the overall size of the composite outcome is a_i.

THE MULTIPLICATION PRINCIPLE FOR GENERATING FUNCTIONS   Consider a sequential counting procedure consisting of m different steps, where the generating function of step j is represented by $A_j(z)$. If the order of the outcomes is unimportant, the number of composite outcomes of size i is given by the coefficient of z^i in the product of the individual generating functions, $A_1(z)A_2(z) \cdots A_m(z)$.

Proof

The product of the m individual generating functions generates the collection of all different products obtained by multiplying together a term from each individual generating function. We assume that each step in the procedure represents a different type of outcome to ensure that each sequence of individual outcomes is associated with a different composite result of the procedure. Also, since the order of the outcomes is unimportant, each sequence represents exactly one composite outcome. Using the ordinary Multiplication Principle, we see that each product in the expansion of $A_1(z)A_2(z) \cdots A_m(z)$ represents exactly the same number of composite outcomes of size i as is given by the product of the individual coefficients of its terms. Since this coincides with the contribution of this product to the coefficient of z^i in the expansion of $A_1(z)A_2(z) \cdots A_m(z)$, this expansion does, in fact, give us the generating function of the entire procedure.

Note that there is also an Addition Principle for generating functions that is used in case-by-case counting. It is often implicitly used in constructing the individual generating functions $A_j(z)$ that we just used.

THE ADDITION PRINCIPLE FOR GENERATING FUNCTIONS   Consider a case-by-case counting procedure consisting of n different steps, where the generating function of step j is represented by $B_j(z)$. The total number of outcomes of size i is given by the coefficient of z^i in the sum of the individual generating functions, $B_1(z) + B_2(z) + \cdots + B_n(z)$.

Example 3   A juggling bag contains 5 yellow, 4 orange, and 5 white juggling balls. A juggler selects 1, 3, or 5 yellow balls; 2, 3, or 4 orange balls; and 1, 4, or 5 white balls. Assuming that balls of the same color are identical, in how many ways can 10 balls be selected?

Solution

The yellow ball generating function is $A_1(z) = (z + z^3 + z^5)$, the orange ball generating function is $A_2(z) = (z^2 + z^3 + z^4)$ and the generating function for the white ball selection is $A_3(z) = (z + z^4 + z^5)$. In the product $A_1(z)A_2(z)A_3(z)$, the products that contribute to the coefficient of z^{10} are $z \times z^4 \times z^5$, $z^3 \times z^2 \times z^5$, $z^3 \times z^3 \times z^4$, and $z^5 \times z^4 \times z$. Thus the coefficient of z^{10} in the composite generating function is 4, meaning that there are four different ways for the juggler to select a subset of 10 balls. ☐

The generating functions we have just introduced are sometimes referred to as ordinary generating functions. We will use ordinary generating functions to count selections with limited repetition, distributions of identical objects, integer solutions of linear equations, and partitions. Since the exponents of the generating function automatically keep track of the size of an outcome, the individual events of the procedure need not be independent in the usual sense. In this situation it is sufficient for the individual generating functions to be independent of the outcomes in the previous steps. In Section 7.4 we study procedures where the order of the outcomes is also considered to be important by using exponential generating functions.

Example 4 If 25 identical juggling balls are distributed to five different jugglers, with each juggler receiving at least 3 juggling balls, how many distributions are possible?

Solution

The order of distribution is normally considered to be unimportant, therefore the distribution process can be thought of as five different steps, distributing at least 3 balls to juggler i, for $i = 1, 2, 3, 4, 5$. The appropriate size of a distribution is the number of balls that are distributed, and there is one distribution of each size since the balls are identical. Thus the generating function of each individual step is $(z^3 + z^4 + z^5 + \cdots)$, and the composite generating function is $(z^3 + z^4 + z^5 + \cdots)^5$. The coefficient of z^{25} is the number of possible distributions of 25 balls. Note that we may consider each individual generating function $(z^3 + z^4 + z^5 + \cdots)$ to stop at z^{25} or not since this will have no effect on the coefficient of z^{25}. We shall see in the next section why it is slightly easier to calculate coefficients using $z^3 + z^4 + z^5 + \cdots$ if it does not stop at z^{25}. This coefficient can be computed using the methods of Chapter 3. First we distribute 3 balls to each juggler, and then we distribute the remaining 10 balls at random to obtain $C(14, 4)$ distributions. ☐

At the end of Chapter 2 we saw that many counting problems could be modeled by looking at integer solutions of linear equations with each coefficient equal to 1. Even if there were restrictions on the variables, it was sometimes still possible to compute the number of solutions. In the next section we give some algebraic methods for computing the coefficients of generating functions, which will give us an alternate method of computing the number of solutions.

Consider the problem of finding the number of integer solutions of $x_1 + x_2 + \cdots + x_n = k$, with $a_i \le x_i \le b_i$. The appropriate size to consider in this case is the numerical sum of the integers involved. The generating function for choosing the size of the variable x_i is $A_i(z) = (z^{a_i} + z^{a_i + 1} + \cdots + z^{b_i})$. Thus the composite generating function is $A_1(z)A_2(z) \cdots A_n(z)$, and the coefficient of z^k is the number of solutions whose overall sum equals k.

Example 5   Find the number of positive integer solutions of $x_1 + x_2 + x_3 + x_4 = 15$, with each $x_i \leq 5$.

Solution
The generating function for choosing the size of each variable x_i is $(z^1 + z^2 + z^3 + z^4 + z^5)$, so the composite generating function is $(z^1 + z^2 + z^3 + z^4 + z^5)^4$. The coefficient of z^{15} is the answer we want. Using our previous methods, we see that the number of solutions is $C(14, 3) - 4C(9, 3) + 6C(4, 3)$.   □

Generating functions can also be used to solve other problems that involve making change, counting partitions of integers, solving linear equations with arbitrary coefficients, and so on that would be difficult to deal with using any of our previous methods. In this case, generating functions give a convenient way to compute a_k, the number of objects whose size is k, though it will not always be easy to find a closed formula.

Example 6   Find a generating function for the number of ways to make n cents postage using only two-cent, three-cent, and five-cent postage stamps.

Solution
We are interested in a_n, the number of combinations of two-cent, three-cent, and five-cent stamps whose total value is n cents. Think of first choosing a number of two-cent stamps, then choosing a number of three-cent stamps, and finally choosing a number of five-cent stamps. Since each two-cent stamp adds 2 to the overall value, $1 + z^2 + z^4 + z^6 + \cdots$ is the generating function for the first choice. Similarly, the generating function for choosing a number of three-cent stamps is $1 + z^3 + z^6 + z^9 + \cdots$, and the generating function for choosing five-cent stamps is $1 + z^5 + z^{10} + z^{15} + \cdots$. Thus we obtain the generating function

$$A(z) = (1 + z^2 + z^4 + \cdots)(1 + z^3 + z^6 + \cdots)(1 + z^5 + z^{10} + \cdots).$$ □

7.1
PROBLEMS

1. Construct a generating function for a_n, the number of ways to select n objects from
    a) Four white, six orange, and four red juggling balls.
    b) Five juggling clubs, four juggling rings, and ten juggling balls if at least one of each kind of object must be chosen.
    c) Unlimited amounts of coins (pennies, nickels, dimes, quarters, and half dollars) contained in a bank vault.

2. Construct a generating function for a_n, the number of distributions of n identical juggling balls to
    a) Six different jugglers with at most four balls distributed to each juggler.
    b) Five different jugglers with between three and seven balls (inclusive) distributed to each juggler.

3. Find a generating function for the number of distributions of n identical dollar bills to four needy families with at least five bills distributed to each family.

4. a) Find a generating function for the number of ways to select n pastries from a bakery that has 10 different types of pastries, if repeated selections are allowed and the order of selection is not important.
    b) Find a generating function if at least one, but no more than 12, pastries of each kind must be selected.

5. Find a generating function for the number of integers whose digits sum to n, among
    a) Integers from 0 to 9999.
    b) Four-digit integers.

6. Find a generating function for the number of ways to select n balls from an infinite supply of red, white, and blue balls subject to the constraints that the number of blue balls selected is at least three, the number of red balls selected is at most four, and an odd number of white balls are selected.

7. A boy has nine packages of gum, each a different flavor and each containing five sticks of gum.
    a) Find a generating function for the number of ways to select n sticks of gum if any number of sticks can be selected from a package.
    b) Repeat part (a) if instead at least one stick of each flavor must be selected.

8. A girl has two each of c types of candy, three each of d types of candy, and four each of e types of candy.
    a) Find a generating function for the number of ways to select n pieces of candy.
    b) Repeat part (a) if instead, at least one piece of each type must be selected.

ADVANCED PROBLEMS

9. a) Find a generating function for the number of ways k distinct dice can show a sum of n.
    b) Find a generating function for the number of ways two indistinguishable dice can show a sum of n.
    c) Find a generating function for the number of ways six distinct dice can show a sum of n if the ith die does not show a value of i.

10. Find a generating function for the number of ways to make n cents in change using only pennies, nickels, and dimes.

11. Each day for a week, a child spends either two quarters on one of three kinds of candy bars or one quarter on popcorn. Find a generating function for the number of ways to spend n quarters during a week.

12. Suppose n identical objects are distributed to k different boxes. Find a generating function for the number of distributions
    a) If at most two objects are distributed to each of the first two boxes.
    b) If no more than two objects total are distributed to the first two boxes.

13. Consider the integer solutions of $x_1 + x_2 + \cdots + x_{10} = n$. Find a generating function for the number of integer solutions consisting of
    a) Nonnegative integers.
    b) Positive integers.
    c) Integers x_i, where $0 \le x_i \le i$.

14. Find a generating function for the number of positive integer solutions of
    a) $2x_1 + 3x_2 + 4x_3 + 5x_4 = n$.
    b) $x_1 + x_2 + x_3 + x_4 = n$, where each x_i satisfies $2 \le x_i \le 5$.

*15. The generating function for the number of outcomes of two different dice that sum to n is given by $(z + z^2 + z^3 + z^4 + z^5 + z^6)^2$. Construct a pair of dice, cubes with positive integers on their faces, that are not ordinary dice but that have the same generating function for the number of outcomes whose sum is n as ordinary dice.

16. Find a generating function for the number of integer solutions of $x_1 + x_2 + x_3 + \cdots + x_{10} = n$ consisting of integers x_i satisfying $-2 \le x_i \le 2$, for each $i = 1, 2, \ldots, 10$.

17. Find a generating function for the number of ways to select n objects from five different types of objects if the total number of objects of type 1 and type 2 selected must be even.

SECTION 7.2   CALCULATING COEFFICIENTS

In this section we look at some simple algebraic ways to manipulate generating functions. Sometimes the formulas we derive will give us a shortcut for computing the coefficients of a generating function, especially when we can relate the generating functions to certain power series. Still, in some complicated cases, the brute force method of computing each possible product and combining like terms to compute the number of outcomes with a particular size will be used. Even this is not so bad because generating functions give a very efficient method of enumerating all possible outcomes with a particular size and we can easily program our multiplication process onto a high-speed computer for quick and accurate computations.

Commonly Used Formulas Involving Generating Functions

Formulas 7-1 and 7-2 can be verified easily by multiplication:

$$(1 - z)(1 + z + z^2 + \cdots + z^n) = (1 - z^{n+1}) \tag{7-1}$$

$$(1 - z)(1 + z + z^2 + \cdots + z^n + \cdots) = 1 \tag{7-2}$$

It is convenient to rewrite formulas 7-1 and 7-2 in the following way. Note that the formulas 7-1* and 7-2* also make sense in the usual way of evaluating polynomials and power series as long as $z \neq 1$ in formula 7-1* and as long as $|z| < 1$ in formula 7-2*.

$$\frac{(1 - z^{n+1})}{1 - z} = (1 + z + z^2 + \cdots + z^n) \tag{7-1*}$$

$$\frac{1}{1 - z} = (1 + z + z^2 + \cdots + z^n + \cdots) \tag{7-2*}$$

It is sometimes helpful to use formulas like these in calculating the coefficients of generating functions since the sums and products of two power series (when they converge) will coincide with the combinatorial sums and products of the corresponding generating functions that we defined in the previous section.

Formulas 7-3 and 7-4 can be computed from the binomial theorem:

$$(1 + z)^n = 1 + \binom{n}{1} z + \binom{n}{2} z^2 + \cdots + \binom{n}{n} z^n \tag{7-3}$$

$$(1 - z^m)^n = 1 - \binom{n}{1} z^m + \binom{n}{2} z^{2m} + \cdots + (-1)^n \binom{n}{n} z^{nm} \tag{7-4}$$

The final formula involves a generating function for the number of nonnegative integer solutions of $x_1 + x_2 + \cdots + x_n = i$. Since we know that the number of solutions of this equation is $\binom{i + n - 1}{i}$, we obtain formula 7-5:

$$\frac{1}{(1 - z)^n} = 1 + \binom{1 + n - 1}{1} z + \binom{2 + n - 1}{2} z^2 + \cdots + \binom{i + n - 1}{i} z^i + \cdots \tag{7-5}$$

Example 1 Count the number of selections of 30 toys from 10 different types of toys if
a) At least two of each kind must be selected.
b) At least two but no more than five of each kind must be selected.

Solution
In part (a) the generating function for selecting each kind of toy is $(z^2 + z^3 + z^4 + z^5 + \cdots)$, so the composite generating function is $(z^2 + z^3 + z^4 + z^5 + \cdots)^{10}$. Factoring out a z^2 from each of the 10 factors, we obtain $z^{20}(1 + z + z^2 + z^3 + \cdots)^{10}$. We are interested in the coefficient of z^{30}, which is also the coefficient of z^{10} in $(1 + z + z^2 + z^3 + z^4 + \cdots)^{10}$. This is another way of seeing that the number of selections can be counted by first selecting two of each kind and then selecting 10 toys arbitrarily. Note that factoring a z^2 from each of the factors in the composite generating function automatically takes care of the combinatorial reasoning we used in this computation. Thus the number of selections is $C(19, 9)$.

In part (b) the composite generating function is

$$(z^2 + z^3 + z^4 + z^5)^{10} = z^{20}(1 + z + z^2 + z^3)^{10} = z^{20} \frac{1}{(1 - z)^{10}} (1 - z^4)^{10}$$

$$= z^{20} \left(1 - 10z^4 + \binom{10}{2} z^8 + \cdots \right) (1 + z + z^2 + \cdots)^{10}$$

The coefficient of z^{30} overall is the coefficient of z^{10} in $(1 + z + z^2 + \cdots)^{10}$, multiplied by the coefficient of z^0 in $(1 - z^4)^{10}$ (which is 1), minus the coefficient of z^6 in $(1 + z + z^2 + \cdots)^{10}$, multiplied by the coefficient of z^4 in $(1 - z^4)^{10}$ (which is -10), plus the coefficient of z^2 in $(1 + z + z^2 + \cdots)^{10}$, multiplied by the coefficient of z^8 in $(1 - z^4)^{10}$ (which is $\binom{10}{2}$). Therefore the number of selections of 30 toys in this case is $C(19, 9) - 10C(15, 9) + 45C(11, 9)$. In Chapter 3 it would have been necessary to use the Principle of Inclusion-Exclusion to perform this calculation, but once again this combinatorial reasoning is taken care of through algebraic manipulations of the generating function. $\qquad \square$

The algebraic methods in this section will give us a new method for solving problems like those in Example 1. In some sense these new methods will be easier because the algebra often seems more automatic and mechanical than in our previous methods.

Example 2   Suppose a combinatorics class consisting of one teacher and 25 students donates 20 dollars to a local charity. In how many ways can this be done if the teacher donates 0, 2, or 4 dollars and each student donates 0 or 1 dollar?

Solution
The composite generating function equals $(1 + z^2 + z^4)(1 + z)^{25}$ and the answer we are looking for is the coefficient of z^{20}. The overall coefficient of z^{20} is the coefficient of z^{20} in $(1 + z)^{25}$, plus the coefficient of z^{18} in $(1 + z)^{25}$, plus the coefficient of z^{16} in $(1 + z)^{25}$, which is $C(25, 20) + C(25, 18) + C(25, 16)$. $\qquad \square$

Example 3   a) In how many ways can 25 identical balls be distributed to nine different boxes if each box receives an odd number of balls?

Solution
In part (a) the generating function for distributing balls to any one box is $(z + z^3 + z^5 + z^7 + \cdots)$, so the composite generating function is $(z + z^3 + z^5 + z^7 + \cdots)^9$. The answer we are looking for is the coefficient of z^{25} in $z^9(1 + z^2 + z^4 + z^6 + \cdots)^9$, which equals the coefficient of z^{16} in $(1 + z^2 + z^4 + z^6 + \cdots)^9$ and also equals the coefficient of z^8 in $(1 + z + z^2 + \cdots)^9$. Therefore the number of distributions is $C(16, 8)$.

b) In how many ways can 25 identical balls be distributed to nine different boxes if each box receives 0, 3, or 7 balls?

Solution
In this case, the composite generating function is $(z^0 + z^3 + z^7)^9$. We can easily check that the only products of nine terms in this expansion whose exponents add up to 25 are sequences consisting of one z^7, six z^3's, and two z^0's. The number of sequences of this kind is $9!/(6!2!1!)$. Thus the number of allowable distributions is 252. $\qquad \square$

A Generating Function for Making Change

A problem that is slightly different than the previous ones involves making change for a dollar. Suppose we wish to make 100 cents in change using pennies, nickels, dimes, quarters, and half dollars. That is, we want to count the selections of the five different types of coins whose monetary value adds up to 100 cents.

We can make the selection by

1. Selecting half dollars
2. Selecting quarters
3. Selecting dimes
4. Selecting nickels
5. Selecting pennies

such that the total monetary value is 100 cents. Of course, since each kind of coin has a different monetary value, the size of a single selection depends on the kind of coin that is selected. The coins of each denomination are considered identical, so there is exactly one way to select n coins of one denomination, and the monetary value of this selection is n times the amount of each individual coin. Thus the generating function for selecting

1. Half dollars is $A_1(z) = (1 + z^{50} + z^{100} + \cdots)$.
2. Quarters is $A_2(z) = (1 + z^{25} + z^{50} + z^{75} + z^{100} + \cdots)$.
3. Dimes is $A_3(z) = (1 + z^{10} + z^{20} + \cdots)$.
4. Nickels is $A_4(z) = (1 + z^5 + z^{10} + \cdots)$.
5. Pennies is $A_5(z) = (1 + z + z^2 + \cdots)$.

The composite generating function for making change is $A_1(z)A_2(z)A_3(z)A_4(z)A_5(z)$. The number of ways to make 100 cents in change is the coefficient of z^{100}. To compute the coefficient of z^{100}, we may ignore the terms in each generating function and subsequent products that have degree greater than 100. We may as well assume that

$$A_1(z) = 1 + z^{50} + z^{100}$$
$$A_1(z)A_2(z) = 1 + z^{25} + 2z^{50} + 2z^{75} + 3z^{100}$$
$$A_1(z)A_2(z)A_3(z) = 1 + z^{10} + z^{20} + z^{25} + z^{30} + z^{35} + z^{40} + z^{45}$$
$$+ 3z^{50} + z^{55} + 3z^{60} + z^{65} + 3z^{70} + 3z^{75} + 3z^{80}$$
$$+ 3z^{85} + 3z^{90} + 3z^{95} + 6z^{100}$$

In the computation of $A_1(z)A_2(z)A_3(z)A_4(z)$ the coefficient of z^{5m} is the sum of all the coefficients in $A_1(z)A_2(z)A_3(z)$ from terms of degree less than or equal to $5m$. In other words, to make change for $5m$ cents using half dollars, quarters, dimes, and nickels, select some amount of half dollars, quarters, and dimes less than or equal to $5m$ in value and make up the rest of the $5m$ cents using nickels. Thus

$$A_1(z)A_2(z)A_3(z)A_4(z) = 1 + z^5 + 2z^{10} + 2z^{15} + 3z^{20} + 4z^{25} + 5z^{30} + 6z^{35}$$
$$+ 7z^{40} + 8z^{45} + 11z^{50} + 12z^{55} + 15z^{60}$$
$$+ 16z^{65} + 19z^{70} + 22z^{75} + 25z^{80} + 28z^{85}$$
$$+ 31z^{90} + 34z^{95} + 40z^{100}$$

To compute the coefficient of z^{100} in $A_1(z)A_2(z)A_3(z)A_4(z)A_5(z)$, we compute the sum of all the coefficients from terms with degree less than or equal to 100 in $A_1(z)A_2(z)A_3(z)A_4(z)$. Therefore the coefficient of z^{100} in the composite generating function is $1 + 1 + 2 + 2 + 3 + 4 + 5 + 6 + 7 + 8 + 11 + 12 + 15 + 16 + 19 + 22 + 25 + 28 + 31 + 34 + 40 = 292$. Since the coefficient of z^{100} is 292, there are 292 ways to change a dollar using half dollars, quarters, dimes, nickels, and pennies.

7.2
PROBLEMS

1. a) Find the coefficient of z^k in $(z^4 + z^5 + z^6 + z^7 + \cdots)^5$, $k \geq 20$.
    b) Find the coefficient of z^k in $(z + z^3 + z^5)(1 + z)^n$, $k \geq 5$.

2. Find a generating function for a_n, the number of ways to distribute n identical juggling balls to five different jugglers, if each juggler receives at most seven balls. Compute a_{25}.

3. Find a generating function for the number of ways to distribute n identical juggling balls to four different jugglers if each juggler receives at least 4 balls. Compute the number of distributions of 24 balls.

4. Let a_n be the number of ways n identical pencils can be distributed to 10 students with each student receiving between two and four pencils. Find a generating function for a_n and compute a_{30}.

5. What is the generating function for a_n, the number of ways to obtain a sum of n when 10 distinct dice are rolled? How many ways are there to get a sum of 35?

6. What is the generating function for a_n, the number of integers from 0 to 99,999, whose digits sum to n? How many of these integers have digits that sum to 27?

7. How many ways are there to paint 12 identical offices in a math department using six colors, assuming that each office is painted entirely one color, that three colors are available in unlimited amounts, and that there is only enough of the three other colors to color two offices each?

8. How many ways are there to distribute 24 dollars to 20 needy children and one needy parent if the parent receives either five or ten dollars and at most one dollar is given to each child?

9. Find a generating function for the number of ways to select n objects from a juggling bag containing 10 rings, 20 clubs, and 30 balls if at least one object of each kind must be selected. Compute the number of ways that 30 objects can be selected.

10. a) Find a generating function for the number of ways to select n coins from a group consisting of five identical pennies, five identical nickels, five identical dimes, and five identical quarters.
    b) Compute the number of ways to select 12 coins.

11. Show that the following formulas hold.
    a) $\dfrac{1}{1-z} = (1+z)(1+z^2)(1+z^4)(1+z^8)\cdots$

b) $\dfrac{1}{1-z} = (1 + z + z^2)(1 + z^3 + z^6)(1 + z^9 + z^{18})\cdots$

12. a) Find the coefficient of z^{2k} in $(1 + z^2 + z^4 + z^6 + \cdots)^n$.
   b) Find the coefficient of z^{2k+1} in $(1 + z^2 + z^4 + \cdots)(z^3 + z^5 + z^7 + \cdots)^3$.

ADVANCED
PROBLEMS

13. Find a generating function for a_n, the number of ways to select five of the first n integers so that any two of the integers selected differ by at least 3. Compute the number of selections possible from the first 25 integers.

14. In how many ways can a charity collect 20 dollars from 12 children and two adults if each child gives one or two dollars and each adult gives from one to five dollars?

15. Find a generating function and a formula for a_n, the number of ways to distribute n similar juggling balls to four different jugglers so that each juggler receives an odd number of juggling balls that is larger than or equal to three.

16. Find the number of ways to change a 20 dollar bill into bills of smaller denominations, namely, 1, 2, 5, and 10 dollar bills.

17. a) How many ways are there to distribute five apples, six bananas, and seven oranges to two different gorillas so that each gorilla receives nine pieces of fruit?
   b) Repeat part (a) if each gorilla receives at least one fruit of each kind.

18. Construct a generating function for a_n, the number of ways to distribute n juggling balls to four different jugglers if unlimited supplies of orange and white balls are available and every juggler receives at least two balls of each color.

19. a) Find the number of solutions in nonnegative integers of the equation $5w + 10x + 25y + 50z = 90$.
   b) Find the number of solutions in positive integers of the equation $5w + 10x + 25y + 50z = 125$.

20. a) Find a generating function for the number of ways to distribute n identical objects to 10 different boxes if each box receives zero, four, or eight balls.
   b) Compute the number of ways in which 12 objects can be distributed in part (a).

21. a) Find a generating function for the number of ways to select n cents bus fare from a group of coins containing 10 identical pennies, 10 identical nickels, 5 identical dimes, and 2 identical quarters.
   b) Compute the number of ways to select a fare of 60 cents.

22. In how many ways can a coin be flipped 25 times in a row so that exactly five heads occur and no more than seven tails occur consecutively?

23. Let $A(z) = a_0 + a_1 z + a_2 z + \cdots + a_n z^n + \cdots$. Show that $A(z)/(1-z)$ is a generating function for $s_n = \sum_{i=0}^{n} a_i$.

24. Find a generating function for a_n, the number of ways to select n dollars from bills of size 1, 1, 2, 5, 10, 10, 20, 50, if
   a) All bills are considered different.
   b) Bills of the same size are considered identical.

7.2

SUPPLEMENTARY
COMPUTER
PROJECT

1. Multiplying Generating Functions
   a) Write a program that will find the first n terms of the product of two generating functions, given the first n terms of each.
   b) Use the program in part (a) to compute the first 100 terms of $(1/(1-z))$ $(1/(1-z^5))(1/(1-z^{10}))(1/(1-z^{25}))(1/(1-z^{50}))$.

SECTION
7.3 PARTITIONS

An important mathematical application of combinatorics is in the study of partitions. In this section we discuss partitions of an integer and their generating functions.

DEFINITION **Partition of an Integer**

A partition of a positive integer n is an unordered collection of positive integers that add up to n. Normally we will write such a collection as a sum and list the integers of the partition in decreasing order.

The partitions of 4, for example, are $4, 3 + 1, 2 + 2, 2 + 1 + 1, 1 + 1 + 1 + 1$. We denote by $p(n)$ the number of partitions of a positive integer n, so $p(4) = 5$. The individual integers in a partition are called the **summands**. From the list of partitions of 4, we see that 4 has one partition with one summand, two partitions with two summands, one partition with three summands, and one partition with four summands.

A partition of an integer n can be thought of as a partition of n identical 1's into smaller subsets. Thus the study of partitions of an integer is also equivalent to the study of partitions of a collection of identical objects. A **partition** of a group of n identical objects divides the group into an unordered collection of subsets of various sizes. Thus such a partition is uniquely determined by the sizes of the respective subsets.

6	4 + 1 + 1	3 + 1 + 1 + 1
5 + 1	3 + 2 + 1	2 + 2 + 1 + 1
4 + 2	2 + 2 + 2	2 + 1 + 1 + 1 + 1
3 + 3		1 + 1 + 1 + 1 + 1 + 1

Figure 7.1
Partitions of 6

In counting partitions we have indicated that order is unimportant, so there are three different partitions of 6 with 3 summands: $4 + 1 + 1$, $3 + 2 + 1$, and $2 + 2 + 2$. (See Fig. 7.1.) On the other hand, in counting the number of solutions of an equation, order is important since the integers represent different variables. Therefore the number of positive integer solutions of $x_1 + x_2 + x_3 = 6$ is not 3, but $C(5, 2) = 10$. However, we can use a slightly different kind of equation to keep track of the number of partitions of an integer.

An arbitrary partition of an integer can be described by specifying the number of 1's, the number of 2's, and in general the number of integers of each type there are in the partition since the order of the integers is unimportant. If x_i is the number of i's in the partition, we have the equation $x_1 + 2x_2 + 3x_3 + \cdots + nx_n = n$. A partition can be constructed by first choosing a number of 1's, then a number of 2's, and so on until integers are chosen with a total numerical value of n. Thus the coefficient of z^n in $P_n(z) = (1 + z + z^2 + z^3 + \cdots)(1 + z^2 + z^4 + z^6 + \cdots)(1 + z^3 + z^6 + \cdots) \cdots (1 + z^n + z^{2n} + z^{3n} + \cdots)$ equals the number of partitions of the integer n. To obtain a generating function for the number of partitions of an arbitrary integer n, we look at the infinite product $P(z) = (1 + z + z^2 + z^3 + \cdots)(1 + z^2 + z^4 + z^6 + \cdots) \cdots (1 + z^i + z^{2i} + \cdots) \cdots$. To find $p(n)$, the number of partitions of the integer n, we again look at the coefficient of z^n since the coefficient in $P_n(z)$ will equal the coefficient in $P(z)$. We can also represent the geometric series $1 + z^i + z^{2i} + z^{3i} + \cdots$ by $1/(1 - z^i)$, obtaining

$$P(z) = \frac{1}{1 - z} \frac{1}{1 - z^2} \frac{1}{1 - z^3} \cdots \frac{1}{1 - z^i} \cdots$$

Example 1
a) Find a generating function for the number of partitions of the integer n into summands no larger than 6.
b) Find a generating function for the number of ways k distinct dice can add up to n.

Solution
a) In this case we use the generating function $A(z) = (1 + z + z^2 + \cdots)(1 + z^2 + z^4 + \cdots) \cdots (1 + z^6 + z^{12} + \cdots)$ since we can choose 1's, 2's,..., and 6's as summands. To find the number of partitions of n using summands no larger than 6, we look at the coefficient of z^n.
b) In this case each die is different, so we use the generating function $A(z) = (z + z^2 + z^3 + \cdots + z^6)^k$. The coefficient of z^n is the number of ways the k

different dice can add up to n. This is not the same as the number of partitions in part (a) with k summands because the dice are different, meaning that the order of the summands is important in part (b).   □

Example 2   Find the generating function for a_n, the number of ways to partition an integer n into distinct summands.

Solution
In this case, any integer $i \geq 1$ is used as a summand exactly once or not at all. The generating function for this individual choice is $(1 + z^i)$. Therefore the generating function for partitions with distinct summands is $B(z) = (1 + z)(1 + z^2)(1 + z^3) \cdots (1 + z^i) \cdots$.   □

A useful way of picturing a partition is by using a diagram known as a Ferrer's graph.

DEFINITION   Ferrer's Graph
The Ferrer's graph of a partition of n with k summands consists of k rows of dots, one row for each summand. The number of dots in a row equals the size of the corresponding summand, and the total number of dots in the graph of the partition is n. The row representing the largest summand is on top, and the rows are listed in order of decreasing size from top to bottom.

The **transpose** of a graph is obtained by interchanging the rows of dots with the columns. Clearly, the transpose is again the graph of a partition of n, and two graphs have the same transpose if and only if they are the same graph.

Example 3

Graph	Transpose
• • • • •	• • •
•	•
•	•
	•
	•
$5 + 1 + 1$	$3 + 1 + 1 + 1 + 1$
• •	• • • •
• •	• • •
• •	
•	
$2 + 2 + 2 + 1$	$4 + 3$

□

Sometimes the Ferrer's graph gives an interesting geometrical way of describing certain facts about partitions.

THEOREM 7.1 | The number of partitions of n into k or fewer summands is the same as the number of partitions of n having summands no larger than k.

Proof
Suppose the original graph represents a partition with k or fewer summands; that is, it has k or fewer rows in its Ferrer's graph. Then the transpose has k or fewer dots in its first and longest row and thus represents a partition having summands no larger than k. Each partition in the first set is paired with its unique transpose in the second set and vice versa. Therefore the one-to-one correspondence between graphs and their transposes also gives a one-to-one correspondence between partitions of n with k or fewer summands and the partitions of n having summands no larger than k, showing that the two sets of partitions are equal in size.

DEFINITION   We denote by $p_k(n)$, the number of partitions of n having k or fewer summands.

For any integer n, there is just one partition, n itself, with at most one summand. Therefore $p_1(n) = 1$. There is also just one partition with n summands and no partition with more than n summands. Therefore we see that $p_n(n) = 1 + p_{n-1}(n)$ and $p_k(n) = p_n(n)$, for $k \geq n$. We also have the following recurrence for these partition numbers, which we prove for all integers n and k satisfying $1 < k < n$.

THEOREM 7.2 If $1 < k < n$, then $p_k(n) = p_{k-1}(n) + p_k(n - k)$.

Proof
We count the $p_k(n)$ partitions of n with no more than k summands by separating them into two types:

1. Partitions with fewer than k summands
2. Partitions with exactly k summands

The type 1 partitions have no more than $k - 1$ summands, so the number of partitions of this type is precisely $p_{k-1}(n)$. Finally we note that there is a one-to-one correspondence between type 2 partitions and partitions of $n - k$ having k or fewer summands in the following way. Starting with a partition of n that has exactly k summands, we subtract one from each summand. By deleting all resulting 0's, we obtain a partition of $n - k$ with k or fewer summands. Since the reverse correspondence is also a function, we have a one-to-one correspondence between the two sets of partitions. Therefore the number of type 2 partitions is $p_k(n - k)$, establishing the preceding recurrence.

Using these results, we can easily obtain the following table.

Values of $p_k(n)$

$k =$	1	2	3	4	5	6	$\cdots$
$n =$							
1	1	1	1	1	1	1	$\cdots$
2	1	2	2	2	2	2	
3	1	2	3	3	3	3	
4	1	3	4	5	5	5	
5	1	3	5	6	7	7	
6	1	4	7	9	10	11	

Example 4 How many distributions are there of n identical objects to k identical boxes?

Solution
For arbitrary distributions, there is a one-to-one correspondence with partitions of n into k or fewer summands, which is $p_k(n)$. On the other hand, if each box receives at least one object, this is just the same as the number of partitions of n into k nonzero summands, which is $p_k(n) - p_{k-1}(n) = p_k(n - k)$. □

7.3
PROBLEMS

1. Find a generating function for the number of solutions of $2w + 4x + 5y + 7z = n$ consisting of
   a) Nonnegative integers.　　b) Positive integers.

2. List all partitions of the integer
   a) 5　　b) 9

3. Find a generating function for a_n, the number of partitions of n into
   a) Odd integers.
   b) Distinct odd integers.

4. Find a product whose expansion can be used to find the number of partitions of
   a) 12 with even summands.
   b) 10 with summands greater than 2.
   c) 9 with distinct summands.

5. Find a generating function for making n cents worth of change using pennies, nickels, dimes, and quarters if there are three distinguishable types of pennies, two distinguishable types of nickels, two distinguishable types of dimes, and two distinguishable types of quarters.

6. a) Show that the number of partitions of $n - 1$ is exactly equal to the number of partitions of n whose smallest summand is 1.

b) Describe the partitions of n that are counted by the expression $p(n) - p(n-1)$.

7. Use the Ferrer's graph to show that the number of partitions of n into exactly k summands equals the number of partitions of n having its largest summand equal to k.

ADVANCED
PROBLEMS

8. Show that the number of partitions of an integer n into summands of even size is equal to the number of partitions into summands such that each summand occurs an even number of times.

9. Show that the number of partitions of n into three summands is equal to the number of partitions of $2n$ into three summands of size less than n.

10. Show that the number of partitions of n is equal to the number of partitions of $2n$ into n summands.

11. a) Find a generating function for the number of partitions of an integer n into powers of 2.
    b) Find a generating function for the number of partitions of an integer n into distinct powers of 2.
    c) Using part (b), explain why each integer n can be expressed uniquely as a sum of distinct powers of 2.

12. Show algebraically that the generating function for partitions of n into distinct parts is equal to the generating function for partitions of n into odd parts, showing that these two types of partitions are always equal in number.

13. a) Find the number of partitions of n into summands no larger than 2.
    b) Find the number of partitions of n into at least $n-2$ summands.

14. Find a generating function for the number of partitions of n into
    a) Summands no larger than 4.
    b) Summands the largest of which is 4.
    c) At most four summands.
    d) Exactly four summands.

15. a) Find a generating function for the number of outcomes when n identical dice are rolled.
    b) Find a generating function for the number of ways to roll n identical dice and obtain an even sum.

16. Show that the number of partitions of $n + k$ into exactly k summands is equal to the number of partitions of n into summands no larger than k.

17. a) Find a generating function for the number of ways to distribute n identical objects to five identical boxes.
    b) Repeat part (a) if each box receives at least one object.
    c) Repeat part (a) if exactly two boxes receive no objects.

18. a) Explain why the number of partitions of 100 into four odd integers is greater than the number of partitions of 100 into four even integers.
    b) Which is larger, the total number of partitions of 100 into even integers or the total number of partitions of 100 into odd integers?

*19. Find a generating function for a_n, the number of different triangles with integral sides and perimeter n.

20. A partition is said to be self-conjugate if the Ferrer's graph of the partition is equal to its own transpose. Show that the number of self-conjugate partitions of n is equal to the number of partitions of n into distinct odd parts.

21. Show that the number of partitions of n into summands not divisible by 3 is equal to the number of partitions of n where no summand occurs more than twice.

7.3
SUPPLEMENTARY COMPUTER PROJECTS

1. Partitions of an Integer
    a) Write a program to compute $p(n)$, the number of partitions of n, for a given positive integer n.
    b) Write a program to list the partitions of n in lexicographic order, for a given positive integer n.

SECTION 7.4 EXPONENTIAL GENERATING FUNCTIONS

We now consider exponential generating functions. In certain situations these exponential generating functions can be used to count permutations with limited repetition as well as distributions of distinct objects. In contrast with the ordinary generating functions, these exponential generating functions are used to count sequences and other arrangements where the order is naturally important.

DEFINITION **Exponential Generating Function**
For any sequence $A = (a_0, a_1, a_2, \ldots, a_i, \ldots)$, we say that $E(z) = a_0 + a_1 z + \dfrac{a_2 z^2}{2!}$
$+ \cdots + \dfrac{a_i z^i}{i!} + \cdots$ is its exponential generating function.

Example 1 Suppose that n is a fixed positive integer. Find the exponential generating function for the sequence $P(n, 0), P(n, 1), P(n, 2), \ldots$.

Solution

Since $P(n,0) = 1$, $P(n,k) = n(n-1)(n-2)\cdots(n-k+1)$ for $0 < k \le n$, and $P(n,k) = 0$ for $k > n$, we obtain the exponential generating function

$$1 + nz + \frac{n(n-1)}{2!}z^2 + \cdots + \frac{n(n-1)\cdots(n-k+1)}{k!}z^k$$

$$+ \cdots + \frac{n!}{n!}z^n = \sum_{k=0}^{n} C(n,k)z^k = (1+z)^n$$

Note that this is the same as the ordinary generating function for the sequence $C(n,0)$, $C(n,1)$, $C(n,2)$, ... As with ordinary generating functions, in some circumstances exponential generating functions can be obtained by multiplying. □

Consider a sequential counting procedure of m different steps. Suppose that each step represents a different type of outcome and that the order of the outcomes is important as well as the number of outcomes of each type. The outcomes of step j in the counting procedure will be represented by the exponential generating function $e_0 + e_1 z + e_2 z^2/2! + \cdots + e_i z^i/i! + \cdots$ if there are e_i ways to have i outcomes of type i, for every $i \ge 0$. In that case we also have a Multiplication Principle for exponential generating functions.

THE MULTIPLICATION PRINCIPLE FOR EXPONENTIAL GENERATING FUNCTIONS   Consider a sequential counting procedure consisting of m different steps, where $E_j(z)$ represents the exponential generating function of step j. If the order of the outcomes is important, the number of ways that i outcomes can occur overall is the coefficient of $z^i/i!$ in the product $E_1(z)E_2(z)\cdots E_m(z)$.

Proof

The product of the m exponential generating functions generates the collection of all products obtained by multiplying together a term from each individual exponential generating function. Suppose that $c_1 z^{i_1}/i_1! c_2 z^{i_2}/i_2! \cdots c_m z^{i_m}/i_m!$ is such a product, whose overall exponent sum is n. This product represents the outcomes consisting of i_1 outcomes of type 1, i_2 outcomes of type 2, ..., and i_m outcomes of type m. Since each outcome can occur in $n!/(i_1! i_2! \cdots i_m!)$ different orders, the product of these m terms represents $c_1 c_2 \cdots c_m n!/(i_1! i_2! \cdots i_m!)$ different sequences of outcomes. This product also contributes the same amount to the coefficient of $z^n/n!$ in the product of the individual exponential generating functions, $E_1(z)E_2(z)\cdots E_m(z)$. Therefore $E_1(z)E_2(z)\cdots E_m(z)$ is the exponential generating function of the entire procedure.

Example 2   Find the number of sequences of length 8 that can be formed using 1, 2, or 3 a's; 2, 3, or 4 b's; and 0, 2, or 4 c's.

Solution

The exponential generating function for the selection of a's is $E_1(z) = (z/1! + z^2/2! + z^3/3!)$. Similarly the exponential generating function for the selection of b's is

$E_2(z) = (z^2/2! + z^3/3! + z^4/4!)$, and the exponential generating function for the selection of c's is $E_3(z) = (1 + z^2/2! + z^4/4!)$. In the product of these three individual generating functions, $E_1(z)E_2(z)E_3(z)$, there are four different products of three terms that contribute to the coefficient of $z^8/8!$. One of these products is $(z/1!)(z^3/3!)(z^4/4!)$, which contributes $8!/(1!3!4!)$ to the coefficient of $z^8/8!$. The other three products are $(z^2/2!)(z^2/2!)(z^4/4!)$, $(z^2/2!)(z^4/4!)(z^2/2!)$, and $(z^3/3!) \cdot (z^3/3!)(z^2/2!)$. Thus we see that the coefficient of $z^8/8!$ in the overall exponential generating function equals $8!/(1!3!4!) + 8!/(2!2!4!) + 8!/(2!4!2!) + 8!/(3!3!2!)$. This also equals the number of sequences of length 8 satisfying the preceding constraints. $\qquad\square$

When analyzing a counting procedure that involves the arrangement of m different types of objects, a selection with unlimited repetition allowed has the exponential generating function

$$1 + z/1! + z^2/2! + z^3/3! + \cdots = e^z \qquad \textbf{(7-6)}$$

We have a few other formulas that are helpful in computing the coefficients of exponential generating functions when the steps in a counting procedure involve selections with limited repetition. For a selection of at least one object of a certain kind, the exponential generating function is

$$z/1! + z^2/2! + z^3/3! + \cdots = e^z - 1 \qquad \textbf{(7-7)}$$

Similarly, for a selection of at least two objects of a certain kind, the exponential generating function is

$$z^2/2! + z^3/3! + \cdots = e^z - z - 1 \qquad \textbf{(7-8)}$$

For a selection involving an even number of objects of a certain kind, the exponential generating function is

$$1 + z^2/2! + z^4/4! + \cdots = (e^z + e^{-z})/2 \qquad \textbf{(7-9)}$$

Likewise, for a selection involving an odd number of objects of a certain kind, the exponential generating function is

$$z + z^3/3! + z^5/5! + \cdots = (e^z - e^{-z})/2 \qquad \textbf{(7-10)}$$

Example 3   a) Find the exponential generating function for the number of ways to form a sequence of length n using any number of five different types of symbols. Use this exponential generating function to compute the number of sequences of length 10 that can be formed.

b) Repeat part (a) if instead each type of symbol must be used at least once

Solution

a) The individual exponential generating function for selecting any one type of symbol is $e^z = 1 + z + z^2/2! + \cdots$, so the composite exponential generating function is $(e^z)^5 = e^{5z}$. The coefficient of $z^n/n!$ in the expansion of e^{5z} is 5^n. Therefore the number of sequences of length 10 is 5^{10}, which coincides with the answer we would have obtained using the regular Multiplication Principle in Chapter 2.

b) In this case, the individual exponential generating function for selecting any one type of symbol is $e^z - 1 = z + z^2/2! + z^3/3! + \cdots$, so the overall exponential generating function is $(e^z - 1)^5 = e^{5z} - 5e^{4z} + 10e^{3z} - 10e^{2z} + 5e^z - 1$. The coefficient of $z^{10}/10!$ is $5^{10} - 5 \times 4^{10} + 10 \times 3^{10} - 10 \times 2^{10} + 5$. Therefore this gives us the number of sequences of length 10, which coincides with the answer we would have obtained using the Principle of Inclusion-Exclusion in Chapter 3.   □

Example 4   Find the number of ways to distribute n different objects to five different boxes if
a) An even number of objects are distributed to box 5.
b) A positive even number of objects are distributed to box 5.

Solution
a) If an unlimited number of objects are distributed to boxes 1–4 and an even number of objects are distributed to box 5, we obtain the exponential generating function $(e^z)^4(e^z + e^{-z})/2 = (e^{5z} + e^{3z})/2$. Since the coefficient of $z^n/n!$ is $(5^n + 3^n)/2$, this is also equal to the number of distributions of n different objects.

b) If an unlimited number of objects are distributed to boxes 1–4 and a positive even number of objects are distributed to box 5, we obtain the exponential generating function $(e^z)^4((e^z + e^{-z})/2 - 1) = (e^{5z} + e^{3z})/2 - e^{4z}$. Since the coefficient of $z^n/n!$ in this expression is equal to $(5^n + 3^n)/2 - 4^n$, this is also equal to the number of distributions of n different objects.   □

7.4
PROBLEMS

1. Find the exponential generating function for the number of ways to arrange $n \geq 0$ letters selected at random from the word MISSISSIPPI.

2. Find the exponential generating function for a_n, the number of different arrangements of n objects chosen from five different types of objects with each object appearing
    a) At least three times.   b) No more than seven times.

3. a) Find the exponential generating function for the number of ways to place n travelers into three different hotel rooms with at least one person in each room.
    b) Repeat part (a) if each room must receive an odd number of travelers.

4. Find the number of n-digit ternary sequences that contain an odd number of 0's and an even number of 1's.

5. a) Find the number of n-digit sequences constructed from the digits $\{1, 2, 3, 4, 5\}$ that contain an even number of 1's and an even number of 2's.
    b) Repeat part (a) if the sequences must contain a positive even number of 1's and a positive even number of 2's.

6. Find the exponential generating function for the number of ways to distribute n different objects to six different jugglers if each juggler receives between three and five objects.

7. Determine the exponential generating function for a_n, the number of different sequences of length n that can be constructed from four different types of objects if
    a) No more than i objects of type i are used.
    b) At least i objects of type i are used.

8. Find the exponential generating function for a_n, the number of n-letter strings with
    a) No vowel used more than once.
    b) Every vowel used at least once.

9. Find an exponential generating function for the number of ordered partitions of an integer n. (See Problem 29, Section 2.4.)

10. Find the number of strings of length n that can be constructed using the alphabet $\{a, b, c, d, e\}$ if
    a) b occurs an odd number of times.
    b) Both a and b occur an odd number of times.

11. Ships often send messages to each other by placing a sequence of colored flags on a pole. If a ship has 4 yellow flags, 4 orange flags, and 4 red flags, how many sequences of 10 flags are possible?

12. Determine the number of ways to arrange red, white, blue, and yellow poker chips in a stack of height n if the stack must contain an even number of red chips and at least one blue chip.

ADVANCED PROBLEMS

13. Use an exponential generating function to find the number of n-digit ternary sequences in which no digit appears exactly once.

14. Use an exponential generating function to find the number of n-digit sequences that can be constructed from the digits $\{0, 1, 2, 3\}$ for which the total number of 0's and 1's is even.

15. Find the number of ways to distribute 10 different toys to four different children if
    a) The first child receives at least one toy.
    b) The second child receives at least two toys.
    c) The first child receives at least one toy and the second child receives at least two toys.

16. Find the exponential generating function for the number of ways to distribute n different objects to five people if person 1 receives fewer objects than person 2 and the total number of objects received by persons 1 and 2 is no more than 5.

REVIEW PROBLEMS

1. a) Find a generating function for the number of ways to distribute n identical balls to 10 different boxes if each box receives 0, 5, or 9 balls.
    b) Compute the number of ways that 23 balls can be distributed.

2. Find a generating function for the number of
    a) Partitions of n whose largest summand is 6.
    b) Ways that 10 distinct dice can add up to n.
    c) Nonnegative integer solutions of $x_1 + 2x_2 + 3x_3 + 4x_4 + 5x_5 + 6x_6 = n$.

3. Find the coefficient of x^{12} in each of these generating functions.
    a) $(z + z^2 + z^3 + \cdots)(z^2 + z^3 + z^4 + \cdots)(z^3 + z^4 + z^5 + \cdots)$
    b) $(z + z^2 + z^3 + \cdots)(z^2 + z^4 + z^6 + \cdots)(z^3 + z^6 + z^9 + \cdots)$

4. Find an exponential generating function and use it to compute the number of 10-digit ternary sequences that contain a positive even number of 0's.

5. Which is greater:
    a) The number of partitions of n into positive even summands?
    b) The number of partitions of n, where each summand appears a positive even number of times?

6. a) Find a generating function for a_n, the number of ways to distribute n balls, from an unlimited supply of red and blue balls, to five different boxes.
    b) Repeat part (a) if no more than three balls per box are allowed.

7. Find a generating function for the number of ways to distribute n different objects to four different boxes if at least one object is distributed to box 1 and an odd number of objects are distributed to box 4.

8. Find a generating function for the number of partitions of an integer n into exactly three positive integer summands.

9. a) Using a generating function find the total number of outcomes when six identical dice are rolled.
    b) Using a generating function find the total number of ways to obtain an even sum when six identical dice are rolled.

10. a) Find a generating function for the number of solutions of $x_1 + 3x_2 + 6x_3 + 12x_4 = n$.
    b) Compute the number of solutions for $n = 25$.

11. Find a generating function for changing n cents into pennies, nickels, and dimes if there are two types of pennies, two types of nickels, and two types of dimes.

CHAPTER

7

SUMMARY

In Chapter 7 we used generating functions to count selections and arrangements with limited repetition, solutions of linear equations, distributions, and partitions of an integer n. Ordinary generating functions are used to count distributions of identical objects and arrangements where the order is not important. On the other hand, exponential generating functions are used to count distributions of different objects and arrangements where the order is important. Generating functions are a standard topic in most combinatorics books, and the reader can check either of the books [2, 3] for a slightly different point of view. Ordinary generating functions can be used to analyze many problems involving partitions of an integer into summands. Partitions are an important topic in number theory and either of the number theory texts [4, 5] can be consulted for more on this topic. Generating functions are also useful in probability, and the reader can consult any of the standard probability texts such as [6] for more about this subject.

BIBLIOGRAPHY

1. Niven, I. Formal power series. *Amer. Math. Monthly*, 76 (1969) 871–889.

Combinatorics
2. Riordan, J. *An Introduction to Combinatorial Analysis*. New York: Wiley & Sons, 1958.
3. Berge, C. *Principles of Combinatorics*. New York: Academic Press, 1971.

Number Theory
4. Niven, I., and H. Zuckerman. *An Introduction to the Theory of Numbers*, 4th edition. New York: Wiley & Sons, 1980.
5. Hardy, G., and E. Wright. *An Introduction to the Theory of Numbers*, 4th edition. London: Oxford University Press, 1960.

Probability
6. Feller, W. *An Introduction to Probability Theory and Its Application*, 3rd edition. New York: Wiley & Sons, 1968.

CHAPTER

8

RECURRENCE RELATIONS

The formulas and counting principles we derived in Chapters 2 and 3 are usually the most direct ways for counting the number of objects in a finite set. However these counting techniques often prove inadequate for many combinatorial problems that are encountered in computer science and other areas. Another important counting technique uses recurrence relations to define the terms of a sequence.

RECURRENCE RELATION MODELS

We have already encountered several examples of recurrence relations. In our study of Pascal's triangle, we saw that combinations satisfied the recurrence $C(n, k) = C(n - 1, k) + C(n - 1, k - 1)$, which expressed a number in the nth row as a sum of two numbers in the $n - 1$st row. This, together with the fact that $C(n, 0) = C(n, n) = 1$, allowed us to compute any entry in Pascal's triangle. Among the other sequences we have encountered are arithmetic sequences that can be described by a recurrence of the form $a_n = a_{n-1} + d$, for some common difference d, and geometric sequences that can be described by a recurrence $a_n = ra_{n-1}$, for some common ratio r. Either of these recurrences, together with an initial term a_0, uniquely determines the sequence in question.

DEFINITION **Recurrence Relation**

A recurrence relation for a sequence $A = (a_0, a_1, a_2, \ldots, a_n, \ldots)$ is a formula that relates a_n to one or more of the preceding terms $a_0, a_1, \ldots, a_{n-1}$ in a uniform way, for any integer n greater than or equal to some initial integer k. The values of the first terms needed to start computing with a recurrence relation are called the initial conditions.

In many instances it is possible to obtain a closed formula for a_n from a recurrence relation. In Section 8.2 and 8.3 we will see how to solve many linear recurrence relations with constant coefficients, however, there are certainly no general techniques that will enable us to solve all recurrence relations for a closed formula. If we can devise a recurrence relation to describe the solutions of a sequence of counting problems and also determine the initial conditions, it is usually not difficult to program a calculator or a computer to compute the terms of the sequence. From a computational standpoint, a recurrence relation can sometimes be more useful than a formula, especially when we need to compute all the terms of a sequence up to some point and not just a single term.

Example 1 Fibonacci Numbers

The following problem was originally posed in the thirteenth century by the mathematician Fibonacci. Initially we start with a pair of newborn rabbits, one male and one female. At the end of the second month, and each month thereafter, the female gives birth to a new pair of rabbits, one of each sex. Each new pair of rabbits also starts reproducing in a like manner at the end of their second month. How many pairs of rabbits will there be at the end of one year?

Solution

Let a_n be the number of pairs of rabbits there will be at the beginning of month n. We wish to compute a_{13}. Obviously $a_1 = 1$ and $a_2 = 1$, but at the end of month 2, a new pair of rabbits is born, so $a_3 = 2$. At the beginning of month 3, there is one newborn pair of rabbits and one mature pair. Thus at the end of month 3, another new pair of rabbits are born making $a_4 = 3$. In this same manner, we can derive a recurrence relation for a_n, from which we can compute the successive values of a_n until a_{13} is obtained. At the beginning of month $n - 1$, there will be a_{n-1} pairs of rabbits and of these there are a_{n-2} pairs of mature rabbits. At the beginning of month n, there will be a_{n-1} pairs of mature rabbits and a_{n-2} pairs of newborn rabbits. Therefore $a_n = a_{n-1} + a_{n-2}$.

The sequence of numbers satisfying the recurrence relation $a_n = a_{n-1} + a_{n-2}$ and the initial conditions $a_1 = 1$ and $a_2 = 1$ is now known as the Fibonacci sequence, and the terms of the sequence are called Fibonacci numbers. It turns out to be such an interesting and widely encountered sequence that there is even a magazine, the *Fibonacci Quarterly*, devoted primarily to research related to the Fibonacci numbers.

Using the relation $a_n = a_{n-1} + a_{n-2}$ and the values that have already been determined, we continue computing the terms of the sequence:

$$a_5 = a_4 + a_3 = 5$$
$$a_6 = a_5 + a_4 = 8$$
$$a_7 = a_6 + a_5 = 13$$
$$a_8 = a_7 + a_6 = 21$$
$$a_9 = a_8 + a_7 = 34$$
$$a_{10} = a_9 + a_8 = 55$$
$$a_{11} = a_{10} + a_9 = 89$$
$$a_{12} = a_{11} + a_{10} = 144$$
$$a_{13} = a_{12} + a_{11} = 233$$

Thus we see that there will be 233 pairs of rabbits at the end of a year. In a similar manner, we could compute as many terms of the Fibonacci sequence as desired. In the next section we will also see how to derive a closed formula for a_n. ☐

Suppose we have a set of similar counting problems, one for each nonnegative integer n. We model each problem by a counting procedure, and let a_n represent the number of outcomes for the procedure with n steps. To obtain a recurrence relation for a_n, break the procedure into two (or more) parts. Often the first part will be either the first or last step of the procedure, and the other part will be the remaining steps of the procedure. We attempt to count the number of outcomes of each part in terms of n and a_j, with $j < n$, and combine these in an appropriate manner to obtain a recurrence for a_n. As usual, when a problem is broken into a sequence of events, we use the Multiplication Principle to compute the total number of outcomes (as in Example 2); and when it is broken into mutually exclusive cases, we use the Addition Principle to compute the total number of outcomes (as in Example 1).

Example 2   Find a recurrence relation for the number of ways to arrange n distinct objects in n distinct positions.

Solution
Let a_n denote the number of arrangements of n objects. There are n places to put the first object, and after that there are $n - 1$ different positions for the remaining $n - 1$ objects. Since $n - 1$ objects can be arranged in a_{n-1} ways, the total number of arrangements of n objects is thus given by the recurrence relation $a_n = na_{n-1}$. Obviously there is just one way to arrange one object, so $a_1 = 1$. Thus we obtain $a_2 = 2 \times 1 = 2!$, $a_3 = 3 \times 2 \times 1 = 3!$, $a_4 = 4 \times 3 \times 2 \times 1 = 4!, \ldots$, and $a_n = n(n-1)(n-2)\ldots 2 \times 1 = n!$, computing our previous formula for the number of permutations of n different objects in a slightly different way. ☐

Example 3   Find a recurrence relation for the number of binary sequences of length n with
a) No consecutive 0's.
b) No block of three consecutive 0's.

Solution

a) Let a_n be the number of binary sequences of length n that contain no consecutive 0's. We obtain a recurrence relation for a_n by considering the start of such a sequence. A sequence of length n with no consecutive 0's may start with a 1, which can be followed by any sequence of length $n - 1$ that contains no consecutive 0's. On the other hand, a sequence may start with a 0, in which case it must be immediately followed by a 1. The remaining digits in such a sequence can be any sequence of length $n - 2$ that contains no consecutive 0's. Thus we obtain the recurrence relation $a_n = a_{n-1} + a_{n-2}$ with the initial conditions $a_0 = 1$ (the empty sequence) and $a_1 = 2$.

b) Similarly let b_n be the number of binary sequences of length n that contain no block of three consecutive 0's. A sequence of length n with no three consecutive 0's may start with a 1 and be followed by any sequence of length $n - 1$ that contains no three consecutive 0's, or it may start with a 01 and be followed by any sequence of length $n - 2$ that contains no three consecutive 0's, or it may start with a 001 and be followed by any sequence of length $n - 3$ that contains no three consecutive 0's. In this case, we obtain the recurrence relation $b_n = b_{n-1} + b_{n-2} + b_{n-3}$, satisfying the initial conditions $b_0 = 1$, $b_1 = 2$, and $b_2 = 4$. □

Example 4   Suppose we have n lines in a plane. We assume that every pair of lines intersect, but that no three lines intersect in a common point. How many regions is the plane divided into by these n lines? (See Fig. 8.1.)

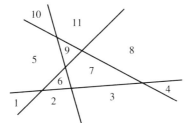

Figure 8.1

Solution

Let a_n be the number of regions into which the plane is divided by n lines. Obviously $a_1 = 2$ because a single line always divides the plane in half. A second line intersecting the first will divide each of these regions in half, so $a_2 = 4$. A third line, however, does not divide each of these four regions in half. The third line crosses from one region to another each time it crosses one of the previous lines. Since the third line crosses the first two lines at two different points, it passes through precisely three of the four regions. Thus a third line always divides three of the regions in half, meaning that $a_3 = 7$.

In general, suppose that $n - 1$ lines are drawn dividing the plane into a_{n-1} regions. When the nth line is drawn, it intersects each of the previous lines, for a total of $n - 1$ intersection points. Therefore the nth line divides precisely n of the previous regions in half, creating n additional regions. We obtain the recurrence relation $a_n = a_{n-1} + n$, for $n \geq 2$. Since $a_1 = 2$, we obtain $a_2 = 2 + 2$, $a_3 = 2 + 2 + 3, \ldots, a_n = 2 + 2 + 3 + \cdots + n = 1 + n(n+1)/2$.   □

Example 5   A bank pays 10% interest at the end of each year on the money in an IRA account at the beginning of the year. Find a recurrence relation for a_n, the amount of money in the account at the end of year n if
a) 2000 dollars is put in the account at the end of year 1 only.
b) 2000 dollars is put in the account at the end of each year.

Solution
In part (a) the amount of money in the account at the end of any year is the amount of money at the beginning of the year plus 10% interest, for $n > 1$. Thus $a_n = a_{n-1} + 0.10a_{n-1} = 1.1a_{n-1}$ and initially $a_1 = 2000$. Obviously this is just the geometric sequence $a_n = 2000(1.10)^{n-1}$. In part (b) the amount of money in the account at the end of any year is the amount at the beginning of the year plus 10% interest and a deposit of 2000 dollars. Thus we obtain the recurrence relation $a_n = 1.10a_{n-1} + 2000$ with the initial condition $a_1 = 2000$. An iterative computation shows that $a_n = 2000(1.10)^{n-1} + 2000(1.10)^{n-2} + \cdots + 2000(1.10) + 2000 = (2000 - 2000(1.10)^n)/(1 - 1.10) = 20000(1.10)^n - 20000$.   □

Example 6   A student visits an ice cream store once a day. During each visit he buys either a banana split for two dollars or a frozen yogurt in one of two possible flavors for one dollar. Find a recurrence relation for the number of different ways to spend n dollars at the ice cream store.

Solution
Let a_n be the number of ways to spend n dollars at the ice cream store. To find a relation between a_n and the previous terms of the sequence, consider the last purchase. If his last purchase was a banana split, there were a_{n-2} other ways to spend the first $n - 2$ dollars. On the other hand, if his last purchase was a frozen yogurt, there were a_{n-1} other ways to spend the first $n - 1$ dollars and two ways to choose the flavor of the yogurt. Thus we obtain the recurrence relation $a_n = a_{n-2} + 2a_{n-1}$, with the initial conditions $a_0 = 1$ and $a_1 = 2$. This is an example of a homogeneous linear recurrence relation with constant coefficients. We discuss techniques for solving these recurrence relations later in this chapter.   □

Example 7   Suppose that $x_1, x_2, x_3, \ldots, x_n$ are real numbers. The product of these n numbers can be computed in many ways by $n - 1$ successive multiplications involving two factors. In how many ways can the product be formed
a) If the numbers can be arranged in any order?
b) If the given order of the numbers must be maintained?

Solution
a) For $n = 2$, there are two ways to multiply two numbers, namely, $x_1 * x_2$ and $x_2 * x_1$. Suppose that $n \geq 2$ numbers $x_1, x_2, \ldots, x_n$ can be multiplied together

in a_n different ways. We can obtain a recurrence relation for a_{n+1} in the following manner. From each product of $x_1, x_2, \ldots, x_n$ we can obtain a product of $x_1, x_2, \ldots, x_n, x_{n+1}$ by either
i) Multiplying the product of $x_1, x_2, \ldots, x_n$ by x_{n+1} on either side.
ii) Multiplying either factor of one of the $n-1$ multiplications in the product of $x_1, x_2, \ldots, x_n$ on either side by x_{n+1}.
For $n=3$ we obtain the following 12 products, six from each product of x_1 and x_2.

$$
\begin{array}{ll}
x_3 * (x_1 * x_2) & x_3 * (x_2 * x_1) \\
(x_1 * x_2) * x_3 & (x_2 * x_1) * x_3 \\
(x_3 * x_1) * x_2 & (x_3 * x_2) * x_1 \\
(x_1 * x_3) * x_2 & (x_2 * x_3) * x_1 \\
x_1 * (x_3 * x_2) & x_2 * (x_3 * x_1) \\
x_1 * (x_2 * x_3) & x_2 * (x_1 * x_3)
\end{array}
$$

In general we obtain $2 + 4(n-1) = 4n - 2$ products of $x_1, x_2, \ldots, x_{n+1}$ from each product of $x_1, x_2, \ldots, x_n$. Thus $a_{n+1} = (4n-2)a_n$, for $n \geq 2$. By iterating this relation, we find that

$$
\begin{aligned}
a_{n+1} &= (4n-2)(4n-6) \ldots 6 \times 2 \\
&= 2^n(2n-1)(2n-3) \ldots 3 \times 1 \\
&= 2^n(2n)!/(2n(2n-2)(2n-4) \ldots 2) \\
&= 2^n(2n)!/(2^n n!) \\
&= (2n)!/n!
\end{aligned}
$$

b) Suppose we let b_n represent the number of products of n different numbers $x_1, x_2, \ldots, x_n$ in their given order. For $n = 2$, there is just one product, $x_1 * x_2$, with the numbers in their given order. For $n = 3$, there are two such products, $(x_1 * x_2) * x_3$ and $x_1 * (x_2 * x_3)$, so $b_2 = 1$ and $b_3 = 2$. By defining $b_1 = 1$, we can obtain a recurrence relation for b_{n+1} in the following way. Consider the last of the n multiplications in the product of the $n+1$ numbers $x_1, x_2, \ldots, x_{n+1}$. This last multiplication involves a product of the first i numbers and a product of the last $n+1-i$ numbers for some $i = 1, 2, \ldots, n$. Thus we obtain the recurrence $b_{n+1} = b_1 b_n + b_2 b_{n-1} + \cdots + b_i b_{n+1-i} + \cdots + b_n b_1$. Although it is difficult to compute b_{n+1} directly from this recurrence relation, we can compute b_{n+1} from the answer in part (a). Since $n+1$ numbers can be arranged in one of $(n+1)!$ different orders, it is clear that $b_{n+1} = a_{n+1}/(n+1)! = C(2n,n)/(n+1)$. These numbers that occur in many combinatorial problems are called the Catalan numbers and are usually denoted by $C_n = \dfrac{1}{n+1}\dbinom{2n}{n}$. $\square$

8.1
PROBLEMS

1. The numbers of the sequence given by $a_0 = A/2$, $(A > 0)$ $a_n = a_{n-1}/2 + A/(2a_{n-1})$, for $n \geq 1$, approach the square root of A. Compute the first five terms of this sequence and their squares for $A = 12$.

2. a) A man climbs a set of 10 steps, taking either 1 or 2 steps in each stride. In how many ways can he climb all 10 steps?
    b) A man climbs a set of 10 steps, taking either 1, 2, or 3 steps in each stride. In how many ways can he climb all 10 steps?

3. a) Consider a $1 \times n$ chessboard. Suppose we can color each square of a chessboard either black or white at random. Let a_n be the number of ways to color the chessboard so that no two white squares are adjacent. Find a recurrence relation for a_n.
    b) Repeat part (a) if instead each square can be colored red, white, or black.

4. Find a recurrence relation for the number of ways to count out bills (order is important) until n dollars are counted
    a) Using one-dollar bills and two-dollar bills.
    b) Using one-, two-, and five-dollar bills.

5. a) Find a recurrence relation for the amount of money in a savings account after n years if the interest rate is 6% and initially the account has 1000 dollars.
    b) Consider the same problem if 100 additional dollars are deposited into the account at the end of each year.
    c) Solve each of these recurrence relations.

6. Find a recurrence relation (and initial conditions) for the number of ways to distribute n distinct objects to four distinct recipients.

7. Find a recurrence relation (and initial conditions) for the number of ways to stack colored flags on an n-foot flag pole if red and white flags are one foot high and blue flags are two feet high.

8. Find a recurrence relation (and initial conditions) for the number of ternary sequences which
    a) Contain no consecutive 0's.
    b) Contain no block of three consecutive 0's.

9. Find a recurrence relation for the number of ways to select a subset (any size, including the empty set) from the set $\{1, 2, 3, \ldots, n\}$ that does not contain a pair of consecutive numbers.

ADVANCED PROBLEMS

10. Find a recurrence relation for the number of ways to pair off $2n$ people for n simultaneous tennis matches.

11. Find a recurrence relation for the number of ways to stack n poker chips if each poker chip is red, white, or blue and
    a) No adjacent chips have the same color.
    b) Blue chips may be adjacent, but no red chips are adjacent and no white chips are adjacent.

12. A husband and wife decide to have one child each year until they have two
     sons, and then they will stop having children. Let a_n be the number of
     sequences of at most n children ending with the second boy. Find a recurrence
     relation for a_n. Find a closed formula for a_n.

13. Find a recurrence relation for the number of regions created by n mutually
     intersecting planes in 3-dimensional space if every three planes meet in one
     point, but no four planes have a point in common.

14. Find a recurrence relation for the number of permutations of the integers
     $\{1, 2, 3, \ldots, n\}$ that have no integer more than one place removed from its
     natural position in the order.

15. Find a recurrence relation for the number of ternary sequences of length n with
     no 1 appearing to the left of any 2.

16. Find a recurrence relation for the number of ways to pair off with non-
     intersecting lines $2n$ different points on a circle.

17. Find a recurrence relation for the number of ways to distribute n coins to k
     different persons so that each person receives between two and four coins
     a) If all the coins are identical.
     b) If three types of coins are available.

18. Let B_n be the number of partitions of a set with n elements. (The numbers in
     this problem are called Bell numbers, after Eric Temple Bell, 1883–1960.)
     Using $B_0 = 1$, show that for $n \geq 1$,

$$B_n = \sum_{i=0}^{n-1} \binom{n-1}{i} B_i$$

19. Let $L_0, L_1, L_2, \ldots$ be the Lucas sequence that is the unique sequence satisfying
     $L_0 = 2$, $L_1 = 1$, and $L_n = L_{n-1} + L_{n-2}$ for $n \geq 2$.
     a) Show that $L_0 + L_1 + L_2 + \cdots + L_n = L_{n+2} - 1$.
     b) Derive a formula for $L_1 + L_3 + L_5 + \cdots + L_{2n-1}$.

20. For a nonnegative integer n, write $[x]_n = s(n, 0) + s(n, 1)x + s(n, 2)x^2 + \cdots +$
     $s(n, n)x^n$, where $[x]_n = x(x - 1)(x - 2) \cdots (x - n + 1)$. The numbers obtained
     in this way are called the Stirling numbers of the first kind.
     a) Show that $s(n, 0) = 0$ and $s(n, n) = 1$.
     b) Show that these numbers satisfy the recurrence relation $s(n, k) =$
        $s(n - 1, k - 1) - (n - 1)s(n - 1, k)$.
     c) Make a table of Stirling numbers of the first kind for $n = 1, 2, \ldots, 6$.

21. Let $a_{n,k}$ be the number of ways to pick k numbers from the set $\{1, 2, \ldots, n\}$ so
     that no two consecutive numbers are chosen. Find a recurrence relation for
     $a_{n,k}$.

*22. Find a recurrence relation for the number of regions into which a convex n-gon
      is divided by its diagonals if no three diagonals intersect at a common point.

*23.   We want to cut a $1 \times n$ strip into unit squares. In how many ways can this be done if at each step
       a) We cut one of the strips consisting of more than one square in two?
       b) We cut all of the strips consisting of more than one square in two?

*24.   Show that the sequence $\sqrt{6}, \sqrt{6 + \sqrt{6}}, \sqrt{6 + \sqrt{6 + \sqrt{6}}}, \ldots$ converges to 3.
       Hint: It may help to consider the recurrence $a_n^2 = 6 + a_{n-1}$.

8.1

SUPPLEMENTARY COMPUTER PROJECT

1.   A Stamp Problem
     Suppose we are given one-cent, two-cent, and five-cent stamps, each in unlimited supply. Let a_n be the number of ways to obtain n cents postage if the order in which the stamps are issued is important.
     a) Find a recurrence relation for a_n.
     b) Use the recurrence relation in part (a) to find a_{24} iteratively.
     c) Write a short program for computing a_n that does not use any arrays whatsoever.

SECTION 8.2   HOMOGENEOUS LINEAR RECURRENCES

In the next two sections we discuss some methods for solving linear recurrence relations with constant coefficients.

DEFINITION   Linear Recurrences

If $A = (a_0, a_1, a_2, \ldots, a_n, \ldots)$ is a sequence, we say that A satisfies a linear recurrence relation with constant coefficients if for all $n \geq m$, $a_n = c_1 a_{n-1} + c_2 a_{n-2} + \cdots + c_m a_{n-m} + g(n)$, where $c_1, c_2, \ldots, c_m$ is some set of constants and $g(n)$ is a function depending on n. If $c_m \neq 0$, we say that the recurrence relation has order m, and in case $g(n) = 0$, we say the recurrence is homogeneous.

In this section we study methods for solving homogeneous recurrence relations, which usually means that we want to find a solution $a_n = f(n)$ of the recurrence that satisfies the initial conditions $a_0 = b_0, a_1 = b_1, \ldots, a_{m-1} = b_{m-1}$, for a given set of constants $b_0, b_1, b_2, \ldots, b_{m-1}$.

The simplest examples of homogeneous linear recurrence relations have order 1. Geometric sequences are described by recurrences of the form $a_n = r a_{n-1}$. Given the initial condition $a_0 = k$, we have seen that the unique solution of this recurrence relation is given by the exponential function $a_n = kr^n$. We shall see that the solutions of many homogeneous linear recurrence relations of order m can also be obtained from exponential functions by taking linear combinations.

Consider the homogeneous linear recurrence relation with constant coefficients of order m given by

$$a_n = c_1 a_{n-1} + \cdots + c_m a_{n-m}, (c_m \neq 0) \tag{8-1}$$

DEFINITION   The Characteristic Equation

The polynomial equation

$$x^m - c_1 x^{m-1} - c_2 x^{m-2} - \cdots - c_m = 0 \tag{8-2}$$

will be called the characteristic equation of the recurrence 8-1.

This equation has m roots $r_1, r_2, r_3, \ldots, r_m$, which are called the characteristic roots. These characteristic roots may be complex numbers and need not be distinct, but since $c_m \neq 0$, they must all be different from zero.

Before trying to solve equation 8-2 for any specific sequence, suppose we look at a broader problem. In general, what kinds of sequences can satisfy this recurrence regardless of initial conditions? Once again let us consider the sequences that are described by functions of the form $a_n = r^n$.

THEOREM 8.1   The sequence $a_n = r^n$, $r \neq 0$, is a solution of the recurrence relation 8-1 if and only if r is a characteristic root.

Proof
To see if the sequence $a_n = r^n$ satisfies the recurrence relation, we simply substitute r^i for a_i in the recurrence to obtain $r^n = c_1 r^{n-1} + c_2 r^{n-2} + \cdots + c_m r^{n-m}$. We can divide both sides by r^{n-m} to obtain $r^m = c_1 r^{m-1} + c_2 r^{m-2} + \cdots + c_m$, or equivalently, $r^m - c_1 r^{m-1} - c_2 r^{m-2} - \cdots - c_m = 0$, which can be obtained by substituting $x = r$ into the characteristic equation.

Let $Y = (y_0, y_1, y_2, \ldots, y_n, \ldots)$ and $Z = (z_0, z_1, z_2, \ldots, z_n, \ldots)$ be sequences. We have previously defined the sequence $Y + Z = (y_0 + z_0, y_1 + z_1, y_2 + z_2, \ldots, y_n + z_n, \ldots)$. We can also define the constant multiple of a sequence Y by $kY = (ky_0, ky_1, ky_2, \ldots, ky_n, \ldots)$.

THEOREM 8.2   If Y and Z satisfy the homogeneous linear recurrence relation 8-1, kY and $X + Y$ also satisfy the same recurrence.

Proof
The proof of this theorem is straightforward, and we omit the details.

Suppose the roots of the characteristic polynomial 8-2 are $r_1, r_2, \ldots, r_m$. From Theorem 8.1 we see that any sequence $a_n = r_i^n$, for $i = 1, 2, \ldots, m$ is a solution of the recurrence relation. We refer to these initial solutions as fundamental solutions. By repeatedly applying Theorem 8.2 we see that any sequence of the following form, for arbitrary constants $k_1, k_2, \ldots, k_m$ is also a solution of the recurrence

$$a_n = k_1 r_1^n + k_2 r_2^n + \cdots + k_m r_m^n \qquad\qquad (8\text{-}3)$$

We say that an expression of the form in 8-3 is a linear combination of the fundamental solutions $r_1^n, r_2^n, \ldots, r_m^n$. In other words, any linear combination of the fundamental solutions is also a solution of the recurrence relation.

The Case of Distinct Roots

Let us now return to the original problem of finding the unique sequence that satisfies the recurrence relation 8-1 and a specific set of initial conditions, $a_0 = b_0$, $a_1 = b_1, a_2 = b_2, \ldots, a_{m-1} = b_{m-1}$. If we are lucky enough, the particular sequence in question will be one of the ones we have already obtained. Sometimes, in fact, this must be the case.

DEFINITION   General Solution

We shall say that equation 8-3 is a general solution of the homogeneous linear recurrence relation 8-1 provided that each solution of 8-1 can be expressed in the form of 8-3 for some choice of constants $k_1, k_2, \ldots, k_m$.

THEOREM 8.3   Let the roots $r_1, r_2, \ldots, r_m$ of the characteristic equation 8-2 be distinct. Then $a_n = k_1 r_1^n + k_2 r_2^n + \cdots + k_m r_m^n$ is a general solution of the homogeneous linear recurrence 8-1.

Proof
We need to show that for some choice of constants $k_1, k_2, \ldots, k_m$, the following system of equations can be satisfied:

$$
\begin{aligned}
k_1 &+ k_2 &+ \cdots + k_m &= b_0 \\
k_1 r_1 &+ k_2 r_2 &+ \cdots + k_m r_m &= b_1 \\
k_1 r_1^2 &+ k_2 r_2^2 &+ \cdots + k_m r_m^2 &= b_2 \\
&\vdots & \vdots \qquad \vdots & \\
k_1 r_1^{m-1} &+ k_2 r_2^{m-1} &+ \cdots + k_m r_m^{m-1} &= b_{m-1}
\end{aligned}
$$

The discussion of the solution of this system of equations requires a little knowledge of linear algebra. For readers who are not familiar with linear algebra, we keep the discussion as brief as possible. A system of m equations and m unknowns $k_1, k_2, \ldots, k_m$ is known to have a unique solution if and only if the determinant of the matrix of coefficients is nonzero. The matrix of coefficients of this system is well known as the Vandermonde matrix and its determinant is nonzero as long as $r_1, r_2, \ldots, r_m$ are all distinct (see Problem 19). Therefore, in the case under consideration, we see that there is a unique choice of constants $k_1, k_2, \ldots, k_m$ for which equation 8-3 satisfies the recurrence relation 8-1 and the initial conditions $a_0 = b_0, a_1 = b_1, \ldots, a_{m-1} = b_{m-1}$.

We now have the following procedure for solving a homogeneous linear recurrence relation with constant coefficients.

1. Find the m roots of the characteristic equation. If the roots are distinct, we obtain m fundamental solutions.
2. Take an arbitrary linear combination of these fundamental solutions to arrive at the general solution of the homogeneous linear recurrence.
3. Solve a system of equations to find the appropriate constants that give a specific solution satisfying the required initial conditions.

Example 1   Each day a young girl goes to a candy store. She buys either a bag of popcorn for one quarter or one of two types of candy bars that cost two quarters each. Find and solve a recurrence relation for a_n, the number of ways she can spend n quarters, assuming that the order of the purchases counts.

Solution
To find a relation between a_n and the previous terms of the sequence, consider the last purchase. If the last purchase was a bag of popcorn, there were a_{n-1} ways that the previous $n-1$ quarters could have been spent. On the other hand, if the last purchase was a candy bar, there were a_{n-2} ways the previous $n-2$ quarters could have been spent and two ways to buy a candy bar. Thus we obtain the recurrence relation $a_n = a_{n-1} + 2a_{n-2}$ with the initial conditions $a_0 = 1$ and $a_1 = 1$. The characteristic equation is $x^2 - x - 2 = 0$, which has roots -1 and 2.

Thus we have the general solution $a_n = k_1(-1)^n + k_2(2)^n$. The constants k_1 and k_2 satisfy the following system of linear equations.

$$k_1 + k_2 = 1$$
$$-k_1 + 2k_2 = 1$$

Therefore $k_1 = 1/3$ and $k_2 = 2/3$, and the solution we seek is

$$a_n = \frac{(-1)^n}{3} + \frac{2(2)^n}{3} \qquad \square$$

Example 2   The Fibonacci numbers satisfy the recurrence relation $a_n = a_{n-2} + a_{n-1}$ with initial conditions $a_0 = 0$ and $a_1 = 1$. Solve this recurrence and find a closed formula for the sequence of Fibonacci numbers.

Solution
The characteristic polynomial of this recurrence relation is $x^2 - x - 1 = 0$. The roots of this equation are $r_1 = (1 + \sqrt{5})/2$ and $r_2 = (1 - \sqrt{5})/2$, so the general solution of the recurrence is $a_n = k_1 r_1^n + k_2 r_2^n$. The constants k_1 and k_2 must satisfy the following system of linear equations to meet the initial conditions.

$$k_1 + k_2 = 0$$
$$\frac{k_1(1 + \sqrt{5})}{2} + \frac{k_2(1 - \sqrt{5})}{2} = 1$$

Solving these equations for k_1 and k_2, we obtain $k_1 = 1/(\sqrt{5})$ and $k_2 = -1/(\sqrt{5})$. Therefore the Fibonacci numbers satisfy the formula $a_n = (r_1^n - r_2^n)/(r_1 - r_2)$, for $n \geq 1$, which we first encountered in Problem 18, Section 1.2.   □

In the following example we see that generating functions can also be used to solve recurrence relations.

Example 3   Find a closed formula for the terms of the sequence satisfying the initial conditions $a_0 = 2$ and $a_1 = 2$ and the recurrence relation $a_n = 2a_{n-1} + 3a_{n-2}$, for $n \geq 2$.

Solution
Denote the generating function of this sequence by $A(z) = a_0 + a_1 z + a_2 z^2 + \cdots + a_n z^n + \cdots$. For each $n \geq 2$, we use the recurrence to obtain $a_n z^n = 2a_{n-1} z^n + 3a_{n-2} z^n$. Thus we have

$$\sum_{n \geq 2} a_n z^n = \sum_{n \geq 2} 2a_{n-1} z^n + \sum_{n \geq 2} 3a_{n-2} z^n$$

Therefore $A(z) - a_0 - a_1 z = 2zA(z) - 2za_0 + 3z^2 A(z)$ and $A(z) = -2z + 2/(1 - 2z - 3z^2)$. Expressing $A(z)$ using partial fractions, we see that $A(z) = 1/(1 - 3z) + 1/(1 + z)$. Each of these two summands is the generating function of a geometric sequence, so we compute the coefficients of $A(z)$ as follows: $A(z) = 2 + 2z + \cdots + (3^n + (-1)^n)z^n + \cdots$ hence $a_n = 3^n + (-1)^n$.   □

The Case of Repeated Roots

In the first part of this section, we saw that when the characteristic equation of a homogeneous linear recurrence relation had distinct roots, a general solution could be obtained by looking at linear combinations of m fundamental solutions, one for each characteristic root. In this case, for each characteristic root, there was an associated fundamental solution $a_n = r_i^n$. However, when the characteristic equation has repeated roots, two or more fundamental solutions coincide. Therefore we have fewer than m fundamental solutions that are exponential functions. Thus the linear combinations of exponential functions cannot form a general solution because there are not enough fundamental solutions.

It is still possible, though, to find a general solution for a homogeneous linear recurrence even when the characteristic equation has repeated roots by looking at a slightly larger class of fundamental solutions. We say that r is a characteristic root of multiplicity j if it appears as a root of the characteristic equation $x^m - c_1 x^{m-1} - c_2 x^{m-2} - \cdots - c_m = 0$ exactly j times, or equivalently that $(x - r)^j$ divides $x^m - c_1 x^{m-1} - c_2 x^{m-2} - \cdots - c_m$ (but $(x - r)^{j+1}$ does not). If we multiply the characteristic equation by x^{n-m}, differentiate, and multiply by x, we obtain $nx^n - (n-1)c_1 x^{n-1} - (n-2)c_2 x^{n-2} - \cdots - (n-m)c_m x^{n-m} = 0$. Since r is a multiple root of the characteristic equation, we see that r is still a root of the new equation (see Problem 20), showing that $a_n = nr^n$ is also a solution of the recurrence. In a similar manner, we can see that $a_n = n^2 r^n, \ldots, a_n = n^{j-1} r^n$ are also solutions. Once again we have j fundamental solutions for these j repeated roots.

Example 4   Solve the recurrence relation $a_n = 6a_{n-1} - 9a_{n-2}$ with initial conditions $a_0 = 1$ and $a_1 = 4$.

Solution

The characteristic equation of this recurrence is $x^2 - 6x + 9 = 0$, so 3 is a characteristic root of multiplicity 2. The corresponding general solution is $a_n = k_1 3^n + k_2 n3^n$. The constants k_1 and k_2 must satisfy the following system of linear equations.

$$k_1 = 1 \qquad 3k_1 + 3k_2 = 4$$

Thus we obtain $k_1 = 1$ and $k_2 = 1/3$ and the closed formula $a_n = 3^n + n3^{n-1}$.

□

In general suppose that the distinct, characteristic roots of a homogeneous linear recurrence of order m are $r_1, r_2, \ldots, r_k$, with root r_i having multiplicity j_i, and satisfying $j_1 + j_2 + \cdots + j_k = m$. For each root r_i having multiplicity j_i, there are j_i fundamental solutions of the recurrence. Overall there are m fundamental solutions $r_1^n, nr_1^n, \ldots, n^{j_1-1}r_1^n, r_2^n, nr_2^n, \ldots, n^{j_2-1}r_2^n, \ldots, r_k^n, nr_k^n, \ldots, n^{j_k-1}r_k^n$. As before, we can show that the linear combinations of these fundamental solutions give a general solution of the homogeneous linear recurrence relation, but we omit the details.

THEOREM 8.4   Suppose that a linear homogeneous recurrence relation of order m has m fundamental solutions $f_1(n), f_2(n), \ldots, f_m(n)$. Then the general solution is given by $a_n = k_1 f_1(n) + k_2 f_2(n) + \cdots + k_m f_m(n)$.

Finding the Roots of a Polynomial

To solve a homogeneous linear recurrence relation with constant coefficients, we are first required to find the roots of a polynomial equation. When faced with the problem of finding the roots of a polynomial $p(x)$, try to factor it as much as possible into polynomials of smaller degree. Here are a few basic facts about factoring and roots that may be helpful in the process of solving homogeneous linear recurrence relations.

1. Any polynomial with real coefficients can be factored into linear factors (degree 1 polynomials) and irreducible quadratic factors (degree 2 polynomials with complex roots) so that each factor also has real coefficients. Each linear factor $ax + b$ corresponds to the real root $x = -b/a$, and each quadratic factor corresponds to two complex conjugate roots that can be computed using the quadratic formula.

2. If r is a root of $p(x)$ (that is, $p(r) = 0$), then $(x - r)q(x) = p(x)$, where $q(x)$ can be obtained by dividing $x - r$ into $p(x)$.

3. Most of the problems we encounter will involve polynomials with integer coefficients and at least some rational roots, for example, $x = j/k$, where j and k are relatively prime integers. If $x = j/k$ is a rational root of $a_n x^n + a_{n-1}x^{n-1} + \cdots + a_0 = 0$, then k divides a_n and j divides a_0. When nothing else

works, we test $p(x)$ for possible rational roots. If a rational root j/k is discovered, we return to Step 2 and factor $p(x)$ into two factors, that is, $p(x) = (x - j/k)q(x)$, where $q(x)$ is a polynomial of degree $n - 1$.

Example 5   Find the general solution of the linear recurrence relation $a_n = 5a_{n-1} - 6a_{n-2} - 4a_{n-3} + 8a_{n-4}$.

Solution
The characteristic polynomial of this recurrence is $x^4 - 5x^3 + 6x^2 + 4x - 8 = 0$. The only possible rational roots are ± 1, ± 2, ± 4, and ± 8. We immediately verify that -1 is a root, so we factor $p(x) = (x + 1)(x^3 - 6x^2 + 12x - 8)$. We also verify that 2 is a root, so we obtain $p(x) = (x + 1)(x - 2)(x^2 - 4x + 4) = (x + 1)(x - 2)^3$. Therefore -1 is a root, 2 is a root of multiplicity 3, and we obtain the general solution $a_n = k_1 2^n + k_2 n 2^n + k_3 n^2 2^n + k_4 (-1)^n$.   □

8.2
PROBLEMS

1. Find the characteristic polynomial of the following recurrence relations.
   a) $a_n = a_{n-1} + 6a_{n-2}$
   b) $a_n = -a_{n-1} + a_{n-2} + a_{n-3}$
   c) $a_n + 3a_{n-1} - 10a_{n-2} = 0$

2. Find the characteristic roots of each of the recurrences in Problem 1.

3. Find the general solution of
   a) $a_n = 2a_{n-1} + 15a_{n-2}$ b) $a_n = 3a_{n-1} + 2a_{n-2}$

4. For each relation in Problem 3, find the specific solution satisfying the initial conditions $a_0 = 1$ and $a_1 = 2$.

5. Find the general solution of
   a) $a_n = -3a_{n-1} + 4a_{n-3}$ b) $a_n = a_{n-1} + 4a_{n-2} - 4a_{n-3}$

6. Solve the following recurrence relations.
   a) $a_n = 4a_{n-1} - 3a_{n-2}$, given that $a_0 = 1$ and $a_1 = 2$.
   b) $a_n + 2a_{n-1} - a_{n-3} = 0$, given that $a_0 = 1$, $a_1 = 2$, and $a_2 = 2$.

7. For the recurrence relation $a_n = 6a_{n-1} - 12a_{n-2} + 8a_{n-3}$, verify that $a_n = 2^n$, $a_n = n 2^n$, $a_n = n^2 2^n$ are solutions by plugging them into the recurrence. Find a specific solution of the recurrence satisfying $a_0 = 1$, $a_1 = 2$, $a_2 = 3$.

ADVANCED
PROBLEMS

8. Consider the recurrence relation $a_n = -a_{n-2}$. Show that $a_n = i^n$ and $a_n = (-i)^n$ are solutions, where $i = \sqrt{-1}$. For any initial conditions $a_0 = b$ and $a_1 = c$, find constants k_1 and k_2 so that $a_n = k_1 i^n + k_2 (-i)^n$ satisfies these initial conditions.

9. Consider the recurrence relation $a_n = a_{n-1} - a_{n-2}$.
   a) Solve the recurrence if $a_2 = 0$ and $a_3 = 1$.
   b) Can you solve the recurrence if $a_0 = 0$ and $a_3 = 0$?
   c) Repeat part (b) if it is known that $a_0 = 0$ and $a_3 = 1$.

10. A man visits a pastry shop each morning. During each visit he buys either one of two types of pastry costing one dollar each or one of three types of pastry costing two dollars each. Find and solve a recurrence for the number of ways to spend n dollars at the pastry shop (order matters).

11. Find the general solution of
    a) $a_n = 3a_{n-1} + 3a_{n-2} - a_{n-3}$ b) $a_n = 3a_{n-1} - 3a_{n-2} + a_{n-3}$

12. Find the general solution of
    a) $a_n = 2a_{n-2} - a_{n-4}$ b) $a_n = -2a_{n-2} - a_{n-4}$

13. Find and solve a recurrence relation for the number of n-digit ternary sequences that have no adjacent 0's.

14. Solve the recurrence relation $a_0 = x = a_1$ and $a_n = a_{n-1}a_{n-2}$ for $n \geq 2$.

15. For the following directed graph determine the number of different directed walks which consist of n directed edges starting at point a and ending at point c.

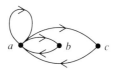

16. A perfect matching M in a graph G with $2n$ vertices is a subset of n edges chosen from the edge set of G so that every vertex in G is incident to exactly one edge of M. Find and solve a recurrence relation for the number of perfect matchings of the following ladder graph with n vertical rungs.

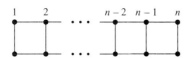

17. Find and solve recurrence relations for the number of n-digit binary sequences
    a) Ending in 11.
    b) Containing 11 for the first time at the end.

18. Solve for a_n and b_n using generating functions.

$$a_n = 5a_{n-1} - 2b_{n-1} \qquad a_0 = 3$$
$$b_n = 6a_{n-1} - 2b_{n-1} \qquad b_0 = 5$$

19. For distinct real numbers $a_1, a_2, \ldots, a_n$ show by induction that

$$\det \begin{bmatrix} 1 & a_1 & a_1^2 & \cdots & a_1^{n-1} \\ 1 & a_2 & a_2^2 & \cdots & a_2^{n-1} \\ \vdots & \vdots & \vdots & & \vdots \\ 1 & a_n & a_n^2 & \cdots & a_n^{n-1} \end{bmatrix} = \prod_{i=2}^{n} \prod_{j=1}^{i-1} (a_i - a_j)$$

Hint: Replace a_n by x and show that the determinant in question is equal to an n-1st degree polynomial of the form $A(x - a_1)(x - a_2)\cdots(x - a_{n-1})$. Continue by substituting a_n for x.

20. a) Show that the polynomial $f(x)$ has a root r of multiplicity m if and only if
$$f(r) = f'(r) = f''(r) = \cdots = f^{(m-1)}(r) = 0 \text{ and } f^{(m)}(r) \neq 0.$$
b) For $n > 1$, the polynomial equation $x^n - nx + n - 1 = 0$ has 1 as a root. What is the multiplicity of this root?

8.2
SUPPLEMENTARY COMPUTER PROJECT

1. **The Dollar Bill Problem Revisited**
    Earlier we found the number of ways to change a dollar using pennies, nickels, dimes, quarters, and half dollars using generating functions. Let us now reexamine this problem from a slightly different viewpoint.

    Definition   Let c_j be the number of ways to make $5j$ cents in change using p pennies, n nickels, and d dimes. In other words, c_j is the number of nonnegative integer solutions of

    $$p + 5n + 10d = 5j. \tag{8-4}$$

    a) Since $5 = 1 + 1 + 1 + 1 + 1$ or $5 = 5$, then $c_1 = 2$. Find c_2, c_3, c_4, c_5.
    b) Equation 8-4 implies that $p = 5q$ for some nonnegative integer q. Thus $q + n + 2d = j$ or $q + n = j - 2d$, where $j - 2d \geq 0$. Explain why $q + n = w$ has $w + 1$ solutions.
    c) Find a recurrence relation for c_j.
    d) Using parts (b) and (c), find a formula (in closed form) for c_{2k}. Verify that $c_{16} = 81$.
    e) Find a formula (in closed form) for c_{2k+1}. Verify that $c_{17} = 90$.
    f) Let d_j be the number of ways to make $5j$ cents in change using pennies, nickels, dimes, and quarters. Find a recurrence relation expressing d_j in terms of c's and d's.
    g) Write a computer program that uses parts (c) and (f) to solve the original dollar bill problem.

SECTION
8.3 NONHOMOGENEOUS LINEAR RECURRENCE RELATIONS

Consider the nonhomogeneous linear recurrence relation of order m with constant coefficients

$$a_n = c_1 a_{n-1} + c_2 a_{n-2} + \cdots + c_m a_{n-m} + g(n) \tag{8-5}$$

where $c_1, c_2, \ldots, c_m$ is some set of constants with $c_m \neq 0$ and $g(n)$ is a nonzero function. Corresponding to 8-5 we have the associated homogeneous linear recurrence relation

$$a_n = c_1 a_{n-1} + c_2 a_{n-2} + \cdots + c_m a_{n-m} \qquad \textbf{(8-6)}$$

which we learned how to solve in the previous section.

Let $Y = (y_0, y_1, y_2, \ldots, y_n, \ldots)$ and $Z = (z_0, z_1, z_2, \ldots, z_n, \ldots)$ be two sequences.

THEOREM 8.5

If Y and Z both satisfy the nonhomogeneous linear recurrence (8-5), then $Y - Z$ satisfies the associated homogeneous linear recurrence (8-6).

Proof
The proof of this theorem is again straightforward, and we omit the details.

As before, the usual kind of problem we consider will be that of determining a specific sequence that satisfies the nonhomogeneous linear recurrence 8-5 and a certain set of initial conditions. It will once again be convenient to first find all the solutions of the nonhomogeneous linear recurrence relation 8-6. Once the general solution is found, we will be able to obtain the specific solution we are looking for by determining the appropriate coefficients in the general solution.

Finding a Particular Solution

From Theorem 8.5 we can see that once a single solution of the nonhomogeneous recurrence 8-5 is found then any other solution differs from it by a solution of the associated homogeneous linear recurrence relation 8-6.

DEFINITION Particular Solution
We say that a single solution $P = (p_0, p_1, p_2, \ldots)$ of the nonhomogeneous linear recurrence 8-5 is a particular solution, regardless of which initial conditions it satisfies.

The general solution of the nonhomogeneous linear recurrence relation 8-5 can be obtained by adding P to the general solution of the associated homogeneous linear recurrence relation 8-6. Thus we have the following procedure for solving a nonhomogeneous linear recurrence relation;

1. Find a particular solution of the original recurrence.
2. Find the general solution of the associated homogeneous linear recurrence relation.
3. Combine Steps 1 and 2 to obtain a general solution for the nonhomogeneous linear recurrence relation.
4. Obtain a specific solution satisfying the required initial conditions from the general solution.

We are familiar with the last three steps, so we concentrate on Step 1. We would like to find a particular solution P of 8-5. When $g(n)$ is a simple function, we can sometimes find a similar function $p(n)$ that describes the terms of a particular solution P. We consider two cases, one when $g(n)$ is a polynomial and the other when $g(n)$ is an exponential function.

When the Nonhomogeneous Part Is Polynomial

Suppose that the function $g(n)$ is a polynomial of degree q, $g(n) = k_q n^q + k_{q-1} n^{q-1} + \cdots + k_1 n + k_0$. When a polynomial $p(n)$ is substituted for the terms on both sides of the equation (that is, $p(n)$ is substituted for a_n, $p(n-1)$ is substituted for a_{n-1}, and so on), the left side of the equation and the right side of the equation are both polynomials. If the two polynomials are equal, $p(n)$ describes the terms of a particular solution P. Ordinarily, when $g(n)$ is a polynomial of degree q, we will be able to find another polynomial of degree q, which is a particular solution of the nonhomogeneous linear recurrence relation 8-5, using the method of undetermined coefficients. We check for a particular solution of the form $p(n) = j_q n^q + j_{q-1} n^{q-1} + \cdots + j_1 n + j_0$. We only have to determine the correct coefficients to obtain the required solution.

Example 1   Find a particular solution of the nonhomogeneous linear recurrence $a_n = a_{n-1} + a_{n-2} + 2n$.

Solution
Since $g(n)$ is a first degree polynomial, we check all first degree polynomials $p(n) = j_1 n + j_0$, in searching for a particular solution. For a particular solution $p(n)$, the following equations are satisfied.

$$j_1 n + j_0 - (j_1(n-1) + j_0) - (j_1(n-2) + j_0) = 2n$$
$$-j_1 n + (3j_1 - j_0) = 2n$$

Thus, equating coefficients, we obtain $j_1 = -2$ and $j_0 = -6$ and the particular solution $p(n) = -2n - 6$.   □

Example 2   Find a solution of the nonhomogeneous linear recurrence relation $a_n = a_{n-1} + 2a_{n-2} - 4$ satisfying the initial conditions $a_0 = 6$ and $a_1 = 7$.

Solution
Since a constant is a degree 0 polynomial, in searching for a particular solution, we consider all constant functions $p(n) = j_0$. A particular solution satisfies the equation $j_0 - j_0 - 2j_0 = -4$. Therefore we obtain the particular solution $p(n) = 2$. Combining this with the general solution of the associated homogeneous linear recurrence relation, we obtain the following general solution of the nonhomogeneous recurrence relation.

$$a_n = 2 + k_1(-1)^n + k_2 2^n$$

Thus $6 = 2 + k_1 + k_2$ and $7 = 2 - k_1 + 2k_2$. This implies $k_1 = 1$ and $k_2 = 3$, so the specific solution we seek is $a_n = 2 + (-1)^n + 3(2^n)$.   □

Normally, when the nonhomogeneous part of a linear recurrence relation $g(n)$ is a polynomial of degree q, we can obtain a particular solution that is also a polynomial of degree q, but this is not always the case as we see by reexamining Example 4 in Section 8.1. There we encountered the recurrence relation $a_n = a_{n-1} + n$ for which the solution is $a_n = (n + 1)n/2 + a_0$. Later in this section we consider recurrences of the form $a_n = a_{n-1} + g(n)$, which we refer to as difference equations. When $g(n)$ is a polynomial, we shall see that the solution is always a polynomial of one higher degree.

When the Nonhomogeneous Part Is Exponential

In solving nonhomogeneous linear recurrence relations, the other case we consider is when $g(n) = kb^n$ is an exponential function. Whenever an exponential function of the form $p(n) = cb^n$ is substituted for the terms on both sides of the recurrence, both sides become exponential functions of the same base. If the two sides are equal, $p(n)$ describes the terms of a particular solution. Normally we will be able to obtain a particular solution $p(n)$ that is an exponential function by determining the proper coefficient.

Example 3   Find a particular solution of the nonhomogeneous linear recurrence relation $a_n = a_{n-1} + 3a_{n-2} + a_{n-3} + 3^n$.

Solution
In searching for a particular solution, we check all exponential functions $p(n) = c3^n$. For a particular solution, the equation $c3^n - c3^{n-1} - 3c3^{n-2} - c3^{n-3} = 3^n$ is satisfied. Dividing boths sides by 3^{n-3}, we solve the resulting equation to find $c = 27/8$ and the particular solution $p(n) = 3^{n+3}/8$.   □

Example 4   Find the solution of the nonhomogeneous linear recurrence $a_n = a_{n-1} + 6a_{n-2} + 2^n$ satisfying the initial conditions $a_0 = 0$ and $a_1 = 1$.

Solution
We check the exponential functions $p(n) = c2^n$ to obtain the particular solution $p(n) = -2^n$. Thus the general solution of the nonhomogeneous linear recurrence relation is $a_n = -2^n + k_1 3^n + k_2(-2)^n$. We are looking for the specific solution satisfying $-1 + k_1 + k_2 = 0$ and $-2 + 3k_1 - 2k_2 = 1$. Therefore $k_1 = 1$ and $k_2 = 0$, and the solution we are seeking is $a_n = -2^n + 3^n$.   □

Normally, when the nonhomogeneous part of a linear recurrence relation $g(n)$ is an exponential function kb^n, we can expect to obtain a particular solution that is also an exponential function. This is obviously not the case when b is a characteristic root of the associated homogeneous linear recurrence relation. However, in this case, it will still be possible to find a particular solution of a slightly different form. When b is a root of multiplicity m, we can show that there will always be a particular solution of the form $p(n) = cn^m b^n$.

Example 5   Find the general solution of $a_n = 2a_{n-1} + 2^n$.

Solution

The functions $a_n = k(2^n)$ are solutions of the associated recurrence, so we look for a particular solution of the form $a_n = cn2^n$. Thus $cn2^n = 2c(n-1)2^{n-1} + 2^n$, so we obtain $c = 1$ and the particular solution $p(n) = n2^n$. Therefore the general solution of the recurrence is $f(n) = k(2^n) + n2^n$.   □

Difference Equations (Optional)

DEFINITION   **Difference Equations**

A simple class of nonhomogeneous linear recurrence relations of the form $a_n = a_{n-1} + g(n)$ are known as difference equations.

We will study the case when $g(n)$ is a polynomial of degree m. Let $A = (a_0, a_1, a_2, \ldots, a_n, \ldots)$ be any sequence. It will be helpful to consider differences between consecutive terms of a sequence, so we define the sequence of differences ΔA to be the sequence $(a'_0, a'_1, a'_2, \ldots, a'_n, \ldots)$, where $a'_n = a_{n+1} - a_n$. For example, if $A = (0, 1, 4, 9, 16, 25, \ldots)$ is the sequence of squares defined by $a_n = n^2$, then $\Delta A = (1, 3, 5, 7, 9, \ldots)$ is the sequence of odd numbers defined by $a'_n = (n+1)^2 - n^2 = 2n + 1$. If $B = (1, 2, 4, 8, 16, 32, \ldots)$ is the sequence defined by $b_n = 2^n$, then $\Delta B = B$.

In a similar manner we can define sequences of repeated differences. The sequence of second differences $\Delta^2 A$ is defined to be the sequence $(a''_0, a''_1, a''_2, \ldots, a''_n, \ldots)$ where $a''_n = a'_{n+1} - a'_n$, and in general the sequence of ith differences is defined recursively to be the sequence $(a^{(i)}_0, a^{(i)}_1, a^{(i)}_2, \ldots, a^{(i)}_n, \ldots)$, where $a^{(i)}_n = a^{(i-1)}_{n+1} - a^{(i-1)}_n$. For the sequence defined by $a_n = n^2$, we see that $\Delta^2 A = (2, 2, 2, 2, 2, \ldots)$ is a constant sequence. For $i > 2$, we see that $\Delta^i A = (0, 0, 0, 0, 0, \ldots)$ is the zero sequence. For the sequence defined by $b_n = 2^n$, we see that $\Delta^i B = B$, for any $i \geq 1$.

DEFINITION   **Arithmetic Sequence**

The simplest kind of difference equation satisfied by a sequence $A = (a_0, a_1, a_2, \ldots, a_n, \ldots)$ is $a_n = a_{n-1} + d$. In this case, ΔA is a constant sequence, and we say that A is an arithmetic sequence. More generally we will say that a sequence A is an arithmetic sequence of degree m if $\Delta^m A$ is a constant sequence but $\Delta^{m-1} A$ is not.

The sequence defined by $a_n = n^2$ is an arithmetic sequence of degree 2, but the sequence $a_n = 2^n$ is not an arithmetic sequence of any degree.

For binomial coefficients our standard recurrence can be written as $\binom{n}{m-1} = \binom{n+1}{m} - \binom{n}{m}$. The following theorem expresses an arithmetic sequence of degree m in terms of binomial coefficients.

THEOREM 8.6

An arithmetic sequence of degree m, $A = (a_0, a_1, a_2,..., a_n,...)$ can be (uniquely) expressed in the form $a_n = b_0 + b_1 \binom{n}{1} + b_2 \binom{n}{2} + \cdots + b_m \binom{n}{m}$ for some set of constants $b_0, b_1, b_2,..., b_m$.

Proof

We shall show that $a_n = a_0 + a_0' \binom{n}{1} + a_0'' \binom{n}{2} + \cdots + a_0^{(m)} \binom{n}{m}$ is the unique way of expressing the sequence A.

If $m = 1$, then $A = (a_0, a_0 + d, a_0 + 2d,..., a_0 + nd,...)$ and $\Delta A = (d, d, d, d,...)$. Therefore $a_n = a_0 + nd = a_0 + a_0' \binom{n}{1}$, as required.

Suppose the result is true for any arithmetic sequence of degree $m - 1$ and that A is an arithmetic sequence of degree m. The sequence ΔA is obviously an arithmetic sequence of degree $m - 1$, so $a_n' = a_0' + a_0'' \binom{n}{1} + a_0''' \binom{n}{2} + \cdots + a_0^{(m)} \binom{n}{m-1}$ by our induction hypothesis. Since

$$a_n = a_0 + (a_1 - a_0) + (a_2 - a_1) + \cdots + (a_n - a_{n-1})$$

$$= a_0 + a_0' + \left(a_0' + a_0'' \binom{1}{1}\right) + \cdots + \left(a_0' + a_0'' \binom{n-1}{1} + \cdots + a_0^{(m)} \binom{n-1}{m-1}\right)$$

$$= a_0 + a_0'(1 + 1 + \cdots + 1) + a_0''\left(\binom{1}{1} + \binom{2}{1} + \cdots + \binom{n-1}{1}\right) + \cdots$$

$$+ a_0^{(m)}\left(\binom{m-1}{m-1} + \binom{m}{m-1} + \cdots + \binom{n-1}{m-1}\right)$$

we see that $a_n = a_0 + a_0' \binom{n}{1} + a_0'' \binom{n}{2} + \cdots + a_0^{(m)} \binom{n}{m}$, as required. It is not hard to show that the coefficients $a_0^{(i)}$ are unique (Problem 13).

THEOREM 8.7

A sequence A is an arithmetic sequence of degree m if and only if it is defined by an mth degree polynomial $a_n = c_0 + c_1 n + c_2 n^2 + \cdots + c_m n^m$.

Proof

If $a_n = c_0 + c_1 n + \cdots + c_m n^m$ is defined by a polynomial of degree $m (c_m \neq 0)$, then ΔA is defined by the polynomial $g(n) = c_0 + c_1(n+1) + \cdots + c_m(n+1)^m - (c_0 + c_1 n + \cdots + c_m n^m)$. Using the Binomial Theorem, we see that the coefficient of n^m in $g(n)$ is 0 and the coefficient of n^{m-1} is $mc_m \neq 0$. Therefore $g(n)$ is a polynomial of degree $m - 1$. Similarly $\Delta^i A$ is defined by a polynomial of degree $m - i$. Therefore $\Delta^m A$ is constant but $\Delta^{m-1} A$ is not, showing that A is an arithmetic sequence of degree m.

On the other hand, suppose that a_n is an arithmetic sequence of degree m. Then, by the previous theorem, $a_n = a_0' + a_0' \binom{n}{1} + \cdots + a_0^{(m)} \binom{n}{m}$, which can be expressed as a polynomial in n since $\binom{n}{k} = n(n-1)\cdots(n-k+1)/(k(k-1)\cdots 1)$. The coefficient of the highest power of n^m is $a_0^{(m)}$, which cannot be 0 since A is an arithmetic sequence of degree m and $\Delta^m A$ is a nonzero constant sequence. Thus A is defined by an mth degree polynomial.

COROLLARY   If $f(n)$ is a polynomial of degree m, the sequence satisfying the recurrence $a_n = a_{n-1} + f(n)$ and $a_0 = c$ is a polynomial of degree $m + 1$.

Example 6   Compute the sum $1^4 + 2^4 + 3^4 + \cdots + n^4$.

Solution
Define the sequence $a_n = 0^4 + 1^4 + 2^4 + \cdots + n^4$. Since $a_n - a_{n-1} = n^4$, we know that a_n is defined by some polynomial of degree 5. Taking repeated differences as follows, we find that $a_0 = 0$, $a_0' = 1$, $a_0'' = 15$, $a_0''' = 50$, $a_0^{(4)} = 60$, $a_0^{(5)} = 24$. Therefore, $a_n = 1^4 + 2^4 + 3^4 + \cdots + n^4 = \binom{n}{1} + 15\binom{n}{2} + 50\binom{n}{3} + 60\binom{n}{4} + 24\binom{n}{5}$.

0		1		17		98		354		979		2275
	1		16		81		256		625		1296	
		15		65		175		369		671		
			50		110		194		302			
				60		84		108				
					24		24	$\cdots$				

$\square$

8.3
PROBLEMS

1. Determine the particular solution for the recurrence relation $a_n - 2a_{n-1} = f(n)$, where
    a) $f(n) = 6n$
    b) $f(n) = 6n^2$
    c) $f(n) = 3^n$

2. Find the general solution of
    a) $a_n = a_{n-1} + 6a_{n-2} + 2n$
    b) $a_n - 5a_{n-1} + 6a_{n-2} = 5^n$

Solve the following recurrence relations.

3. $a_n + 4a_{n-1} + 4a_{n-2} = 2^n$ with $a_0 = 1$, $a_1 = 2$

4. $a_n + 3a_{n-1} + 2a_{n-2} = 2n^2$ with $a_0 = 1$, $a_1 = 5$

5. $a_n - 7a_{n-1} + 10a_{n-2} = 3^n + 1$ with $a_0 = 2$, $a_1 = 6$

6. $a_n + 2a_{n-1} + 2a_{n-2} = 4^n$ with $a_0 = 2$, $a_1 = 4$

7. $3a_n - 5a_{n-1} - 2a_{n-2} = n + 1$ with $a_0 = 3$, $a_1 = 5$

8. $a_n + a_{n-1} + a_{n-2} + a_{n-3} = 2$ with $a_0 = 1$, $a_1 = 2$, $a_2 = 3$

9. In a savings account there is initially $1000 and at the end of year n, 10% interest is paid and $10n$ is withdrawn. Find and solve a recurrence relation for the amount of money in the account at the end of the nth year.

10. Find a formula for $\sum_{i=0}^{n} i^5$.

11. Suppose $a_n = n^3 - 2n^2 + 3n - 4$.

    a) Find constants c_0, c_1, c_2, c_3 so that $a_n = c_0 + c_1\binom{n}{1} + c_2\binom{n}{2} + c_3\binom{n}{3}$.

    b) Find constants b_0, b_1, b_2, b_3, b_4 so that $\sum_{i=0}^{n} a_i = b_0 + b_1\binom{n}{1} + b_2\binom{n}{2} + b_3\binom{n}{3} + b_4\binom{n}{4}$

12. Show by induction that

$$a_n^{(m)} = a_{n+m} - \binom{m}{1}a_{n+m-1} + \binom{m}{2}a_{n+m-2} + \cdots + (-1)^m\binom{m}{m}a_n$$

13. Suppose $a_n = c_0 + c_1\binom{n}{1} + c_2\binom{n}{2} + \cdots + c_m\binom{n}{m}$. Explain why the constants $c_0, c_1, c_2, \ldots, c_m$ are unique.

14. Suppose A is a sequence whose nth term is given by the formula $a_n = n^4 + 3n^2 + 6$. Compute formulas for the sequences $\Delta A, \Delta^2 A, \Delta^3 A, \Delta^4 A, \Delta^5 A$.

ADVANCED PROBLEMS

15. Find and solve a recurrence relation for the number of n-digit ternary sequences with an even number of zeros.

16. Find and solve a recurrence relation for the number of n-digit ternary sequences with no 1 anywhere to the right of any 2.

17. Solve the following recurrences
    a) $a_n^2 = a_{n-1}^2 + 2a_{n-2}^2$, $a_0 = 0$, $a_1 = 1$ **Hint:** First find $b_n = a_n^2$.
    b) $na_n + (n-1)a_{n-1} = 2^n$, $a_0 = 1$, $a_1 = 2$ **Hint:** First find $b_n = na_n$.

*18. What is the smallest amount that someone can invest at interest rate i compounded annually in order that the person may withdraw one dollar at the end of the first year, four dollars at the end of the second year, $\ldots, n^2$ dollars at the end of the nth year in perpetuity.

8.3
SUPPLEMENTARY COMPUTER PROJECT

1. The Rods Problem
   We are given n rods ($n \geq 3$) of lengths $1, 2, 3, \ldots, n$ (one of each length). The problem is to find $f(n)$, the number of different (nondegenerate) triangles that can be formed using these rods. For example, $f(3) = 0$; $f(4) = 1$: $(2,3,4)$; $f(5) = 3$: $(2,3,4), (2,4,5), (3,4,5)$; and so on.

a) Verify that the following use of three nested loops yields the desired result.

```
PROGRAM ONE
INTEGER  I,J,K,N,T
READ N
T = 0
DO 10 I=1,N-2
    DO 20 J=I+1,N-1
        DO 30 K=J+1,N
            IF(I+J.GT.K) T=T+1
30          CONTINUE
20      CONTINUE
10  CONTINUE
PRINT N,  'RODS YIELD',  T,  'TRIANGLES'
END
```

b) Show that the outermost loop in Program ONE may start with I = 2.
c) Positive integers I, J, K represent the lengths of the sides of a triangle if and only if the sum of any two is greater than the third. Explain why only one comparison (instead of three) was made in Program ONE.
d) Determine the values of $f(n)$ for $n = 6, 7, 8, 9, 10$. Carefully notice any patterns in the differences. Use your observations to find a recurrence relation for $f(n)$. Construct a proof of this result.
e) Use part (d) to express $f(n)$ as a sum.
f) Find a new recurrence relation for $f(n)$ that involves only $f(n-1)$ and $f(n-2)$.
g) Suppose n is even. Prove that $f(n)$ can be expressed as a polynomial in n.
h) For odd n, express $f(n)$ as a polynomial in n and prove your claim.

CHAPTER 8   REVIEW PROBLEMS

1. a) Find the number of ordered partitions of 12 with only 1's and 2's as summands.
   b) Find the number of ordered partitions of 12 with 1's, 2's, and 3's as summands.

2. Find a recurrence relation for the number of n-digit ternary sequences containing at least one 1, for which the first 1 occurs to the left of any 0.

3. Find a recurrence relation for the number of binary sequences of length n that do not contain the subsequence 011.

4. Find and solve a recurrence relation for the number of ways to make a stack of

n poker chips using red, white, blue, and gold chips
a) If the stack has no adjacent red chips.
b) If the stack has no adjacent red chips and no adjacent white chips.

5. Find a closed formula for a_n satisfying the following recurrence relations.
   a) $a_n = a_{n-1} + 6a_{n-2}$ with $a_0 = 1$ and $a_1 = 1$
   b) $a_n = a_{n-1} + 6a_{n-2} + 2^n$ with $a_0 = 0$ and $a_1 = 0$
   c) $a_n - 5a_{n-1} + 6a_{n-2} = 3n + 2$ with $a_0 = 0$ and $a_1 = 1$

6. For the recurrence relation $a_n = 6a_{n-1} - 11a_{n-2} + 6a_{n-3}$,
   a) Find the characteristic equation.
   b) Find the characteristic roots.
   c) Find the general solution.

7. Repeat Problem 6 for the recurrence relation $a_n = 4a_{n-1} - a_{n-2} - 6a_{n-3}$.

8. A man visits a pastry shop each morning. During each visit he buys either one of two types of pastry costing one dollar each or one of eight types of pastry costing two dollars each. Find and solve a recurrence relation for the number of ways to spend n dollars at the pastry shop.

9. Suppose a savings account earns 5% interest at the end of each year. Initially there is $1000 in the account, and at the end of each year an additional $100n$ is deposited. Let a_n be the amount of money in the account at the end of the nth year. Find and solve a nonhomogeneous recurrence relation for a_n.

10. Find a closed formula that is a polynomial for the sequence 1, 3, 7, 37, 141, 391, 883, 1737, ...

CHAPTER

8

SUMMARY

In this chapter we looked at recurrence relations as a method for computing the answer to a counting problem. Using this method, the size of the problem usually depended on a nonnegative parameter i, and we described our answer as a sequence $A = (a_0, a_1, a_2, \ldots)$. A recurrence relation is often useful for computing the terms of a sequence and is usually easier to find than a closed formula because we need only express the answer a_n in terms of the answers for smaller values of i. Sometimes it is difficult to solve a collection of problems explicitly. However, it may be easy to find an algorithm that solves a larger problem by reducing it to smaller problems of the same type. We say that an algorithm of this type is recursive. Recurrence relations are often encountered in computing the complexity of an algorithm of this type. In the last two sections, we also saw how certain simple recurrence relations could be used to explicitly find a formula for a_n. It is also possible to solve these recurrences using generating functions (see [3]).

BIBLIOGRAPHY

1. Ryser, H. J. *Combinatorial Mathematics*, Monograph No. 14, Washington, D.C.: MAA, 1963.
2. Goldberg, S. *Introduction to Difference Equations.* New York: Wiley & Sons, 1978.
3. Hillman, A., G. Alexanderson, and R. Grassl. *Discrete and Combinatorial Mathematics.* San Francisco: Dellen Publishing, 1987.

9

THE POLYA THEORY OF COUNTING

In this chapter we use algebraic systems to study a special class of counting problems. Sometimes a combinatorial problem involves coloring the vertices, edges, or faces of a geometrical object such as an n-gon or a cube. The difficulty in counting these colorings is that two colorings that appear to be different may be essentially identical when the geometrical symmetry of the object is considered. These geometrical symmetries form a group, and we use them to develop a formula for the inequivalent colorings of the object in question. George Polya was one of the first mathematicians to use this theory while he was analyzing a problem involving chemical isomers.

9.1 SYMMETRY GROUPS AND BURNSIDE'S THEOREM

A **binary operation** $*$ on the set G assigns a value to each ordered pair (a, b) in $G \times G$, which we denote by $a * b$. Normally we think of $a * b$ as the product of a and b. If $a * b$ is in G for every pair a and b in G, we say that the binary operation $*$ is **closed**. A set G together with one or more closed binary operations is called an **algebraic system**. Algebraic systems are used in many combinatorial constructions involving symmetry.

Many algebraic systems involve sets of numbers. The set of integers Z, together with the binary operations of addition and multiplication, form a well-known algebraic system.

Example 1   Integers Modulo n

The binary relation, congruence modulo n, can also be used to describe other useful algebraic systems. Congruence modulo n partitions the set of integers into n distinct equivalence classes $Z_n = \{\langle 0 \rangle, \langle 1 \rangle, \ldots, \langle n-1 \rangle\}$. We define the corresponding binary operations on the set Z_n by 1) $\langle a \rangle + \langle b \rangle = \langle a+b \rangle$, and 2) $\langle a \rangle \langle b \rangle = \langle ab \rangle$. According to Theorem 1.9 (Section 1.3) these operations are well defined. The algebraic system formed by Z_n, together with these two binary operations, is referred to as the integers modulo n. For example, in Z_7 it is easy to calculate that $\langle 4 \rangle + \langle 5 \rangle = \langle 2 \rangle$ and $\langle 4 \rangle \langle 5 \rangle = \langle 6 \rangle$. ☐

For a binary operation $*$, on the set G, we define the following properties. The operation $*$ is said to be **associative** if $(a * b) * c = a * (b * c)$ for all triples a, b, c in G. An element e in G is said to be an **identity** if $a * e = a = e * a$, for all a in G. Also an element a^{-1} in G, satisfying $a * a^{-1} = e = a^{-1} * a$, is said to be an **inverse** of a.

DEFINITION   Group

The algebraic system $(G, *)$ is said to be a group if the following conditions are satisfied:

1. $*$ is a closed operation.
2. $*$ is an associative operation.
3. G contains an identity.
4. Every element in G has an inverse.

Permutation Groups

Let $X = \{1, 2, \ldots, n\}$. A bijection from X to itself is sometimes referred to as a permutation or symmetry of X. The $n!$ permutations of X form a set that we denote by S_n. We use the symbol $\begin{pmatrix} 1 & 2 & \cdots & n \\ f(1) & f(2) & \cdots & f(n) \end{pmatrix}$ to represent the permutation f that assigns 1 to $f(1)$, 2 to $f(2)$, ..., and n to $f(n)$. Using this notation, the set S_3 consists of the following six permutations:

$$\left\{ \begin{pmatrix} 1 & 2 & 3 \\ 1 & 2 & 3 \end{pmatrix}, \begin{pmatrix} 1 & 2 & 3 \\ 1 & 3 & 2 \end{pmatrix}, \begin{pmatrix} 1 & 2 & 3 \\ 2 & 1 & 3 \end{pmatrix}, \begin{pmatrix} 1 & 2 & 3 \\ 2 & 3 & 1 \end{pmatrix}, \begin{pmatrix} 1 & 2 & 3 \\ 3 & 1 & 2 \end{pmatrix}, \begin{pmatrix} 1 & 2 & 3 \\ 3 & 2 & 1 \end{pmatrix} \right\}$$

If f and g are permutations of X, we define a binary operation $\circ$ on S_n to be the composition of the functions, $f \circ g(a) = f(g(a))$, for all a in X. For example, in S_3 we see that

$$\begin{pmatrix} 1 & 2 & 3 \\ 1 & 3 & 2 \end{pmatrix} \circ \begin{pmatrix} 1 & 2 & 3 \\ 3 & 1 & 2 \end{pmatrix} = \begin{pmatrix} 1 & 2 & 3 \\ 2 & 1 & 3 \end{pmatrix}$$

Example 2   **The Symmetric Group**

We denote by S_n the entire set of $n!$ permutations on $\{1, 2, \ldots, n\}$. Show that S_n forms a group together with the binary operation $\circ$ (S_n is sometimes called the symmetric group on n elements).

Solution

To prove this, we first note that composition is a closed binary operation on S_n. To show that the function $f \circ g$ from X to X is also a permutation of X, it suffices to show that no two elements of X have the same image under $f \circ g$. If a and b are distinct elements of X, then $g(a)$ and $g(b)$ are also distinct since g is a permutation of X. Since f is a permutation, $f(g(a)) = f \circ g(a)$ and $f(g(b)) = f \circ g(b)$ are still distinct. Therefore $f \circ g$ is a permutation of X. (See Problem 20, Section 1.4.)

To show that $\circ$ is an associative operation, consider three permutations f, g, and h in S_n. For any a in X, we see that $(f \circ g) \circ h(a) = f(g(h(a))) = f \circ (g \circ h)(a)$. Thus the algebraic system $(S_n, \circ)$ satisfies the associative property.

We denote by 1_X the permutation that maps every element of X to itself, that is, $1_X(a) = a$, for all a in X. It is easy to see that for any permutation f in S_n, $f \circ 1_X = f = 1_X \circ f$. Therefore 1_X is an identity for S_n under the operation $\circ$, and 1_X is referred to as the identity permutation.

Finally, we note that any permutation f in S_n has an inverse. We define f^{-1} to be the permutation (see Theorem 1.10, Section 1.4) that assigns $f(1)$ to 1, $f(2)$ to 2,..., and $f(n)$ to n. We see that $f \circ f^{-1}(a) = a = f^{-1} \circ f(a)$, for any a in X. Therefore $f \circ f^{-1} = 1_X = f^{-1} \circ f$. $\qquad\square$

In many problems that we encounter in this chapter, there will be some set S of the vertices, edges, or faces of a geometrical object that are to be colored. We denote by C the colorings of S. In addition, we will consider a set of permutations (symmetries) G that act on the set S being colored and thus on C. The set G may not contain all the permutations of the objects in S, but if G is a group, we refer to G as a permutation group (acting on S). For any permutation group G that also acts on C, there is a binary relation R on C that is induced by G. For any pair a and b in C, we say that aRb if and only if there is a permutation in G that takes a to b. We will show that the binary relation R is always an equivalence relation.

THEOREM 9.1

If G is a group of permutations (symmetries) acting on a set S and also on a collection C of colorings of S, then G induces a partition of $C(S)$ into equivalence classes.

Proof

Since G is a group, the identity permutation is in G, and the identity permutation takes any element a to itself. Therefore every element in C is related to itself, and the reflexive property is satisfied. If there is a permutation f in G that takes a to b, the inverse permutation f^{-1} is also in G and it takes b to a, so the binary relation R satisfies the symmetric property. If there is a permutation f in G that takes a to b and a permutation g in G that takes b to c, the permutation $g \circ f$, which is also in G, takes a to c. Thus the binary relation R satisfies the transitive property. When a group of symmetries G acts on a set of colorings C, the induced relation R is an equivalence relation.   □

In this way the colorings are partitioned into equivalence classes, and often we want to determine the number of equivalence classes there are.

Example 3 Suppose that n different objects are equally spaced around a circle. (See Fig. 9.1.) How many different arrangements of these objects are possible?

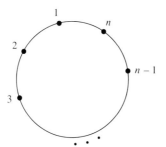

Figure 9.1

Solution
If the circle is not allowed to move, we find that there are $n!$ arrangements using the Multiplication Principle. However, we saw earlier in Section 4.1 that there were n different rotations that can be applied to a circular arrangement of n objects (including the identity). Written as permutations the set of rotations G is

$$\left\{ \begin{pmatrix} 1 & 2 & \cdots & n \\ 1 & 2 & \cdots & n \end{pmatrix}, \begin{pmatrix} 1 & 2 & \cdots & n \\ 2 & 3 & \cdots & 1 \end{pmatrix}, \begin{pmatrix} 1 & 2 & \cdots & n \\ 1 & 2 & \cdots & n \end{pmatrix}, \dots, \begin{pmatrix} 1 & 2 & \cdots & n \\ n & 1 & \cdots & 2 \end{pmatrix} \right\}$$

Since the n objects are different, all n rotations of one arrangement result in different fixed arrangements. Therefore the equivalence classes induced by the group of rotations will all have n elements. As before, we see that when any rotation is allowed, the number of distinct equivalence classes of circular permutations of n different objects is $n!/n = (n-1)!$.   □

Note that the problem in Example 3 is equivalent to the problem of finding the number of ways to color the vertices of a regular n-gon using n different colors when any rotation is allowed. Later in this section we will see that it is also possible to allow a slightly larger group of symmetries to act on the regular n-gon.
We consider another type of coloring problem in the next example.

Example 4 A baton is divided into five cylindrical bands of equal length, as shown in Fig. 9.2. In how many different ways can the five bands be colored if n colors are available, and unlimited repetition of the colors is allowed?

Figure 9.2

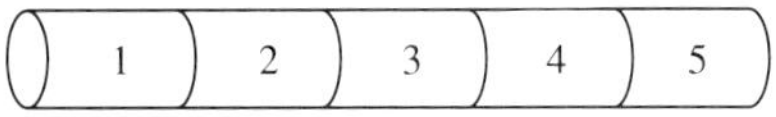

Solution

If the position of the baton is fixed, we use the Multiplication Principle to count n^5 colorings. When the baton is allowed to move freely, there are two symmetries, the identity and a 180° rotation. Written as permutations the identity is $\begin{pmatrix} 1 & 2 & 3 & 4 & 5 \\ 1 & 2 & 3 & 4 & 5 \end{pmatrix}$ and the 180° rotation is $\begin{pmatrix} 1 & 2 & 3 & 4 & 5 \\ 5 & 4 & 3 & 2 & 1 \end{pmatrix}$. In this case, we need to count the number of equivalence classes of colorings under these symmetries. Since there are only two symmetries, an equivalence class will contain either one coloring that remains unchanged after a 180° rotation or two different colorings. If a coloring remains unchanged after a 180° rotation, the first and last bands must have the same color. In addition, we see that the second and fourth bands must receive the same color as well. Using the Multiplication Principle again, we obtain n^3 colorings by assigning one of n colors to each of the two pairs of bands and one to the third band. The remaining $n^5 - n^3$ colorings will be in equivalence classes of size 2. Therefore, the total number of different equivalence classes of colorings will be $n^3 + (n^5 - n^3)/2 = (n^5 + n^3)/2$. $\qquad\square$

Suppose we have a set S acted on by a group of symmetries G. In considering the equivalence relation induced by G on a set of colorings C for the simplest problems (like Example 3), any permutation will take one fixed coloring to a different one. In this case, each equivalence class will contain $|G|$ different colorings, and the number of equivalence classes is simply $|C|/|G|$. In general, it may become rather tedious to analyze a coloring problem directly when the sizes of the equivalence classes vary a great deal. However, we will prove a result, first discovered by Burnside, that allows the number of equivalence classes to be computed in a slightly different manner.

We say that a coloring is fixed by a permutation f if it remains unchanged when f is applied. We denote by $\text{Fix}(f)$ the set of colorings that are fixed by a given permutation f. For any c in C, the set of permutations in G that fix c is called the stabilizer of c and is written $G(c)$. As in Section 1.3, we denote by $\langle c \rangle$, the equivalence class of colorings containing c.

Example 5
Black and white chairs are arranged around a square table, with one chair on each side. (See Fig. 9.3.) If an unlimited number of chairs of each color are available and two arrangements that differ by just a rotation of the table are considered identical, how many different seating arrangements are possible?

Solution
There are $2^4 = 16$ different seating arrangements when the position of the table remains fixed. We also have four different rotations of the table, which are represented by the permutations

$$G = \left\{ \begin{pmatrix} 1 & 2 & 3 & 4 \\ 1 & 2 & 3 & 4 \end{pmatrix}, \begin{pmatrix} 1 & 2 & 3 & 4 \\ 2 & 3 & 4 & 1 \end{pmatrix}, \begin{pmatrix} 1 & 2 & 3 & 4 \\ 3 & 4 & 1 & 2 \end{pmatrix}, \begin{pmatrix} 1 & 2 & 3 & 4 \\ 4 & 1 & 2 & 3 \end{pmatrix} \right\}$$

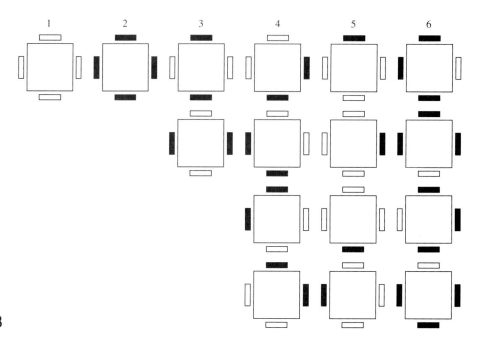

Figure 9.3

By analyzing the 16 fixed arrangements, when 0°, 90°, 180°, and 270° rotations are allowed (see Fig. 9.3), we see that there are six different equivalence classes of fixed arrangements and that an equivalence class may contain one, two, or four colorings. Thus we cannot apply the formula $|C|/|G|$ to obtain the number of different equivalence classes. However, Burnside's theorem will use a formula similar to this in computing the number of equivalence classes. In problems where a coloring may be fixed by a permutation, rather than mapped to another different coloring, the numerator of the ratio $|C|/|G|$ must be corrected to make sure that each equivalence class is counted $|G|$ times.

Note that in each equivalence class of size 1, a coloring is fixed by each of the four rotations. Also note that in the equivalence class of size 2, each coloring is fixed by precisely two rotations, the identity and the 180° rotation, and in an equivalence class of size 4, each coloring is only fixed by the identity. If we replace $|C|$ by the sum $|\text{Fix}(0°)| + |\text{Fix}(90°)| + |\text{Fix}(180°)| + |\text{Fix}(270°)|$, each element in an equivalence class of size 1 is counted four times, each element in an equivalence class of size 2 is counted twice, and each element in an equivalence class of size 4 is counted once. Therefore each equivalence class is counted a total of four times in this sum, and the number of equivalence classes can be obtained from the ratio $(|(\text{Fix}(0°)| + |\text{Fix}(90°)| + |\text{Fix}(180°)| + |\text{Fix}(270°)|)/4 = (16 + 2 + 4 + 2)/4 = 6$. $\qquad\square$

In general, we have the following results.

THEOREM 9.2 $|G(c)||\langle c \rangle| = |G|$.

Proof

Suppose that $G(c) = \{g_1, g_2, \ldots, g_m\}$ are the distinct elements of G that fix c and let $\langle c \rangle = \{c_1, c_2, \ldots, c_k\}$. For any c_i in $\langle c \rangle$, there exists an f in G that takes c to c_i. In fact, the permutations g that take c to c_i are precisely those permutations $f \circ g_i$, $i = 1, 2, \ldots, m$, since $g(c) = c_i$ implies $f \circ (f^{-1} \circ g)(c) = c_i$ and $f^{-1} \circ g$ is in $G(c)$. These permutations are all distinct since $f \circ g_i = f \circ g_j$ if and only if $g_i = g_j$ (see Problem 1). For example, consider the equivalence class of size 2 in Fig. 9.3. Each coloring is fixed by the $0°$ and $180°$ rotations, whereas the $90°$ and $270°$ rotations interchange the two colorings. Since exactly $|G(c)|$ permutations in G take c to c_j, for $j = 1, 2, \ldots, k$, then $|G| = |G(c)||\langle c \rangle|$.

THEOREM 9.3

Let G be a permutation group that acts on a set of colorings C. If we let N be the number of different equivalence classes of C induced by G, then N is given by the following formula.

$$N = \frac{1}{|G|} \sum_{f \in G} |\text{Fix}(f)|$$

Proof

In the sum $\sum_{f \in G} |\text{Fix}(f)|$, consider a given equivalence class $\langle c \rangle$. For any coloring c_i in $\langle c \rangle$, there is a permutation f taking c to c_i, so $f(c) = c_i$. If g fixes c_i, then $g \circ f(c) = f(c)$. But $g \circ f(c) = f(c)$ if and only if $g(c) = c$. Thus each coloring in $\langle c \rangle$ is fixed by precisely those permutations in $G(c)$ so the equivalence class $\langle c \rangle$ is counted a total of $|\langle c \rangle||G(c)| = |G|$ times in this sum. Therefore the number of equivalence classes is obtained by dividing $|G|$ into the sum, proving Burnside's theorem.

9.1
PROBLEMS

1. If $(G, *)$ is a group, show that the following cancellation laws hold.
    a) If $a * b = a * c$, then $b = c$.
    b) If $b * a = c * a$, then $b = c$.

2. Let a and b be arbitrary elements of a group $(G, *)$. Show that the following laws hold.

    a) $(a^{-1})^{-1} = a$
    b) $(a * b)^{-1} = b^{-1} * a^{-1}$

3. For any element a in a group $(G, *)$, we define $a^0 = e$ (where e is the identity of the group), and we also define $a^n = a^{n-1} * a$ and $a^{-n} = (a^n)^{-1}$, for any integer $n \geq 1$. Show that $a^p * a^q = a^{p+q}$, for any integers p and q.

4. Let $(G, *)$ be a group that has a finite number of elements. For any element a in G, we define the order of a, denoted by $o(a)$, to be the total number of distinct powers of a. Show that $a^{o(a)} = e$.

5. Compute the following permutations.

a) $\begin{pmatrix} 1 & 2 & 3 & 4 & 5 \\ 2 & 3 & 5 & 1 & 4 \end{pmatrix} \circ \begin{pmatrix} 1 & 2 & 3 & 4 & 5 \\ 3 & 2 & 1 & 5 & 4 \end{pmatrix}$

b) $\begin{pmatrix} 1 & 2 & 3 & 4 & 5 \\ 1 & 4 & 5 & 3 & 2 \end{pmatrix}^{-1}$

c) $\begin{pmatrix} 1 & 2 & 3 & 4 & 5 \\ 5 & 3 & 2 & 1 & 4 \end{pmatrix}^{3}$

6. a) Show that the set $\{\langle 0 \rangle, \langle 2 \rangle, \langle 4 \rangle, \langle 6 \rangle\}$ is a group using the operation of addition modulo 8.

   b) Show that the set $\{\langle 1 \rangle, \langle 3 \rangle, \langle 5 \rangle, \langle 7 \rangle\}$ is a group using the operation of multiplication modulo 8.

7. At a rectangular table, two chairs are placed along the top and bottom sides and one chair is placed at each end. If an unlimited number of black and white chairs are available, how many different seating arrangements are possible?

8. A baton is divided into six cylindrical bands of equal length.

   a) In how many different ways can the six bands be colored if n colors are available and unlimited repetition of the colors is allowed?

   b) In how many different ways can the six bands be colored if n colors are available and no two adjacent bands can receive the same color?

ADVANCED PROBLEMS

9. Suppose that $(G, *)$ is a group, with $|G| = n$. We say that G is a cyclic group if and only if some g in G has order n.

   a) Show that $(Z_m, +)$ is a cyclic group, for all $m \geq 1$.

   b) Show that $(S_m, \circ)$ is not a cyclic group, for all $m \geq 3$.

10. Describe the group of symmetries of a 3×5 rectangle. In how many different ways can we clip c corners $(0 \leq c \leq 4)$ off of a 3×5 card if all symmetries are allowed.

11. We say that a group $(G, *)$ is abelian if $a * b = b * a$, for every pair of elements a and b in G. Show that G is abelian if and only if $a^2 * b^2 = (a * b)^2$, for every pair of elements a and b in G.

12. Suppose that $(G, *)$ is a group with $G = \{g_1, g_2, \ldots, g_n\}$. Show that f_i, defined by $f_i(g) = g * g_i$ for all g in G, is a permutation of G.

13. Show that for any prime p, the set $Z_p^* = \{\langle 1 \rangle, \langle 2 \rangle, \ldots, \langle p-1 \rangle\}$, together with the operation of multiplication modulo p, forms a group.

14. Suppose that $(G, *)$ is a group, with identity e, where $|G|$ is even. Show that there must be an element g in G, with $g \neq e$ and $g * g = e$.

15. A domino is a 1×2 rectangular tile. Normally a domino is marked so that both squares on one side of the domino receive $0, 1, 2, \ldots,$ or 6 dots. How many different dominos can be formed if both sides are marked in this way?

16. A decimal sequence is a sequence whose digits are $0, 1, 2, \ldots, 9$. The digits $0, 1, 6, 8, 9$ become $0, 1, 9, 8, 6$, respectively, when they are turned upside down. We say

that two decimal sequences are equivalent if one can be transformed into the other by a $180°$ rotation. Find the number of different n-digit decimal sequences.

9.2 THE CYCLE INDEX

An important contribution that Polya made to this theory of counting was to show how $|\text{Fix}(f)|$ can be calculated by expressing the permutation f in terms of simpler permutations known as cycles.

Disjoint Cycle Notation

Consider the permutation $f = \begin{pmatrix} 1 & 2 & 3 & 4 & 5 \\ 3 & 1 & 5 & 4 & 2 \end{pmatrix}$ in S_5. Note that $f(1) = 3$, $f(3) = 5$, $f(5) = 2$, and $f(2) = 1$, whereas $f(4) = 4$. Thus f moves the elements $1 \to 3 \to 5 \to 2 \to 1$ in a cycle, while fixing the element 4. We say that f is a 4-cycle and represent it by $(1\ 3\ 5\ 2)$. Note that the cycle notation is not unique since f can also be represented by $(3\ 5\ 2\ 1)$, $(5\ 2\ 1\ 3)$, or $(2\ 1\ 3\ 5)$.

DEFINITION   Cycle

If f is a permutation of $X = \{1, 2, \ldots, n\}$, defined by $f(i_1) = i_2$, $f(i_2) = i_3, \ldots$, $f(i_{k-1}) = i_k$, $f(i_k) = i_1$, and $f(a) = a$ for all other a in X, we say that f is a k-cycle and denote it by $(i_1\ i_2\ i_3 \cdots i_{k-1}\ i_k)$.

Permutations that are not cycles can be expressed as a product of disjoint cycles in the following way. For a fixed permutation f in S_n and a in X, we define the orbit of a to be the distinct elements $\{a, b, \ldots, z\}$ where $f(a) = b$, $f(b) = c, \ldots, f(z) = a$. Each element of X is contained in a unique orbit, and each orbit will lead to a single cycle. For example, consider the permutation $f = \begin{pmatrix} 1 & 2 & 3 & 4 & 5 & 6 & 7 & 8 & 9 \\ 9 & 7 & 5 & 2 & 3 & 6 & 1 & 4 & 8 \end{pmatrix}$ in S_9. The orbits are $\{1, 9, 8, 4, 2, 7\}$, $\{3, 5\}$, and $\{6\}$, and f can be expressed as the product $(1\ 9\ 8\ 4\ 2\ 7)(3\ 5)(6)$.

For a permutation group G, we associate to any f in G whose disjoint cycle representation has e_1 1-cycles, e_2 2-cycles, e_3 3-cycles, $\ldots$, and e_n n-cycles, the monomial $x_1^{e_1} x_2^{e_2} x_3^{e_3} \cdots x_n^{e_n}$.

DEFINITION   Cycle Index

The cycle index of a permutation group G is the sum of the monomials associated with each of the permutations in G, divided by $|G|$.

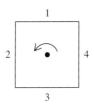

Figure 9.4

To see how the cycle index can be used in applying Burnside's theorem, we reconsider the problem of counting the number of black-white seating arrangements around a square table. First label the positions of the chairs around the table 1, 2, 3, and 4, as in Fig. 9.4.

The identity gives us the permutation (1)(2)(3)(4); the $90°$ rotation gives us the permutation (1 2 3 4); the $180°$ rotation gives us the permutation (13)(24); and the $270°$ rotation gives us the permutation (1 4 3 2). Therefore the cycle index of this group of rotations is $(x_1^4 + x_2^2 + 2x_4^1)/4$. Let c be a coloring that is fixed by a permutation $f = (i_1 i_2 \ldots i_m)\ldots$. Since $f(i_1) = i_2$, then i_2 has the same color as i_1. In a similar way, we can show that all the elements $i_1, i_2, \ldots, i_m$ must have the same color. Thus we see that in a coloring fixed by a permutation f, the objects in a cycle must all receive the same color. Since two colors are available, we can use the Multiplication Principle to show that $\text{Fix}(f) = 2^n$, where n is the number of cycles in the disjoint cycle representation of the permutation f. Alternately we can substitute 2 for each x_i in the monomial associated to f. Therefore by substituting 2 for each x_i in the cycle index, we obtain $(2^4 + 2^2 + 2 \times 2)/4 = 6$, which equals the total number of different seating arrangements. Many similar counting problems can be solved easily by first computing the cycle index of the appropriate permutation group G.

Example 1 **Symmetries of the Regular n-gon**
Label the vertices of the regular n-gon $1, 2, \ldots, n$ in counterclockwise order around its perimeter as in Fig. 9.5. Describe the symmetries of this figure.

Solution
First consider the group of symmetries of the n-gon that can be performed in the plane, that is, without turning it over. After any symmetry performed in the plane, the vertices will remain in their original counterclockwise order, so any symmetry is determined by the image of the vertex 1. The vertex 1 can be taken to any of the n vertices by a rotation. Thus the symmetry group consists of the n rotations, $k(360°/n)$, for $k = 0, 1, \ldots, n - 1$. This group of symmetries is sometimes called the group of rotations of the n-gon and is denoted by C_n.

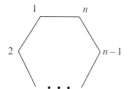

Figure 9.5

Now consider the entire group of symmetries of the regular n-gon. Any symmetry will be determined by the images of the two vertices 1 and 2. Vertex 1 can be taken to any of the n vertices, and after that vertex 2 must be taken to either of the two vertices adjacent to the image of vertex 1. Either vertex 2 is taken to the vertex that is adjacent to the image of vertex 1 in the counterclockwise direction, in which case we obtain one of the n rotations discussed earlier; or vertex 2 is taken to the vertex that is adjacent to the image of vertex 1 in the clockwise direction, in which case we obtain a symmetry that reverses the original clockwise order of the vertices. We let f be the symmetry of the n-gon that flips it 180° about an axis that passes through vertex 1 and the center of the n-gon. By first applying the flip f and then one of the n rotations, we obtain n different symmetries that reverse the original order of the vertices. Therefore we see that a total of $2n$ different symmetries can be obtained, and these $2n$ symmetries form the entire group of symmetries of the regular n-gon. This group of symmetries is referred to as the dihedral group and is denoted by D_n.

$\square$

Example 2   Carbon Compounds

In a benzene ring, six carbon atoms are attached to each other in the shape of a regular hexagon. If two kinds of radicals can be attached to each carbon atom and all the C–C bonds in the ring are assumed to be equivalent, how many different chemical compounds can be formed? (See Fig. 9.6.)

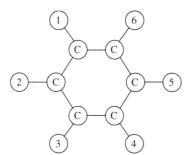

Figure 9.6

Solution

If the position of the ring were fixed, there would be 2^6 different ways of attaching the radicals. However, the dihedral group D_6 acts on these arrangements, and we wish to find the number of equivalence classes. We start by computing the cycle index of D_6. The group D_6 contains rotations of 0°, $\pm 60°$, $\pm 120°$, and 180°, and these are represented by the permutations (1)(2)(3)(4)(5)(6), (1 2 3 4 5 6), (1 6 5 4 3 2), (1 5 3)(2 6 4), (1 3 5)(2 4 6), (1 4)(2 5)(3 6). To the identity rotation, we associate the monomial x_1^6; to the second kind of rotation, we associate the monomial x_6^1; to the third kind, we associate the monomial x_3^2; and to the fourth kind of rotation, we associate the monomial x_2^3.

There are also two kinds of flips in D_6. We have three symmetries that flip the regular hexagon 180° about an axis that passes through diagonally opposite vertices on the hexagon. We also have three symmetries that flip the regular hexagon 180°

about an axis that passes through the midpoints of diagonally opposite edges of the hexagon. To the first kind of flip, we associate the monomial $x_1^2 x_2^2$ since its disjoint cycle representation contains two 1-cycles and two 2-cycles. To the second kind of flip, we associate the monomial x_2^3 because its disjoint cycle representation contains three 2-cycles. Since the cycle index of D_6 acting on these arrangements is given by $(x_1^6 + 2x_6^1 + 2x_3^2 + 4x_2^3 + 3x_1^2 x_2^2)/12$, the number of different compounds is $(2^6 + 2 \times 2 + 2 \times 2^2 + 4 \times 2^3 + 3 \times 2^4)/12 = 13$. $\square$

Note that in computing the number of equivalence classes of a set C of colorings that are induced by a permutation group G, there is a rather simple way to detect most errors. After the computations have been made, the calculated number of equivalence classes must be an integer; otherwise, an error has been detected.

Example 3   Fermat's Little Theorem

Let p be any prime number. Given that n different colors are available and that unlimited repetition of the colors is allowed, we color the vertices of the regular p-gon. Find the number of different colorings that are possible when two colorings are considered to be equivalent if and only if they differ by just a rotation.

Solution

The disjoint cycle representation of the identity rotation consists of p 1-cycles. Consider any other rotation by $k(360°/p)$, for $k = 1, 2, \ldots, p - 1$. Since p is prime, the numbers $0, k, 2k, \ldots, (p - 1)k$ are all distinct modulo p. This means that the vertices of the p-gon are all contained in a single orbit of size p under the action of such a rotation, and thus its disjoint cycle representation consists of a single p-cycle. Therefore the cycle index of this group is $(x_1^p + (p - 1)x_p^1)/p$, and the total number of colorings is given by $(n^p + (p - 1)n)/p$. Because the total number of colorings is an integer, we see that $n^p + (p - 1)n$, and thus $n^p - n = n(n^{p-1} - 1)$ are both divisible by p. If p does not divide n, then p divides $n^{p-1} - 1$ (or $n^{p-1} \equiv 1 \pmod{p}$), which is precisely the statement of Fermat's little theorem. This famous result has many applications in number theory. $\square$

Occasionally we encounter a coloring problem that involves a 3-dimensional object. In this case, a natural group of symmetries to consider is the group of symmetries that can be realized in 3-dimensional space. This collection of symmetries is often called the group of proper rotations. Because our own physical world is 3-dimensional, these symmetry groups are often used in applications involving chemistry and physics.

Example 4   Proper Rotations of the Cube

Theorem 9.2 can sometimes be used to help count the number of proper rotations of a geometrical object. Describe the group G of proper rotations of the cube acting on the faces of the cube.

Solution

The relation induced by G has one equivalence class that contains all six faces because one face can always be moved to any other by a proper rotation. Thus we see

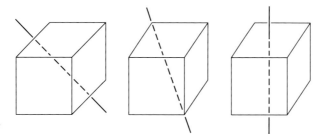

Figure 9.7

that $|G| = 6|G(a)|$, where $G(a)$ is the set of proper rotations that fix a given face a. Clearly $|G(a)| = 4$, so $|G| = 24$.

The 24 proper rotations of G can be described in more detail, as follows (see Fig. 9.7). There is, of course, a single identity rotation. There are a total of eight rotations of $\pm 120°$, about one of four different axes that pass through pairs of diagonally opposite vertices of the cube. There are also a total of six rotations of $180°$ about one of six axes that pass through the midpoints of opposite edges of the cube. Finally, there are a total of nine rotations of $\pm 90°$ or $180°$ about one of three axes that pass through the centers of opposite faces of the cube.   ☐

Example 5   Suppose that the six faces of the cube are each colored with one of n available colors and that unlimited repetition of the colors is allowed. How many different colorings are possible if two colorings that differ by a proper rotation are considered to be identical?

Solution
Obviously the disjoint cycle representation of the identity rotation acting on the six faces of the cube consists of six 1-cycles. The disjoint cycle representation of a $\pm 120°$ rotation, about an axis that passes through opposite vertices of the cube, consists of two 3-cycles. In addition, the disjoint cycle representation of a $180°$ rotation, about an axis that passes through the midpoints of opposite edges, consists of three 2-cycles. The disjoint cycle representation of a $\pm 90°$ rotation, about an axis that passes through the centers of opposite faces, consists of two 1-cycles and one 4-cycle, whereas the disjoint cycle representation of a $180°$ rotation about such an axis consists of two 1-cycles and two 2-cycles. Therefore the cycle index of the group of proper rotations is $(x_1^6 + 8x_3^2 + 6x_2^3 + 6x_1^2 x_4^1 + 3x_1^2 x_2^2)/24$. Substituting n for each of the variables, we obtain $(n^6 + 8n^2 + 12n^3 + 3n^4)/24$ different colorings.   ☐

Burnside's theorem can also be applied to counting problems that do not involve geometrical symmetry. When certain objects in an arrangement are considered identical, it is possible to count the number of inequivalent colorings using the entire permutation group S_n.

Example 6   Consider the different switching circuits that can be obtained by using three switches, labeled 1, 2, and 3. Every alignment of the three switches can be represented by a three-digit sequence w_1, w_2, w_3, where $w_i = 1$ if switch i is closed

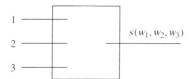

Figure 9.8

and $w_i = 0$ if switch i is open. To each switching circuit we associate a switching function $s(w_1, w_2, w_3)$, which assigns to each binary sequence, representing an alignment of the three switches, a value of 1 if electricity flows through the circuit and a value of 0 if it doesn't. In this context it is convenient to think of a circuit as having three input wires, with one switch controlling the electrical flow on each input wire, and one output wire whose electrical flow is described by the switching function $s(w_1, w_2, w_3)$. (See Fig. 9.8.)

Two circuits are obviously identical if they have the same switching function, so the total number of switching functions for a circuit with three switches is $2^{2^3} = 2^8 = 256$ (see Section 2.1). Thus for each switching function it is only necessary to keep track of one circuit with this switching function. In fact, this inventory of circuits can be further reduced using symmetry. Two circuits are also essentially the same if they have the same switching function after a permutation of the input wires. Thus we consider the equivalence classes of circuits under this action of S_3.

The permutations of S_3 consist of the identity, three 2-cycles, and two 3-cycles. Obviously all 2^8 circuits are fixed by the identity. A permutation that switches two wires, say, 1 and 2, will fix a circuit if and only if $s(0, 1, 0) = s(1, 0, 0)$ and $s(0, 1, 1) = s(1, 0, 1)$. To count the number of circuits whose switching function is fixed by this 2-cycle, we assign a value of 0 or 1 to each of the preceding pairs of sequences $\{(0, 1, 0), (1, 0, 0)\}$ and $\{(0, 1, 1), (1, 0, 1)\}$, as well as the four remaining sequences. Thus there are 2^6 switching functions fixed by a 2-cycle.

Similarly, a permutation that permutes the input wires in a 3-cycle will fix a circuit if and only if $s(0, 0, 1) = s(0, 1, 0) = s(1, 0, 0)$ and $s(0, 1, 1) = s(1, 0, 1) = s(1, 1, 0)$. To count the number of circuits whose switching function is fixed by a 3-cycle, we assign a value of 0 or 1 to each of the preceding triples of sequences $\{(0, 0, 1), (0, 1, 0), (1, 0, 0)\}$ and $\{(0, 1, 1), (1, 0, 1), (1, 1, 0)\}$, as well as to the two remaining sequences. Thus there are 2^4 circuits fixed by a 3-cycle. To find the total number of switching functions under this action of S_3, we apply Burnside's theorem to obtain $(2^8 + 3 \times 2^6 + 2 \times 2^4)/6 = 80$ different circuits. Note that this number can be reduced even further by allowing both permutations and inversions of the switches, but we do not pursue this.   □

9.2

P R O B L E M S 1. Find the disjoint cycle representation for each of the following permutations.

a) $\begin{pmatrix} 1 & 2 & 3 & 4 & 5 & 6 & 7 & 8 \\ 7 & 1 & 3 & 6 & 5 & 4 & 8 & 2 \end{pmatrix}$ b) $\begin{pmatrix} 1 & 2 & 3 & 4 & 5 & 6 & 7 & 8 & 9 \\ 2 & 4 & 6 & 8 & 1 & 3 & 5 & 9 & 7 \end{pmatrix}$

2. Show that any permutation in S_n can be written as a product of 2-cycles (not necessarily disjoint).

3. In how many different ways can the faces of a cube be painted using 6 different colors if every face must receive a different color?

4. Describe the symmetry groups of each of the following figures.
   a)   b)   c)   d)

5. Describe the group of proper rotations of a rectangular solid that is 12 inches wide, 12 inches high, and 18 inches long.

6. Find the cycle index of the group of proper rotations of the cube acting on
   a) The vertices of the cube.   b) The edges of the cube.

7. In how many different ways can the vertices of a cube be labeled if each vertex is labeled with either a 0 or a 1?

8. a) Find the cycle index of C_{10} acting on the vertices of the regular 10-gon.
   b) Find the cycle index of D_{10} acting on the vertices of the regular 10-gon.

9. a) Describe the group of symmetries of the regular tetrahedron.
   b) In how many different ways can the faces of a regular tetrahedron be painted if n different colors are available and unlimited repetition of the colors is allowed?

10. Find the cycle index of the group of proper rotations of the tetrahedron acting on
   a) The vertices of the regular tetrahedron.
   b) The edges of the regular tetrahedron.

11. A circular necklace contains nine beads.
   a) How many different necklaces can be constructed if an unlimited number of red and white beads are available?
   b) How many different necklaces can be constructed from three white and six red beads?

12. The nine squares of a 3 × 3 chessboard are painted red, white, and black. Assuming that the board can be rotated, but not flipped
   a) Find the number of chessboards that have two white, two red, and five black squares.
   b) Find the number of chessboards that have three squares of each color.

13. How many different merry-go-rounds can be formed using eight horses if two of the horses are white, two are black, and four are brown (horses of the same color are considered identical)?

14. A symmetry of a polynomial is a permutation of the variables that leaves the value of the polynomial unchanged. Describe the group of symmetries of each of the following polynomials.

a) $x_1 x_2 + x_3 x_4$ b) $x_1 x_2 x_3 + x_2 x_3 x_4$

15. In S_n, show that an r-cycle has order r.

16. a) Compute the order of (1 2 3)(4 5).
    b) Compute the order of (1 2 3 4)(5 6).

ADVANCED
PROBLEMS

17. In how many different ways can the faces of a cube be painted using three different colors if each color must be used at least once?

18. Suppose that each vertex of a regular n-gon is labeled with either a 0 or a 1. For which values of n is the number of different labelings under the action of C_n equal to the number of different labelings under the action of D_n?

19. a) Find the number of different binary relations on a set with four elements (Section 1.3).
    b) Find the number of different binary relations that are not equivalent under any permutation of the four elements.

20. Find the number of ways to distribute three red balls, three white balls, and three blue balls to three (indistinguishable) piles (empty piles allowed).

21. Compute the number of switching circuits, constructed using four switches, that are not equivalent under any permutation of the switches.

22. Show that there are 114 ways of labeling the vertices of the cube with letters a, b, c, d if each letter occurs exactly twice.

23. How many different chemical compounds can be formed by attaching one of two kinds of radicals to each of the four bonds of a carbon atom, assuming that the radicals lie at the vertices of a regular tetrahedron?

9   REVIEW PROBLEMS

1. a) A rod divided into six equal segments is to be colored with one or more of three different colors. In how many ways can this be done?
   b) Repeat part (a) if each color is used twice.

2. a) In how many ways can the 16 squares of a 4×4 chessboard be colored using three colors, if the board is free to rotate?
   b) Repeat part (a) if each color is used at least once.

3. For any $n \geq 3$, show that there are 3-colorings of the vertices of the regular n-gon that are inequivalent under any rotation but are equivalent under a flip.

4. Using the permutation group S_3, compute the number of ways to distribute
   a) 12 identical balls to three identical boxes.
   b) 4 red, 4 white, and 4 blue balls to three identical boxes.

5. In how many ways can the faces of a square pyramid be colored if three colors are available?

6. In how many ways can a $2 \times 2 \times 2$ cube be constructed from eight $1 \times 1 \times 1$ cubes if an unlimited number of red, white, and blue cubes are available?

7. In how many ways can a triangular array of 10 balls be constructed using orange and white balls, assuming that the array is free to rotate?

8. In how many ways can a merry-go-round be constructed using 10 horses if 4 different types of horses are available?

9. In how many ways can the edges of a square be colored using n colors if adjacent edges cannot receive the same color?

CHAPTER 9

SUMMARY

In this chapter, we encountered a powerful method for solving counting problems which takes into consideration the symmetry of the objects being counted. The theory was first developed by Polya in 1937 while he was analyzing models proposed for the benzene molecule. More recently this theory has also been used to solve counting problems involving various families of graphs [4].

BIBLIOGRAPHY

1. Burnside, W. *Theory of Groups of Finite Order*, 2nd edition. New York: Dover, 1955.
2. DeBruijn, N. G. *Polya's Theory of Counting in Applied Combinatorial Mathematics*. New York: John Wiley & Sons, 1964.
3. Gilbert, W. *Modern Algebra with Applications*. New York: John Wiley & Sons, 1976.
4. Harary, F., and E. Palmer. *Graphical Enumeration*. New York: Academic Press, 1973.

CHAPTER

10

GRAPH AND NETWORK ALGORITHMS

In Chapter 5 we saw that undirected graphs were useful in representing a variety of combinatorial problems. By allowing edges to have a direction and a weight, we obtain even more versatile models. A set of vertices together with a set of directed edges joining them is usually called a **directed** graph or **digraph**, whereas a directed graph that has a weight assigned to each directed edge is referred to as a **network**. Several important problems in computer science and operations research can be represented by optimization problems on a directed graph or network. In the last two sections of this chapter, we will encounter problems involving the optimal scheduling of activities in a project and also problems about optimal assignments of jobs to applicants. Since these problems have many practical applications, it is important to find efficient algorithms for solving them. In this section we discuss some basic definitions and examples related to directed graphs.

DIRECTED GRAPHS

A directed graph D consists of a finite set of vertices V and a finite set of directed edges or arcs $A \subseteq V \times V$. A directed graph or digraph is represented by a diagram with one point for each $v \in V$ and one edge directed from u to v for each $(u, v) \in A \times A$. For any vertex $v \in V$, the indegree $\deg^-(v)$ is the number of arcs directed into v and the outdegree $\deg^+(v)$ is the number of arcs directed out of v. (See Fig. 10.1.)

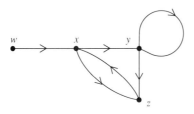

$$\deg^-(w) = 0 \qquad \deg^-(x) = 2 \qquad \deg^-(y) = 2 \qquad \deg^-(z) = 2$$

Figure 10.1 $\deg^+(w) = 1 \qquad \deg^+(x) = 2 \qquad \deg^+(y) = 2 \qquad \deg^+(z) = 1$

In traversing the arcs of a digraph D, any directed edge (u, v) must be traveled in the proper direction from u to v. With this in mind, we define the concept of a **directed walk** as follows. A directed walk joining u to v is an alternating sequence of vertices and arcs $u = u_0, a_1, u_1, a_2, u_2, \ldots, a_n, u_n = v$, with $a_i = (u_{i-1}, u_i)$. The length of a directed walk is equal to the number of arcs that it traverses. The definitions of directed trail, directed path, directed cycle, directed Eulerian circuit, and so on for a digraph are analogous.

Two vertices u and v in $V(D)$ are said to be strongly connected if there is a directed path from u to v as well as a directed path from v to u. Since this defines an equivalence relation, it partitions the vertices of D into equivalence classes. An equivalence class of vertices together with the arcs in D joining pairs of these vertices is referred to as a strongly connected component of D. If there is just one such equivalence class, we say that D is a strongly connected digraph.

Tournaments

An interesting class of digraphs are those that can be obtained from a complete graph by giving each edge a direction. Since these graphs arise naturally in the analysis of round-robin tournaments (Section 5.1, Example 1), any digraph of this kind is known as a tournament. A round-robin tournament is a competition in which every pair of teams play a match, and every match has a winner. In the corresponding digraph, every vertex represents a team and every arc (u, v) represents a match in which u beat v. Thus a tournament can be described as a digraph in which there is precisely one of the arcs (u, v) or (v, u) for every pair of different vertices u and v.

Figure 10.2
Tournaments on
Four Vertices

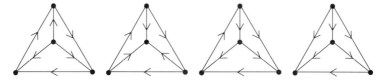

A directed Hamiltonian path of a digraph D is a directed path that includes every vertex of D.

THEOREM 10.1

Every tournament has a directed Hamiltonian path.

Proof
The proof is by induction on n, the number of vertices in the tournament. It is certainly true that any tournament with one vertex has a directed Hamiltonian path. Let T be any tournament on the vertices $t_1, t_2, \ldots, t_n$, for $n > 1$. We assume that any tournament with $n - 1$ vertices has a directed Hamiltonian path. In particular, the tournament consisting of vertices $t_1, t_2, \ldots, t_{n-1}$ and the arcs in T joining them has a directed Hamiltonian path. Without loss of generality, we assume that $t_1 t_2 \cdots t_{n-1}$ is such a path. Consider the following three cases.

i)   If the arc between t_n and t_1 is directed from t_n to t_1, then $t_n t_1 t_2 \cdots t_{n-1}$ is a directed Hamiltonian path of T. (See Fig. 10.3.)

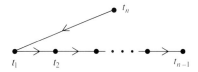

Figure 10.3

ii) If the arc between t_n and t_{n-1} is directed from t_{n-1} to t_n, then $t_1 t_2 \cdots t_{n-1} t_n$ is a directed Hamiltonian path of T. (See Fig. 10.4.)

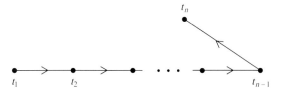

Figure 10.4

iii) If neither part (i) nor part (ii) applies, then T contains the arcs (t_1, t_n) and (t_n, t_{n-1}). Let i be the smallest subscript for which T contains the arc (t_n, t_i). Since $1 < i \le n - 1$, then T contains the arcs (t_n, t_i) and (t_{i-1}, t_n). Therefore $t_1 t_2 \cdots t_{i-1} t_n t_i t_{i+1} \cdots t_{n-1}$ is a directed Hamiltonian path of T. (See Fig. 10.5.)

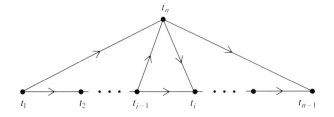

Figure 10.5

Note that a directed Hamiltonian path in a tournament has the property that it arranges the competitors in order $a, b, c, \ldots, z$ so that a beat b, b beat c, and so on. Although this might seem like a desirable way to rank the teams in the tournament, this ranking is not necessarily unique (see Problem 17).

Eulerian Digraphs

A directed Eulerian circuit in a digraph D is a directed circuit that traverses each arc of D exactly once.

THEOREM 10.2

A strongly connected digraph D contains a directed Eulerian circuit if and only if $\deg^+(v) = \deg^-(v)$ for every vertex v in D.

Proof
The proof is essentially the same as that of Theorem 5.2 in Section 5.3. It is easy to see that any digraph D with a directed Eulerian circuit satisfies $\deg^+(v) = \deg^-(v)$ for every vertex v in D, and in case $\deg^+(v) = \deg^-(v)$ for every v we have the following algorithm for constructing a directed Eulerian circuit in D.

i) Starting at any vertex v, we traverse a directed trail C by successively adding any unused arc to the end of the trail. We can only be forced to stop at v after all the arcs incident to v have been used. If, at this point, all the arcs in D have been used, we are done since a directed Eulerian circuit has been constructed.

ii) If unused arcs remain in D, the number of unused arcs entering any vertex u equals the number of unused arcs leaving u. Since D is strongly connected, we can find a vertex x on C that is incident to unused arcs. Starting at x, we construct a nontrivial closed directed trail B that has no arcs in common with C as in Step (i). By joining these two trails at x, we obtain a larger closed trail. This process eventually terminates with a closed directed trail that contains every arc of D. The resulting trail is a directed Eulerian circuit.

Example 1   An Efficient Computer Drum
The surface of a rotating drum is divided into 16 sections. Each section is constructed with either a conducting material or a nonconducting material. Four fixed electrical contacts are used to recognize the position of the drum. When a contact is at rest against a section of nonconducting material, no electricity flows; when it is against a section of conducting material, electricity does flow. We use these patterns of electrical flow to recognize the different positions of the drum. How can we design a drum with 16 distinguishable positions?

Solution
For the 16 positions to be clearly distinguishable, the sections of the drum must be constructed in such a way that no two conducting and nonconducting patterns of four consecutive sections are the same. We let the binary digit 0 represent a non-conducting section and the binary digit 1 represent a conducting section. Thus we

would like to construct a circular arrangement of 16 binary digits for which each of the 16 sequences of four consecutive digits is distinct. The existence of such an arrangement can be discovered by looking at the following digraph model.

While the computer drum rotates from one position to the next, the binary pattern recognized by the four electrical contacts changes from $b_1b_2b_3b_4$ to $b_2b_3b_4b_5$. Note that these two patterns have the three-digit sequence $b_2b_3b_4$ in common, so we consider the digraph D with eight vertices, each of which is labeled by a different three-digit binary sequence. Each four-digit binary sequence $b_1b_2b_3b_4$ corresponds to an arc in D that joins $b_1b_2b_3$ to $b_2b_3b_4$ (see Fig. 10.6).

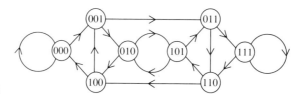

Figure 10.6

Note that two four-digit binary patterns can appear consecutively in a circular arrangement if and only if the corresponding arcs can appear consecutively in a directed trail of D. Therefore the 16 consecutive positions of the desired computer drum correspond to a directed Eulerian circuit of D and vice versa. Each vertex $b_1b_2b_3$ of D has two edges $b_1b_2b_30$ and $b_1b_2b_31$ leaving it, so its outdegree is 2. In a similar way, we see that every vertex also has indegree 2. Since D is strongly connected, it has a directed Eulerian circuit. Each circuit of this kind corresponds to the type of circular arrangement that we are trying to find. For example, we see one directed Eulerian circuit and the corresponding circular drum in Fig. 10.7.

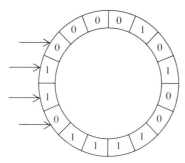

Figure 10.7 $0000 \to 0001 \to 0010 \to 0101 \to 1010 \to 0100 \to 1001 \to 0011 \to 0111 \to 1111 \to$
$1110 \to 1101 \to 1011 \to 0110 \to 1100 \to 1000 \to 0000$

In a similar way, we can construct a computer drum with 2^n different sections whose position can be recognized using n different electrical contacts (see Problem 12). Obviously no fewer than n contacts will suffice since there are only 2^n different binary patterns of length n.   □

10.1

PROBLEMS

1. A digraph is strict if it has no loops and no two arcs joining the same pair of vertices in the same direction. If D is a strict digraph with minimum indegree k, show that D contains a directed path of length k.

2. For which values of p is it possible to have a digraph with p vertices such that every vertex has odd outdegree and every vertex has odd indegree?

3. For which values of p is it possible to have a strict digraph with p vertices such that no two vertices have the same indegree and no two vertices have the same outdegree?

4. A digraph D is called r-regular if $\deg^+(v) = \deg^-(v) = r$ for every vertex v of D. For which integers r and p with $0 \le r < p$ is there a strict r-regular digraph with p vertices?

5. Let D be a digraph with no directed cycle. Show that D must have at least one vertex with indegree zero.

6. For any digraph D, show that $\sum_{v \in V} \deg^-(v) = \sum_{v \in V} \deg^+(v)$.

7. In a digraph D, let $d(u, v)$ represent the minimum length of a directed path from u to v. If D is a tournament, show that $d(u, v) \ne d(v, u)$, for any pair of vertices u and v.

8. Show that the digraph D is strongly connected if and only if it has a closed directed walk that contains every vertex of D.

9. If a vertex u of D is contained on a directed circuit of D, show that u is also contained on a directed cycle of D.

10. Show that every tournament is either strongly connected or that it can be made strongly connected by changing the direction of just one arc.

11. Show that a tournament has no more than one vertex with indegree 0.

12. a) Explain the digraph model needed to prove the existence of a circular arrangement containing 2^n binary digits for which every block of n consecutive digits is different.
    b) Find a circular arrangement containing 32 binary digits for which every block of five consecutive digits is different.

ADVANCED PROBLEMS

13. Let $v_1, v_2, \ldots, v_p$ be the vertices of a digraph D. The adjacency matrix of D is the $p \times p$ matrix $A = [a_{ij}]$ for which a_{ij} equals the number of arcs joining v_i to v_j. Show that the (i, j)th entry of A^k equals the number of directed walks in D from v_i to v_j that have length k.

14. Let $D_1, D_2, \ldots, D_n$ be the strongly connected components of a digraph D. The

condensation of D, denoted by $\tilde{D}$, is a directed graph with n vertices, $v_1, v_2, \ldots, v_n$. There is an arc in $\tilde{D}$ joining v_i to v_j $(i \neq j)$ if and only if there is an arc in D joining some vertex in D_i to some vertex in D_j. Show that the condensation $\tilde{D}$ has no directed cycle.

15. We say that the score of a vertex in a tournament is its outdegree. The score sequence of a tournament is the sequence of scores arranged in nondecreasing order. Show that the score sequence of a tournament with n vertices satisfies:

   a) $s_1 + s_2 + \cdots + s_n = \binom{n}{2}$

   b) $s_1 + s_2 + \cdots + s_k \geq \binom{k}{2}$

16. A tournament is said to be transitive if it represents a transitive relation. In other words, a relation is transitive if the existence of arcs (x, y) and (y, z) implies the existence of arc (x, z). Show that a tournament is transitive if and only if it contains no directed cycle.

17. Show that a tournament T has a unique Hamiltonian path if and only if it is transitive.

18. An orientation of a graph G is a digraph D obtained by inserting an arrow on each edge of D. Show that a graph G always has an orientation D with $|\deg^+(v) - \deg^-(v)| \leq 1$, for every vertex v.

19. Let A be any alphabet of n letters. Explain the digraph model needed to prove the existence of a circular arrangement containing n^3 letters from A, for which every block of three consecutive letters is different.

*20. Show that any orientation D of a graph G, with chromatic number $X(G)$, has a directed path of length $X(G) - 1$.

21. Let D be a digraph that has a single vertex u with $\deg^-(u) = 0$ and $\deg^+(u) > 0$, and a single vertex v with $\deg^-(v) = 0$. For any other vertex w in D, suppose that $\deg^-(w) = \deg^+(w)$. Show that there is a directed path in D joining u to v.

10.1
SUPPLEMENTARY COMPUTER PROJECTS

1. Strongly Connected Digraphs
   Given the adjacency matrix of a digraph D
   a) Write a program to compute the indegrees and outdegrees of its vertices.
   b) Write a program to determine whether or not D is strongly connected.

2. Round-Robin Tournaments
   Suppose you have N teams (for the moment we assume N is even). In a round-robin tournament, each team is required to play every one of the other $N - 1$ teams exactly once. In each of the $N - 1$ rounds, all the teams are paired. Thus,

for $N = 4$, we could have the following schedule:

Team Round	1	2	3	4
1	3	4	1	2
2	4	3	2	1
3	2	1	4	3

Equivalently, we could represent this schedule on the complete graph with $N = 4$ vertices. (See Fig. 10.8.)

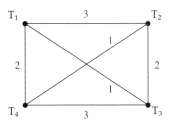

Figure 10.8

Edge $T_1 T_2$ is labeled "3" since team 1 plays team 2 in round 3, and so on.

If N is odd, not all teams can have an opponent in each round. It is then customary to add a dummy team. If a team is paired with the dummy team in a round, it gets a "bye" and does not play.

Define $A(R, X)$ to be the opponent of team X in round R. (Note that $1 \leq R \leq N - 1$.) Let our schedule be represented by an $N - 1$ by N matrix A, where the entry in row R and column X is $A(R, X)$. We may use the following algorithm.

    i) Let t be the unique integer satisfying $t \equiv R - X \pmod{N - 1}$ and $t \in S = \{1, 2, \dots, N - 1\}$.

    ii) If $t \neq X$, then $A(R, X) = t$; otherwise, set $A(R, X) = N$ and $A(R, N) = t$.

a) Prove the following theorems.

    1. If $R \neq R^*$, then $A(R, X) \neq A(R^*, X)$. (The opponents of team X in distinct rounds are distinct.)

    2. If $X, Y \in \{1, 2, \dots, N - 1\}$ with $X \neq Y$, there is a unique round R such that $A(R, X) = Y$. (Each team plays every other team exactly once.)

    3. $A(R, X) \neq X$. (No team plays itself.)

    4. If $A(R, X) = Y$, then $A(R, Y) = X$. (In round R, if X plays Y, then Y plays X.)

b) Write a program to generate the schedule matrix A for a round-robin tournament. Your input should be N, the number of teams.

NETWORKS

A useful model for many combinatorial problems is a digraph to which each arc has been assigned a numerical weight. We use the term network to refer to a digraph with weighted arcs. In a network we say that the weight of a directed path is equal to the sum of the weights of the arcs in the path.

Activity Networks

A large project often consists of a number of smaller activities that are interrelated. Although some of the activities may occur simultaneously, one activity often must be completed before another can even begin. Project analysis is one of the many practical problems where networks are used. In planning a project, we consider a network where each arc represents an activity. The weight of an activity is an estimate of the amount of time needed to complete that activity. The most important goal of this analysis is to find a schedule for the activities that minimizes the overall time needed to complete the project.

Example 1   A Computer Science Curriculum

A student must complete nine courses before he or she can graduate in computer science. The courses and their prerequisites are listed in the following table.

Course	Prerequisites
Calculus 1(C1)	None
Calculus 2(C2)	C1
Discrete Math(DM)	C1
Programming 1(P1)	C1
Combinatorics(C)	C2, DM
Programming 2(P2)	C2, P1
Pascal (P)	C1, P1
Data Structures(DS)	P
Advanced Programming(AP)	C, P2, DS

The activity network for this curriculum is shown in Fig. 10.9. Each course is represented by a solid arc and each such arc has weight 1 because a course can be completed in one semester. Course A is seen to be a prerequisite for course B if there

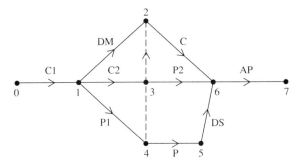

Figure 10.9

is a directed path in the network from the terminal vertex of arc A to the initial vertex of arc B. Thus we have added two dotted arcs of weight 0 to ensure that all the prerequisites will be met. These arcs do not represent activities and are known as dummy arcs. Find a schedule for completing the required courses in the smallest amount of time.

Solution
A vertex in an activity network can be thought of as the event that marks the completion of all the activities ending at that vertex. In particular, the vertex labeled 0 can be thought of as the starting time of the project, and the vertex labeled 7 can be thought of as the completion time. We shall see that the smallest amount of time needed to complete this project coincides with the maximum weight of a path from vertex 0 to vertex 7 in this network, which equals 5. Another important kind of question that we do not consider is how long it would take, if, say, no more than two courses per semester could be taken.   □

A digraph that contains no directed cycle is said to be acyclic. It is easy to see that an activity network must be acyclic. For example, suppose that abcd ... za was a cycle in the network. Activity (a, b) would then have to be completed before activity (b, c) could be started, activity (b, c) would have to be completed before activity (c, d) could be started, ..., activity (y, z) would have to be completed before activity (z, a) could be started, and activity (z, a) would have to be completed before activity (a, b) could be started. Therefore activity (a, b) cannot be started, which means that it is impossible to complete the project.

Consider an acyclic activity network. Each arc in an activity network will have a nonnegative weight since its weight equals the amount of time required to complete the corresponding activity. We denote by $w(a, b)$ the weight of arc (a, b). In scheduling the activities of a project, we may as well assume that the first activity starts at time 0. In addition, suppose that the network contains a directed path of weight t that ends at vertex a. In this case we see that the event corresponding to vertex a can occur no earlier than time t, so activity (a, b) can start no earlier than time t. We denote by $e(a)$ the maximum weight of a directed path ending at a. Since activity (a, b) cannot start earlier than event a occurs, $e(a)$ is also referred to as the earliest starting time of (a, b).

THEOREM 10.3

In an acyclic activity network, we can finish all the activities in the smallest possible amount of time by starting each activity at its earliest starting time.

Proof
Given any activity (a, b), it suffices to show that the proposed schedule leaves enough time to complete activity (a, b) before the activities that have (a, b) as a prerequisite are started. The starting time of (a, b) is $e(a)$, and any activity that has (a, b) as a prerequisite starts after $e(b)$. The maximum weight of a directed path ending at b is at least as large as the maximum weight of a directed path ending at a plus $w(a, b)$. Since $e(b) \geq e(a) + w(a, b)$, there will be enough time to finish activity (a, b).

Finally, we present an algorithm for determining the earliest starting time schedule of an activity network. Note that this is equivalent to finding, for each vertex in the network, the maximum weight of a directed path ending at the vertex. Suppose that the network under consideration has n vertices and m arcs. The algorithm consists of two basic steps. First, we find a **source** vertex in the network, that is, a vertex with indegree 0. If no such vertex exists, the network has a cycle (see Problem 5, Section 10.1). In the second step, we process the arcs that start at the chosen vertex. Finally, we remove the chosen source and the processed arcs, returning to Step 1 until no vertices remain. Since each arc is processed once, when its initial vertex is the chosen source, the number of steps required by this algorithm is $O(m)$.

The Earliest Starting Time Algorithm

Initially we set $j = 1$ and $e(i) = 0$, for $i = 1, 2, \ldots, n$.

1. Find a source vertex in the network and label it j. If no such vertex exists, the network has a cycle, so it cannot be solved.
2. For each arc (j, v) with initial vertex j, set $e(v) = \max\{e(v), e(j) + w(j, v)\}$.
3. Remove vertex j and the arcs incident to it from the network. Increase j by 1 and return to Step 1 until no vertices remain.

THEOREM 10.4

For an acyclic network with n vertices, the earliest starting time algorithm terminates with $e(i)$ equal to the maximum weight of a directed path ending at i, for $i = 1, 2, \ldots, n$.

Proof

We proceed by induction on i. For $i = 1$, the algorithm terminates with $e(1) = 0$, which also equals the length of a longest path ending at 1 since 1 is a source vertex. Assume that the algorithm terminates with $e(i)$ equal to the maximum weight of a directed path ending at i, for $i \leq j - 1$. The final value of $e(j)$ is equal to $\max\{e(i) + w(i, j)\}$, where the maximum is taken over all predecessors of j. By the induction hypothesis, $e(i) + w(i, j)$ will be equal to the weight of a path ending at j that passes through vertex i. Thus $e(j)$ is no larger than the maximum weight of a directed path ending at j. On the other hand, a maximum-weight path ending at j consists of a maximum-weight path ending at i followed by the arc (i, j), for some predecessor i of j. Therefore $e(j)$ is equal to $e(i) + w(i, j)$, the maximum weight of a directed path ending at j.

The last vertex chosen by the earliest starting time algorithm will have no arcs leaving it. A vertex with outdegree 0 in a network is referred to as a **sink**. In a typical activity network, a single source represents the start of the project and a single sink represents the finish of the project. Otherwise, we can take the starting vertex to be the initial vertex of the maximum-weight path in the network and the final vertex to be the terminal vertex of the maximum-weight path. If we denote by T the maximum weight of a directed path from start to finish, T will equal the minimum overall time needed to complete the entire project.

Example 2   Consider a home building project. The activities that must be completed and their estimated completion times are listed in the following table.

Activity	Time required (in days)	Prerequisites
a. Planning	15	—
b. Foundation	8	a
c. Framing	7	b
d. Plumbing	5	c
e. Electrical	6	c
f. Interior	16	d, e
g. Exterior	14	c
h. Septic system	10	d
i. Painting	9	f, g
j. Landscaping	7	h
k. Moving in	6	i

What is the minimum amount of time needed to complete this project?

Solution
To analyze this project, we construct the activity network shown in Fig. 10.10.

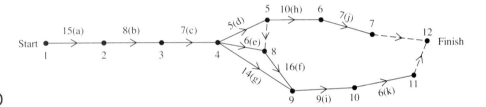

Figure 10.10

The maximum-weight directed path in this network consists of arcs, a, b, c, e, f, i, and k, and has overall weight 67. Thus the smallest amount of time needed to finish this project is 67 days.   □

Critical Path Analysis

Another important goal when analyzing a project is to identify the activities that might delay the entire project if they were not completed on time. In an activity network we have already seen that the earliest completion time, $e(x)$, of an event x equals the maximum weight of a directed path (beginning at the start) ending at x. In a similar manner we can define the latest completion time, $l(y)$, of an event y. If T is the minimum overall completion time of the project, $l(y)$ is defined to be T minus the maximum weight of a directed path starting at y (ending at the finish). Any activity (x, y) must start after $e(x)$, and it must be completed by $l(y)$ if the project is to be finished by time T. The maximum delay that can be allowed in the completion of activity (x, y) is thus $f(x, y) = l(y) - e(x) - w(x, y)$. The quantity $f(x, y)$ is referred to as the **float time** of activity (x, y). In Example 2, the float time of activity j

is $f(j) = l(7) - e(6) - w(6,7) = 67 - 41 - 6 = 19$ and $f(k) = l(11) - e(10) - w(11,10) = 67 - 61 - 6 = 0$. The float times of the activities in this project are as follows.

Activity	a	b	c	d	e	f	g	h	i	j	k
Float time	0	0	0	1	0	0	8	15	0	19	0

An activity for which the float time is 0 is said to be critical because it must be started at the earliest possible time and completed without delay if the project is to finish on time. For example, any activity on a maximum-weight path in the activity network is critical. A maximum-weight path from the start to the finish in an activity network is also referred to as a critical path.

In Example 2, there is a unique critical path containing the arcs a, b, c, e, f, i, k and one dummy arc from vertex 11 to the finish.

Critical path analysis is an important topic in operations research with widespread industrial application, and we hope that this brief discussion will give the reader an idea of what is involved.

Compaction of an Integrated Circuit Design (Optional)

To describe the layout of an integrated circuit design, we assume that it is drawn in a coordinate plane. To each vertical line we associate its x-coordinate, and to each horizontal line we associate its y-coordinate, as shown in Fig. 10.11. The simplest design rules are constraints on the distances between pairs of parallel lines in the design. Usually such a constraint indicates that a distance must be greater than or equal to a given amount, but less-than-or-equal-to constraints and equality constraints also arise occasionally.

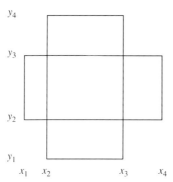

Figure 10.11

A feasible solution of an integrated circuit compaction problem will be a set of nonnegative integer values for the endpoints of these line segments that satisfy the constraints given by the design rules. An optimal solution will be a feasible solution for which the overall area is minimized. In these simple design problems, the x-values and the y-values are independent, so we can compact the area by first minimizing the spread in the x-direction and then in the y-direction. In our examples we will consider the x-values only, but the same technique can be used to find the y-values. Our goal will be to find nonnegative integer values for the x-coordinates that satisfy the constraints and minimize the overall spread in the x-direction.

We consider a network with one vertex for each x-coordinate. For each constraint of the form $x_j \geq x_i + k$, there is one arc of weight k joining x_i to x_j. Less-than or equal-to constraints are algebraically transformed into greater-than-or-equal-to constraints with a negative constraint value. Equality constraints are represented as two constraints, one greater-than or equal-to constraint and one less-than or equal-to constraint. Figure 10.12 gives a set of constraints for the example in Fig. 10.11 along with the corresponding constraint network.

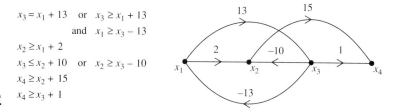

$x_3 = x_1 + 13$ or $x_3 \geq x_1 + 13$
                     and $x_1 \geq x_3 - 13$
$x_2 \geq x_1 + 2$
$x_3 \leq x_2 + 10$ or $x_2 \geq x_3 - 10$
$x_4 \geq x_2 + 15$
$x_4 \geq x_3 + 1$

Figure 10.12

Other relationships between the x-coordinates can be determined by looking at the constraint network.

THEOREM 10.5

If there is a directed walk W from vertex x_i to vertex x_j, then $x_j \geq x_i +$ length of W.

Proof
The proof is by induction on the number of arcs in the directed walk W. The statement is obviously true for walks with one arc, by definition. Assume that the result is true for directed walks consisting of $n - 1$ arcs, and let W be any directed walk consisting of $n > 1$ arcs. Suppose that the last arc of W starts at x_h and ends at x_j. Denote by W^* the directed walk from x_i to x_h that consists of the first $n - 1$ arcs of W. The induction hypothesis implies that $x_h \geq x_i +$ weight of W^*. If arc (x_h, x_j) has weight w, then $x_j \geq x_h + w$. Combining these inequalities, we obtain $x_j \geq x_i +$ weight of $W^* + w$. Since the weight of $W^* + w$ equals the weight of W, this completes the proof.

Similarly, if there is a directed cycle C in the constraint network containing a vertex x_i, we see that $x_i \geq x_i +$ length of C. This last statement shows that a set of constraints will not have a feasible solution if the constraint network has a positive weight cycle. On the other hand, if the constraint network has no positive weight cycle, there is a convenient description of an optimal solution for this compaction problem.

THEOREM 10.6

In a constraint network without positive weight cycles, we obtain an optimal solution by setting x_i equal to the maximum weight of a directed path that ends at x_i.

Proof
Since the proof is very similar to that of Theorem 10.4, we omit it.

The maximum-weight path solution for the problem described in Fig. 10.12 gives us the values $x_1 = 0$, $x_2 = 3$, $x_3 = 13$, and $x_4 = 18$. To find this optimal solution, in general, we can use the previous maximum-weight path algorithm as long as the constraint network is acyclic. However, it often happens that a constraint network has cycles of nonpositive weight. For example, an equality constraint introduces a cycle of weight 0. The following algorithm can be used on an arbitrary constraint network to find, for each vertex x_i in the network, the maximum weight of a directed path ending at x_i.

Consider a constraint network with n vertices, $x_1, x_2, \ldots, x_n$, and m arcs. Initially we set each x_i equal to 0. The complete set of constraints is processed in some order. If no changes are made after a pass through the constraints, a solution has been found. Otherwise, continue by making another pass through the constraints. If changes are still made after the nth pass through the constraints, the constraint network has a positive weight cycle and no solution exists. Thus the efficiency of this algorithm is $O(nm)$.

A Maximum-Weight Path Algorithm (For Arbitrary Networks)

1. Set $p = 1$ (the number of the pass), $C = 0$ (the number of changes in the present pass), and v_i(the value of x_i) $= 0$, for $i = 1, 2, \ldots, n$.
2. For each constraint $x_j \geq x_i + k$,
   i) Increase C by 1 if $v_j < v_i + k$.
   ii) Set $v_j = \max \{v_j, v_i + k\}$.
3. If $C = 0$, stop since all the constraints are satisfied. If $p = n$, stop since no solution exists. Otherwise, increase p by 1, set $C = 0$, and return to Step 2.

We briefly indicate the idea behind this algorithm. Consider a constraint network N with vertices $x_1, x_2, \ldots, x_n$, that has no cycle of positive weight. After p passes of the maximum-weight path algorithm, we can show by induction that the value of v_j equals the weight of some directed walk ending at x_j. In addition, this value will be greater than or equal to the weight of any directed walk ending at x_j that consists of p or fewer arcs. By backtracking we find that a change made on the pth pass will come from a walk consisting of p or more arcs. In a network with n vertices, any walk consisting of n or more arcs that causes a change must contain a positive weight cycle. Thus the algorithm will terminate after n passes unless a positive weight cycle is present.

10.2
PROBLEMS

1. In an acyclic digraph D show that a directed walk from u to v is also a directed path from u to v.

2. Explain the difficulty that might arise in finding the maximum-weight path between a pair of vertices in a network that has a positive weight cycle.

3. Describe a procedure that exhibits a cycle in a network or determines that no cycle exists.

4. A family picnic consists of the following activities:

Activity	Minutes required	Prerequisites
a. Shopping	45	—
b. Gather kids	25	—
c. Pack basket	20	a
d. Drive	75	b, c
e. Get water	15	d
f. Start fire	35	d
g. Cooking	40	f
h. Set table	10	d
i. Eating	30	g, h
j. Cleanup	25	i
k. Return home	75	j

a) Draw the corresponding activity network.
b) Find the smallest amount of time needed to complete the family picnic.
c) Determine the float time of each activity.
d) Find a critical path in the activity network.

5. A construction project consists of ten activities.

Activities	a_1	a_2	a_3	a_4	a_5	a_6	a_7	a_8	a_9	a_{10}
Hours required	7	3	2	8	4	6	1	10	5	9
Prerequisites	—	a_1	a_1	a_3	a_2, a_4	a_5	a_4	a_7	a_6, a_7	a_8, a_9

a) Find the earliest starting time of each activity.
b) Find the earliest possible completion time of the entire project.

6. In the following IC design, find the smallest nonnegative x-values that satisfy the given list of constraints. (See the figure following Problem 7.)

$$x_2 \geq x_1 + 2$$
$$x_3 \geq x_2 + 1$$
$$x_3 \leq x_1 + 5$$
$$x_4 \geq x_1 + 7$$
$$x_4 \geq x_3 + 2$$
$$x_5 \geq x_4 + 1$$
$$x_5 = x_3 + 4$$
$$x_6 \geq x_5 + 3$$
$$x_6 \geq x_2 + 8$$

7. Find a set of nonnegative y-values that satisfy the following set of constraints:

$$y_2 \geq y_1 + 2$$
$$y_3 \geq y_2 + 1$$

$$y_4 \geq y_3 + 3$$
$$y_5 \geq y_4 + 3$$
$$y_6 \geq y_5 + 4$$
$$y_3 \geq y_1 + 5$$
$$y_6 \geq y_4 + 6$$
$$y_5 \geq y_2 + 7$$
$$y_2 - y_1 = y_6 - y_5$$

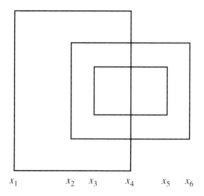

x_1 x_2 x_3 x_4 x_5 x_6

8. For an acyclic network with n vertices and m arcs, describe an $O(m)$ algorithm that finds the minimum-weight path between any given pair of vertices.

9. For a network with n vertices and m arcs that has no negative weight cycle, describe an $O(nm)$ algorithm that finds the minimum-weight path between any given pair of vertices.

10. The vertices of a network are denoted by $1, 2, \ldots, n$. In addition, the weight of the arc joining i to j is denoted by w_{ij} (if there is such an edge) or ∞ (if there is no such edge). Show that the final value of d_{ij}, determined by the following algorithm, is equal to the minimum-weight path from vertex i to vertex j, for every pair i and j.

    1. Set $k = 1$.
    2. For every $1 \leq i, j \leq n$, set $d_{ij} = \min\{d_{ij}, d_{ik} + d_{kj}\}$.
    3. If $k = n$, stop. Otherwise, increase k by 1 and return to Step 2.

SECTION 10.3   NETWORK FLOWS

In this section we study a type of network that serves as a useful model for the transportation of a commodity from its source to a destination through shipping routes with a limited capacity. In a transport network (see Fig. 10.13), each arc (x, y) is assigned a nonnegative weight $c(x, y)$ known as the capacity of (x, y). The capacity

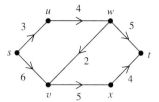

Figure 10.13
A Transport
Network

of (x, y) represents the maximum amount of the commodity that can be shipped through the corresponding route from x to y. In addition, a transport network has a single vertex s with indegree 0, and a single vertex t with outdegree 0. The vertex s represents the origin of the commodity and is known as the source, whereas the vertex t represents the destination of the commodity and is known as the sink.

DEFINITION **Network Flow**

A flow in a transport network is a function that assigns to each arc (x, y) a nonnegative number $a(x, y)$ such that the following conditions are satisfied:

1. $a(x, y) \leq c(x, y)$, for every $(x, y) \in A$.
2. $\sum_{\text{all } u} a(u, v) = \sum_{\text{all } w} a(v, w)$, for each vertex $v \neq s, t$.

The quantity $a(x, y)$ is the amount of material to be shipped through the route (x, y). Condition 1, known as the feasibility condition, states that the amount shipped through any route cannot exceed the capacity of that route. Condition 2, known as the conservation condition, states that the amount of material shipped into any intermediate point equals the amount shipped out of that point. This ensures that no material is allowed to accumulate at any intermediate point. Thus the amount of material shipped from the source, $\sum_{\text{all } u} a(s, u)$, will equal the amount of material that is shipped into the sink, $\sum_{\text{all } w} a(w, t)$ [see Problem 1]. This quantity is denoted by A and is referred to as the value of the flow a. To diagram a flow in a network, we assign an ordered pair to each arc (see Fig. 10.14). The first number represents the amount of the flow, and the second number represents the capacity of the arc.

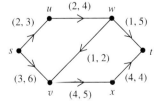

Figure 10.14
A Network Flow

A maximum flow in a transport network is a flow with the largest possible value. In a typical application of network flows, we want to determine the largest amount of material that can be shipped from the source to the destination. This can be found by constructing a maximum flow in the corresponding network. Eventually we will present an algorithm that finds a maximum flow in a given network. We use the original algorithm of Ford and Fulkerson [1] because it is the easiest to understand. To explain this algorithm, we use the notion of a cut. Note that there are newer, more complex algorithms for finding the maximum flow in a network that are more efficient.

DEFINITION   Capacity of a Cut

In a transport network we say that (S, T) is a cut if $\{S, T\}$ is a partition of the vertices with $s \in S$ and $t \in T$. The capacity of the cut (S, T), denoted by $\text{cap}(S, T)$, is equal to $\sum_{\substack{u \in S \\ v \in T}} c(u, v)$. A cut with the smallest possible capacity is known as a minimum cut.

The following fundamental result gives an upper bound on the value of a flow in a transport network.

THEOREM 10.7   If a is a flow in a given transport network with value A and (S, T) is any cut, then $A \leq \text{cap}(S, T)$.

Proof

For any vertex $v \in S$, consider the quantity $\sum_{\text{all } w} a(v, w) - \sum_{\text{all } u} a(u, v)$. When v is the source s, this quantity equals A, the value of the flow. For any other vertex v, this quantity equals 0, so

$$A = \sum_{v \in S} \left[\sum_{\text{all } w} a(v, w) - \sum_{\text{all } u} a(u, v) \right]$$

For any arc (u, v) with $u \in S$ and $v \in S$, $a(u, v)$ appears once in the sum with a positive sign and once with a negative sign, so these terms cancel. For an arc (u, v) with $u \in T$ and $v \in S$, $a(u, v)$ appears once with a negative sign. Similarly for an arc (v, w) with $v \in S$ and $w \in T$, $a(v, w)$ appears once with a positive sign. Thus the sum reduces to

$$A = \sum_{\substack{v \in S \\ w \in T}} a(v, w) - \sum_{\substack{u \in T \\ v \in S}} a(u, v)$$

The first sum is less than or equal to cap (S, T), whereas the second sum is nonnegative because each individual flow is nonnegative. Therefore $A \leq \text{cap}(S, T)$.

Theorem 10.7 states that the value of any flow is always less than or equal to the capacity of any cut. In particular, for a given transport network, the value of a maximum flow is less than or equal to the capacity of a minimum cut. We will present an algorithm, known as the labeling algorithm, for constructing a flow whose value is equal to the capacity of some cut. Thus the resulting flow is a maximum flow, and the corresponding cut is a minimum cut.

Consider a transport network with integer-valued capacities. We say that an arc (x, y) is a forward arc if $a(x, y) < c(x, y)$. Thus along a forward arc (x, y) we are able to increase the amount of material that is shipped from x to y by increasing the flow on (x, y) toward $c(x, y)$. We say that an arc (y, x) is a backward arc if $a(y, x) > 0$. For a backward arc (y, x) we are able to increase the amount of material reaching vertex y by decreasing the flow on (y, x) toward 0. In fact, suppose that there is a chain of arcs with forward arcs traversed in the forward direction and backward arcs traversed in the backward direction that starts at x and ends at y. Then it is possible to increase the amount of material shipped from x to y along this chain. A chain of forward arcs and backward arcs starting at the source s and ending at the sink t is referred to as a flow augmenting chain since it can be used to increase the value of the flow.

The flow in Fig. 10.14 has a value of 5. The flow augmenting chain in that network consists of three forward arcs (s, u), (u, w), and (w, t). The value of the original flow can be increased by at most 1 along this chain because a larger increase would force the flow on arc (s, u) to exceed its capacity. Increasing the flow on each of these arcs by 1, we obtain the flow in Fig. 10.15, which has value 6.

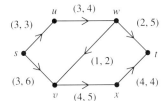

Figure 10.15

The flow augmenting chain in Fig. 10.15 consists of the three arcs $(s, v), (w, v), (w, t)$, where the arc (w, v) is a backward arc. Once again the value of the flow can be increased by at most 1 along this chain because any further increase would make the flow on (w, v) negative. In this way we obtain a flow of value 7 as in Fig. 10.16. It is a maximum flow since (S, T), where $S = \{s, v, x\}$, and $T = \{u, w, t\}$, is a cut with capacity 7.

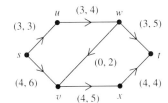

Figure 10.16

The labeling algorithm starts with an initial flow on a transport network. For example, we can always start with an all-zero flow, though it is usually easy to find a larger flow by inspection. The algorithm then finds a flow augmenting chain that can be used to find a flow whose value is larger. If no such chain can be found, the algorithm exhibits a cut whose capacity equals the value of the present flow. This shows that the present flow is a maximum flow, and the algorithm terminates.

The Labeling Algorithm

We start with an initial flow a and proceed to label the vertices of the network. A vertex label consists of an ordered pair. The first coordinate is the vertex from which the labeling has occurred, and the second coordinate is the maximum amount of material that can be shipped from that point. We start by assigning the label $(-, \infty)$ to the source s. Other vertices are assigned labels in one of two ways:

1. A new vertex labeling can occur in the forward direction along a forward arc (x, y). If vertex x has the label (w, Δ) and vertex y is unlabeled, vertex y will receive the label $(x, \min \{\Delta, c(x, y) - a(x, y)\})$. (Note that $c(x, y) - a(x, y) > 0$ for a forward arc (x, y).)

2. A new labeling can also occur in the backward direction along a backward arc (y, x). If vertex x has the label (w, Δ) and vertex y is unlabeled, vertex y will receive the label $(x, \min \{\Delta, a(x, y)\})$. (Note that $a(x, y) > 0$ for a backward arc (y, x).)

We repeat this process of labeling the unlabeled vertices along forward and backward arcs until one of the following two cases occurs:

1. Suppose that the sink t receives a label (v, Δ). Note that $\Delta > 0$ and the flow can be increased by Δ along the arc (v, t). Backtracking we find the vertex u from which v was labeled. Either (u, v) is a forward arc and the flow can be increased by Δ along this arc, or (v, u) is a backward arc and the flow can be decreased by Δ along this arc. Continuing in this manner, we would eventually make changes in the original flow along an augmenting chain until a new flow whose value is increased by Δ results. At this point we remove all the vertex labels and restart the labeling process with the new flow.

2. Suppose that no vertices incident to or incident from a labeled vertex can be labeled, and the sink t remains unlabeled. We denote by S the set of labeled vertices and by T the set of unlabeled vertices. Note that $s \in S$ and $t \in T$. If (x, y) is an arc with $x \in S$ and $y \in T$, then $c(x, y) = a(x, y)$ because we are assuming that y cannot be labeled. Similarly, if (x, y) is an arc with $y \in S$ and $x \in T$, then $a(x, y) = 0$ because we are assuming that x cannot be labeled. As in the proof of Theorem 10.7 we see that

$$A = \sum_{\substack{v \in S \\ w \in T}} a(v, w) - \sum_{\substack{u \in T \\ v \in S}} a(u, v)$$

Therefore,

$$A = \sum_{\substack{v \in S \\ w \in T}} c(v, w) = \mathrm{cap}(S, T)$$

According to Theorem 10.7, the value of any flow is less than or equal to $\text{cap}(S, T)$, so the flow is a maximum flow.

THEOREM 10.8

For a given transport network, the value of a maximum flow is equal to the capacity of a minimum cut.

Proof

For a network with integer capacities, we can always start with an integer-valued flow. After applying Step 1, any resulting flow is also integer-valued and the value of the flow is increased by at least 1. Since the value of any flow is obviously bounded above by $\sum_{\text{all } v} c(s, v)$, the labeling algorithm must terminate with a maximum flow after a finite number of steps. Thus, we obtain the maximum-flow–minimum-cut theorem that was first discovered by Ford and Fulkerson. Even for networks with noninteger capacities, the labeling algorithm can be modified to ensure that it terminates after a finite number of flow augmentations.

Example 1

A certain material is mined at three sites m_1, m_2, and m_3. The material is to be shipped through the network in Fig. 10.17 to three processing plants p_1, p_2, and p_3. The amount of material that can be mined at the three sites m_1, m_2, m_3 is 5, 10, and 15 tons per day, respectively. Each day 14 tons of the material can be processed at p_1, 9 tons can be processed at plant p_2, and 7 tons can be processed at plant p_3. Determine a shipping schedule that maximizes the amount of material that can be mined at the three sites and processed at the three plants in a single day.

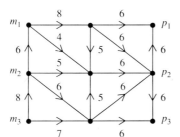

Figure 10.17

Solution

To analyze this problem using flows, we add a source and a sink to the network. The source s is joined to each of the mining sites m_1, m_2, m_3 by an arc whose capacity equals the limited amount of material that can be mined at the corresponding site. In addition, each of the processing plants p_1, p_2, p_3 is joined to the sink t by an arc whose capacity equals the limited amount of material that can be processed at the corresponding site. Since the associated network has a maximum flow of 26, the maximum amount of material that can be mined and processed in a single day is 26 tons.

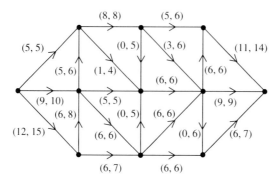

Figure 10.18

Matchings

Let G be any undirected graph. An important application of network flows is in the analysis of matchings on a graph. A **matching** M is a set of edges in G that satisfy the property that no two edges in M have a vertex in common. A **maximum matching** of G is a matching that contains the largest possible number of edges. We say that a vertex v of G is **matched** if v is incident to an edge of M. Otherwise, we say that v is **unmatched**.

Example 2   The Assignment Problem

Suppose that an employer has k job openings to be filled by n applicants. What is the largest number of job openings that can be filled at one time?

Solution

This situation can be represented by a bipartite graph. We let the k vertices in $X = \{x_1, x_2, \ldots, x_k\}$ represent the k job openings and the n vertices in $Y = \{y_1, y_2, \ldots, y_n\}$ represent the n applicants. Vertices x_i and y_j are joined by an edge if and only if applicant j is a suitable candidate for job i. Thus the graph in Fig. 10.19 represents a situation where the only suitable applicants for job 1 are applicants a, c, f, and so on. A matching M in this bipartite graph corresponds to an assignment of

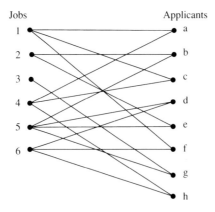

Figure 10.19

applicants to jobs, with at most one applicant assigned to any job and at most one job assigned to any applicant. The best possible assignment for the employer corresponds to a matching that matches each vertex in X. We refer to a matching of this kind as a complete X-matching.   □

The assignment problem in Example 2 can be solved by looking at the appropriate network and finding a maximum flow. To find a maximum matching in a bipartite graph, we first change the graph into a network by directing each edge from X to Y and giving each arc a capacity of 1. Next we add two new vertices s and t to the network. Vertex s will be the source of the network and is joined to each vertex $x_i, i = 1, 2, \ldots, k$ by an arc of capacity 1. Each vertex $y_j, j = 1, 2, \ldots, n$ is joined to vertex t, which is the sink of the network by an arc of capacity 1. Given any flow, the set of edges from X to Y will form a matching M since the flow from each job x_i will be at most 1 and the flow into each applicant y_j will also be at most 1. Thus a flow in this network corresponds to an allowable assignment of applicants to jobs, and clearly the value of a maximum flow will equal the largest number of jobs that the employer can fill from this group of applicants.

Let G be a bipartite graph with bipartition (X, Y). For any subset $S \subseteq X$, we denote by $N(S) = \{y \in Y \mid xy \in E(G) \text{ for some } x \in S\}$ the set of neighbors of S. The following theorem of Philip Hall [2] characterizes those bipartite graphs for which a complete X-matching is possible.

THEOREM 10.9

The bipartite graph G has a complete X-matching if and only if $|N(S)| \geq |S|$, for every $S \subseteq X$.

Proof
If G has a complete X-matching, every vertex in S is matched to a distinct neighbor in Y. Thus $|N(S)| \geq |S|$.

Conversely, suppose that $|N(S)| \geq |S|$, for every $S \subseteq X$. Consider the associated network flow problem. We will show that the labeling algorithm always terminates with a flow that corresponds to a complete X-matching.

Let $M = \{x_1 y_1, x_2 y_2, \ldots, x_m y_m\}$ be any initial matching. In the corresponding network, flow edges sx_i, $y_i t$, and $x_i y_i$, for $i = 1, 2, \ldots, m$, have flow 1 and the remaining arcs have flow 0. If $m = |X|$, then M is a complete X-matching. Otherwise, there is an edge sx' with flow 0. The labeling process starts by labeling s and then x'. Since $|N(\{x'\})| \geq 1$, there is at least one forward arc $x'y'$ in the network. Thus the vertex y' can be labeled. If y' is unmatched in M, the sink t can be labeled and the resulting flow corresponds to the matching $M \cup \{x'y'\}$ with one more edge. If y' is matched, there is a backward arc $x''y'$ through which a new vertex x'' can be labeled.

Continue labeling in this manner until either the sink t can be labeled, in which case the size of the initial matching can be increased, or until no further labelings can be made. In the latter case, denote by L the set of vertices that can be reached from s by flow augmenting paths, and set $S = L \cap X$ and $T = L \cap Y$. Clearly every vertex in T is matched with a corresponding vertex in

S. However, S contains at least one unmatched vertex x', so $|T| < |S|$. It is also clear that $N(S) = T$. Therefore $|N(S)| < |S|$, which contradicts the original assumption. Thus the labeling algorithm always terminates with a complete X-matching.

The assignment graph in Fig. 10.19 can be analyzed by looking at the network in Fig. 10.20 where each edge in the network has weight 1.

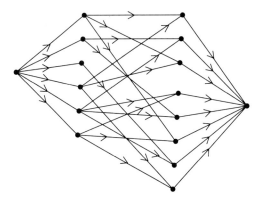

Figure 10.20

A maximum flow is pictured in Fig. 10.21. Each marked edge has a flow of 1 and each unmarked edge has a flow of 0. This flow represents the complete X-matching 1a, 2b, 3g, 4c, 5d, 6h.

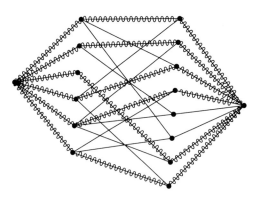

Figure 10.21

Theorem 10.9 can also be applied to the following well-known puzzle (See Section 5.1).

Puzzle 1 The Marriage Puzzle

In a small village each woman knows exactly k men, and each man knows exactly k women ($k \geq 1$). Explain why the men and women in this village can marry so that each woman marries a man she knows and vice versa. [See Problem 17.]

10.3

PROBLEMS

1. For a transport network with source s and sink t prove that

$$\sum_{\text{all } v} a(s, v) = \sum_{\text{all } w} a(w, t)$$

2. Use the labeling procedure to find a maximum flow in the following transport network.

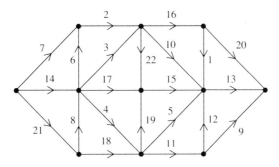

3. Five ships are assigned to deliver six kinds of military equipment to a common destination. There are four units of each type of equipment, and the five ships can carry seven, six, five, four, and three units, respectively. To reduce the possibility of sabotage, the equipment is shipped so that no two units of the same kind are on one ship. Use a transport network to determine whether or not the equipment can be shipped in a single convoy of the five ships.

4. Consider a distribution problem with three origins and four destinations. Let a_i denote the supply available at the ith origin, b_j the demand at the jth destination, and c_{ij} the maximum amount that can be shipped from the ith origin to the jth destination. Is there a feasible shipping flow that meets all demands, and doesn't exceed the following capacities?

i	a_i		j	b_j		i	j	1	2	3	4
1	9		1	6		1		5	2	6	2
2	11		2	6		2		3	3	7	6
3	11		3	12		3		6	2	5	1
			4	7							

5. Let M be any matching in a bipartite graph. Show that there is a maximum matching M' for which every vertex matched under M is also matched under M'.

6. A matching M in a graph G is said to be a perfect matching if every vertex in G is matched by M. Compute the number of perfect matchings of
a) $K_{n,n}$ b) K_{2n}

7. Andy is liked by Amy, Carol, and Eloise; Bob is liked by Amy, Brenda, and Carol; Carl is liked by Carol and Diane; Dennis is liked by Amy, Carol, and Diane; and Emmett is liked by Carol and Eloise.
   a) Use a transport network to match each boy with a girl who likes him.
   b) Suppose we want to match each boy with two different girls who like him (and each girl with two boys). Use a transport network to determine the matchings.

8. A mathematics department has five different committees. Committee 1's members are a, b, c; committee 2's members are a, c, g; committee 3's members are b, c, d, e; committee 4's members are a, b, e; and committee 5's members are d, e, f. The department wants each committee to send a different representative to a meeting of the academic senate. Use a transport network to determine whether or not a set of distinct representatives, one for each committee, can be chosen.

ADVANCED PROBLEMS

9. Let $S_1, S_2, \ldots, S_n$, be finite sets. A set of n different elements $\{r_1, r_2, \ldots, r_n\}$ is called a system of distinct representatives (SDR) if $r_i \in S_i$ for each $i = 1, 2, \ldots, n$.
   a) Describe an algorithm that finds an SDR, if one exists.
   b) Prove that an SDR exists if and only if the union of any k of these sets contains at least k elements, for $k = 1, 2, \ldots, n$.

10. Show that a bipartite graph G has a perfect matching if and only if $|N(S)| \geq |S|$, for all $S \subseteq V(G)$.

11. In a school there are n boys and n girls attending a dance. Suppose that each boy knows exactly k girls and each girl knows exactly k boys. Show that in k consecutive dances everyone can dance with each person he or she knows.

12. Let N be a network with source s and sink t for which each arc has unit capacity. We say that a set of directed paths is arc-disjoint if no two of them have an arc in common.
    a) Show that the value of a maximum flow in N equals the maximum number of arc-disjoint directed paths from s to t.
    b) Show that the capacity of a minimum cut in N equals the smallest number of arcs whose removal destroys all directed paths from s to t.

13. Let u and v be two vertices of a digraph D. Show that the maximum number of arc-disjoint directed paths from u to v in D equals the minimum number of arcs whose deletion destroys all directed paths from u to v.

14. The associated digraph $D(G)$ of a graph G is the digraph obtained when each edge e of G is replaced by two oppositely oriented arcs with the same endpoints as e. For any two vertices u and v, show that there are k arc-disjoint directed paths from u to v in $D(G)$ if and only if there are k edge-disjoint paths from u to v in G.

15. After a severe storm several messengers are sent from town a to town b. The

highways between a and b are shown in the following (undirected) graph. Because certain highways might be blocked, we require that no two messengers use the same highway. What is the largest number of messengers that can be sent simultaneously from a to b?

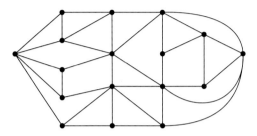

16. For a given transport network, we want a flow with minimum value satisfying the property that the flow in each edge is larger than or equal to the capacity of the edge.
    a) Define the minimum-flow–maximum-cut condition analogous to that of Theorem 10.7.
    b) Describe an algorithm that finds a minimum flow.

17. Solve the marriage puzzle.

18. In the following bipartite graph, we want to select a set of edges so that every vertex is incident with at least one of the edges in the set. Find the smallest number of edges that can be selected by analyzing a minimum-flow problem.

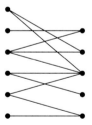

10 │ SUMMARY

In this chapter we encountered several combinatorial optimization problems that could be solved by looking at networks. The analysis of an activity network, the maximum-flow problem on a transport network, and the assignment problem are all important topics in operations research. For a more thorough discussion of network flows, the reader is referred to either of the books [1,6]. The book by Minieka [4] contains a wide variety of graph and network optimization problems. Many of these same problems can also be solved using linear and integer programming techniques [5].

BIBLIOGRAPHY

1. Ford, L., and D. Fulkerson. *Flows in Networks.* Princeton, N.J.: Princeton University Press, 1962.
2. Hall, P. On Representatives of Subsets. *J. London Math. Soc.,* 10 (1935) 26–30.
3. Knuth, D. *The Art of Computer Programming, Vol. III, Sorting and Searching.* Reading, Mass.: Addison-Wesley, 1973.
4. Minieka, E. *Optimization Algorithms for Networks and Graphs.* New York: Marcel-Dekker, 1978.
5. Papadimitriou, C., and K. Steiglitz. *Combinatorial Optimization: Algorithms and Complexity.* Englewood Cliffs, N.J.: Prentice-Hall, 1982.
6. Wilf, H. *Algorithms and Complexity.* Englewood Cliffs, N.J.: Prentice-Hall, 1986.

HINTS AND ANSWERS TO ODD-NUMBERED PROBLEMS

CHAPTER I

Section 1.1

1. Only 2 is a root, not -3.
3. Let x be the chosen number, $x \to x + 6 \to 2x + 12 \to 2x + 8 \to x + 4 \to 4$. The result is always 4.
5. 119 cents
7. a) The second player wins by making sure that the pile always has a multiple of four coins after each turn.

   b) The first player wins by adding three coins at the start and making sure that the pile always contains one less than a multiple of four coins after each turn.
9. a) $n(n + 1)/2$ b) n^2 c) $n(3n - 1)/2$ d) $(2a + (n - 1)d)n/2$.
11. $(a - b)^2 \geq 0 \to (a + b)^2 \geq 4ab \to ((a + b)/2)^2 \geq ab \to (a + b)/2 \geq \sqrt{ab}$
13. No, color the cubicles black and white.
15. Ask person A: Is B normal? Yes $\to C$ is a truthteller, No $\to B$ is a truthteller. Ask the known truthteller: Is A normal?
17. a) $(n - 1) + (n - 2) + \cdots + 2 + 1 = n(n - 1)/2$ b) $n - 1$ c) $2n - 2$ or $2n - 1$

Section 1.2

1. $(0.03)2^{12} = 122.88$ inches
3. b) $13 + 3 \times 199 = 610$ c) $1 + 2 \times 999 = 1999$

299

5. **Hint:** $1 \times 1! + 2 \times 2! + \cdots + n \times n! + (n + 1) \times (n + 1)! = (n + 1)! - 1 + (n + 1) \times (n + 1)! = (n + 2)! - 1$

7. **Hint:** $1^3 + 3^3 + \cdots + (2n - 1)^3 + (2n + 1)^3 = n^2 \times (2n^2 - 1) + (2n + 1)^3 = (n + 1)^2 \times (2(n + 1)^2 - 1)$

9. **Hint:** $1 \times 2 + 2 \times 3 + \cdots + n(n + 1) + (n + 1)(n + 2) = n(n + 1)(n + 2)/3 + (n + 1)(n + 2) = (n + 1)(n + 2)(n + 3)/3$

11. **Hint:** $1/2! + 2/3! + \cdots + n/(n + 1)! = ((n + 1)! - 1)/(n + 1)!$

13. $2000((1.05)^n - 1)$

15. **Hint:** Use strong induction. $\quad a_n = 5(2^{n-1} + 3^{n-1}) - 6(2^{n-2} + 3^{n-2})$

17. a) $f(40) = 41^2$

    b) **Hint:** Assume $f(0), f(1), \ldots, f(39)$ are all primes greater than or equal to 41 and $p \mid f(x)$, for some $1 < p < 41$. Let $x = pq + r$, and compute the remainder of $f(x)$ when divided by p in another way.

19. **Hint:** $(1 + x)^{n+1} \geq (1 + nx)(1 + x) \geq 1 + (n + 1)x$

21. If $n = 3x + 5y$ for nonnegative integers x and y, proceed to $n + 1$ in cases depending on whether $y > 0$ or $y = 0$.

23. a) **Hint:** $(n + 1)^2 > (4n + 1) + (2n + 1)$ b) **Hint:** $2^{n+1} > 2n^2$

25. **Hint:** $n(n - 1) \cdots (n - k + 1)/k! = (n - 1) \cdots (n - k)/k! + (n - 1) \cdots (n - k + 1)/(k - 1)!$

27. If $n < m = 2^k$, consider $a_1, a_2, \ldots, a_n, b_{n+1}, \ldots, b_m$ where $b_i = (a_1 + a_2 + \cdots + a_n)/n$

29. a) **Hint:** Obtain a balanced ternary expansion of $n + 1$ from the balanced ternary expansion of n by adding 1 to the first coefficient that is not already 1 and changing the previous 1 coefficients to -1.

    b) 1, 3, 9, 27

Section 1.3

1. a) 166   b) 100   c) 233   d) 267

3. a) 25   b) 13

5. 62

7. 6^n

9. Start with $n = 2$ and use induction on n.

11. There are $n + 1$ equivalence classes containing subsets of size $0, 1, 2, \ldots, n$.

13. Prove by induction: To list the subsets of $\{x_1, x_2, \ldots, x_{n+1}\}$ first list the subsets not containing x_{n+1}, then list the others.

15. Use congruence modulo 100 and note that $3^{20} \equiv 1 \pmod{100}$.

17. a) Use induction.   b) Consider sums modulo 3.

Section 1.4

1. a) 7^5 b) 5^7

3. n

5. The n differences between consecutively chosen integers add up to at most $3n - 1$, so at least one difference is less than 3.

7. a) In any arrangement $x_1, x_2, \ldots, x_{10}$, one of the numbers x_1, x_4, x_7, x_{10} is no more than 6. The other nine form 3 blocks of 3 consecutive integers whose total is at least 39, so one adds up to at least 13.

    b) The nine nonzero integers form 3 blocks of 3 consecutive integers whose total is 45 so one adds up to at least 15.

9. a) Two of the 51 chosen integers must belong to the same pair $\{1, 100\}, \{2, 99\}, \ldots, \{50, 51\}$ and sum up to 101 since there are only 50 such pairs.

    b) $\{50, 51, \ldots, 100\}$.

11. For each x_i, let a_i be the length of the longest decreasing sequence that begins with x_i and let b_i be the length of the longest increasing sequence that begins with x_i. Show that $f(x_i) = (a_i, b_i)$ defines an injection.

13. Each integer can be factored into a power of two times an odd part. Since there are 50 odd numbers, two of the chosen numbers must have the same odd part and thus one divides the other.

15. a) Differentiate between subsets containing x_{n+1} and those not containing x_{n+1}.
    b) Pair a subset containing the first element to the corresponding subset obtained by deleting the first element and vice versa.

17. *Hint:* Consider congruence classes modulo 12, then modulo 11.

Chapter I Review

1. a) The second player wins by adding enough coins to make the total number of coins in the pile a multiple of 6 after each of his turns.
   b) The first player should always win by adding enough coins to make the total number of coins in the pile 4 more than a multiple of 6 after each of his turns.

3. For $n = 1, 3^2 - 1 = 8 = 8(1)$ is a multiple of 8. Assume $3^{2n} - 1$ is divisible by 8 for some $n \geq 1$, thus we can let $3^{2n} - 1 = 8m$ for some integer m. Then $3^{2(n+1)} - 1 = 3^{2n+2} - 1 = 9(3^{2n}) - 1 = 9(8m + 1) - 1 = 8(9m + 1)$. Therefore $3^{2(n+1)} - 1$ is divisible by 8 and the result holds for all integers $n \geq 1$ by induction.

5. a) $|X| = 200 + 150 - 50 = 300$
   b) $(3 + 6 + \cdots + 600) + (4 + 8 + \cdots + 600) - (12 + 24 + \cdots + 600) = 60300 + 45300 - 15300 = 90300$

7. a) $(n + 1)^n$ b) $(n + 1)n(n - 1) \cdots (3)(2)$

9. If d_i is the number of games played by team i, then $d_1 + d_2 + d_3 + \cdots + d_{10} = 2(23) = 46$. The average number of games played per team is more than 4 so at least one team plays five (or more) games.

11. For $n = 2$, $(0.99)^2 = 0.9801 > 1 - (0.01)2 = 0.98$. Assume $(0.99)^n > 1 - (0.01)n$, for some $n \geq 2$. Then $(0.99)^{n+1} > 0.99(1 - (0.01)n) = 0.99 - 0.99(0.01)n > 0.99 - (0.01)n = 1 - (0.01)(n + 1)$. Thus $(0.99)^{n+1} > 1 - (0.01)(n + 1)$ and the result holds for all integers $n \geq 2$ by induction.

CHAPTER 2

Section 2.1

1. $n(n - 1)$ 3. a) 320   b) 72   5. 6,400,000   7. a) 511   b) 767
9. a) 24   b) 12   11. a) 12   b) 24   13. 1452   15. a) 9^{10} b) 9^{10}
17. a) 2^{nm} b) n^{nm} 19. $(n + 1)^n - 1$ 21. a) m^{m^2} b) $m^m \times m^{m(m-1)/2}$
23. 180

Section 2.2

1. $26^3 \times 2000, 26^3 \times 2000 - 26 \times 25 \times 24 \times 10 \times 9 \times 8 \times 2$ 3. 108
5. a) $25^4 + 4 \times 25^3$ b) $26^4 - 25^4$ 7. a) 2240   b) 2296
9. a) $20 \times 48 \times 47 \times 46 \times 45$ b) $52 \times 51 \times 50 \times 49 \times 48 - 48 \times 47 \times 46 \times 45 \times 44$
11. 10,080   13. a) 700×21^6 b) 525×21^6

15. $9 + 9 \times 9 + 9 \times 9 \times 8 + 9 \times 9 \times 8 \times 7 + \cdots + 9 \times 9 \times 8 \times \cdots \times 2 \times 1$
17. $3^n - 3 \times 2^{n-1}$ 19. 768
21. a) 9^n
     b) For n odd, more odd integers. For n even, more even integers.

Section 2.3

1. a) $P(20, 3)$ b) $C(20, 3)$
3. a) $C(9, 3)$ b) $9C(10, 2)$ c) $C(19, 3) - C(10, 3)$ d) $9C(10, 2) + C(9, 3)$
5. a) $8!$ b) $C(7, 2)5!$ 7. a) $C(8, 5)$ b) $C(5, 4)C(5, 3) + C(5, 2)$
9. a) $P(50, 6)$ b) $C(50, 3)C(47, 3)$ 11. $54{,}912/C(52, 5)$
13. a) $C(9, 2)/C(10, 3)$ b) $C(6, 2)/C(10, 3)$ 15. $(C(52, 5) - C(13, 5)4^5)/C(52, 5)$
17. $1/2$ 19. $C(20, 15)P(30, 15)$ 21. $3C(10, 4)C(6, 3)$ 23. $C(n, k)2^{n-k}$
25. b) $C(13, 3)C(39, 2) + C(13, 4) \times 39 + C(13, 5)$
27. a) $C(25, 4) - C(20, 4)$ b) $C(19, 3)$ 29. $5/7$ 31. $(8 \times 7 - 6 \times 5)/(8 \times 7)$
33. a) $C(13, k)C(39, 13 - k)/C(52, 13)$ b) $k = 3$ 35. a) $C(n, 2)$
37. $C(m, 2)C(n, 2)$

Section 2.4

1. $C(16, 4); C(11, 4)$ 3. a) $C(n + 2, 2)$ b) $C(n + 3, 3)$
5. a) $C(14, 2)$ b) $C(n + 2, 2)$
7. a) $C(10, 5)$ b) $C(n + 5, 5)$ c) $C(n - 1, 5)$ d) $C(10, 5) \times C(15, 5) \times C(20, 5)$
9. b) $C(7, 2)6!$ 11. $C(19, 4)$ 13. $51C(52, 2)$ 15. a) $C(24, 4)$ b) $C(14, 4)$
17. $C(33, 6)$ 19. a) $nC(k - 1, n - 2)$ b) $C(n, m)C(k - 1, n - m - 1)$
21. $C(30, 5)$ 23. $C(22, 5)5!21!$ 25. a) $C(9, 4)$ b) $C(9, 4) + 3C(9, 3) + C(9, 2)$
27. $C(2n + 3, 3) - 4C(n + 2, 3)$ 29. Use the method of Example 2.

Section 2.5

1. a) (Combinatorial Proof) Given n people, select a committee of k with one person designated chairperson.

    b) Use the factorial notation $C(n, k) = \dfrac{n!}{k!(n - k)!}$

    c) Prove by induction for $k \geq 0$.
3. 1792
7. $a = 6, b = 6, c = 1, 6C(n + 1, 4) + 6C(n + 1, 3) + C(n + 1, 2)$
9. $20/64; 30/64$
11. $49/64$
13. $(C(n, 0)5^n + C(n, 2)5^{n-2} + \cdots)/6^n$ 15. $C(n, j)5^{n-j}/6^n$
17. **Hint:** Integrate $(1 + x)^n$.
19. The coefficient of x^i is the sum of all products of the form $r_{j_1} r_{j_2} r_{j_3} \cdots r_{j_{n-i}}$
21. a) $k = n$ b) $k = 0$
23. **Hint:** Represent the exponent using binary notation and consider $(x + y)^{2^m}$.
31. a) Look at all the subsets containing a given element.
     b) Look at collections of subsets all the same size.

Section 2.6

1. $(x + y + z)^4 = x^4 + y^4 + z^4 + 4(xy^3 + xz^3 + yx^3 + yz^3 + zx^3 + zy^3) + 6(x^2 y^2 + y^2 z^2 + x^2 z^2) + 12(x^2 yz + y^2 xz + z^2 xy)$

3. $(2n)!/2^n$
5. a) $14!/(3!4!7!)$ b) $12!/(2!4!6!)$
7. If $m \neq n, (m + n)!/(m!n!)$; if $m = n, (2m)!/(2!m!m!)$.
9. $(2n - 1)(2n - 3) \cdots 5 \times 3 \times 1$
11. $a^5 c^2 (7!/(2!5!)) + a^4 b^2 c(7!/(4!2!1!)) + a^3 b^4 (7!/(3!4!))$
13. $2^4 (8!/(3!3!2!))$
15. a) $C(12,5)11!/(8!3!)$ b) $2C(8,3) + 14C(6,4)$
17. $4(10!/(2!^3 4!)) + C(4,2)(10!/(2!^2 3!^2)$
19. $3 \times (8!/(3!3!2!))(4!/2!)$

Chapter 2 Review

1. **Hint:** $C(n, k + 1)/C(n, k) = (n - k)/(k + 1)$
3. a) $C(23,3)$ b) $C(19,3)$
5. $C(15,4) - C(10,4) - C(5,4)$
7. a) $13C(4,3)(C(48,4) - 12) - C(13,2)C(4,3)C(4,3)44$
   b) $C(52,7) - 4(C(13,7) + C(13,6)39)$
9. $(8(9^4) - 7(8^4))/(9(10^4))$
11. $C(30,2)C(28,2)C(26,2)C(24,2)/4!$

CHAPTER 3

Section 3.1

1. a) 8   b) 60   3. 480   5. $10!/4 - 9! + 8!$
7. a) $9^4 + 8 \times 9^3 - 8^4$ b) $9 \times 10^3 - 8^4$
9. a) $10 \times 26^5 - 25 \times 26^4$ b) $10P(25,5) - 20P(24,4)$ 11. $3 \times 7! - 3 \times 5! + 3!$
13. a) $C(n,3)$ b) $C(n,3) - n(n - 3)$ 15. $C(9,4)5!$
17. $1,000,000 - 1000 - 100 - 15 + 10 + 3 + 2 - 1$
19. a) $5^{10} - 5 \times 4^{10} + \cdots + C(5,4)1^{10}$ b) $10!/2^5$
21. $9 \times 10^6 - 9^7 - 16 \times 9^6 + 2 \times 8^7 + 7 \times 8^6 - 7^7$
23. $5! - 6 \times 4! + 12 \times 3! - 2^4$
25. a) $S_m - C(m + 1, m)S_{m+1} + C(m + 2, m)S_{m+2} - \cdots + (-1)^{n-m}C(n,m)S_n$ b) 150
27. 61

Section 3.2

1. a) $C(8,2)P(8,2)$ b) $C(8,8)P(8,8)$ c) $C(8,8)D(8)$
3. a) $nD(n - 1)$ b) $C(n,m)D(n - m)$
5. $12! - 6 \times 11! + C(6,2)10! - \cdots + C(6,6)6!$
7. $C(34,5) - C(25,5) - 5C(24,5) + 5C(15,5) + C(5,2)C(14,5) - C(5,2)$
9. $C(13,3) - C(3,3) - C(6,3) - C(8,3) - C(9,3) + C(4,3)$
11. $P(8)$ is the greatest.
13. $C(39,9) - 10C(33,9) + \binom{10}{2}C(27,9) - \binom{10}{3}C(21,9) + \binom{10}{4}C(15,9) - \binom{10}{5}C(9,9)$
15. $C(102,2) - 3C(51,2)$
17. a) all $n \geq 2$ b) all $n \geq 2$ c) all $n \geq 1$ d) all odd $n \geq 1$ e) all $n \geq 1$

19. $(n-1)(n-1)! - C(n-1,2)(n-2)! + C(n-1,3)(n-3)! - \cdots + (-1)^n C(n-1,n-1)1!$
21. $10! - 5 \times 2 \times 9! + C(5,2) \times 2^2 \times 8! - \cdots - C(5,5) \times 2^5 \times 5!$
23. a) $(2n-1)(2n-3)\cdots 3 \times 1$
    b) $(2n-1)(2n-3)\cdots 3 \times 1 - C(n,1)(2n-3)\cdots 3 \times 1 +$
    $C(n,2)(2n-5)\cdots 3 \times 1 - \cdots + (-1)^n C(n,n)$
25. $(C(28,3) - 14 \times 13)/2$
27. Use Theorem 3.3.

Section 3.3

1. a) $C(44,4)$ b) $C(39,4)$ c) $C(19,4)$
3. a) $C(17,5)$ b) $6^{18} - 6 \times 5^{18} + C(6,2)4^{18} - \cdots - C(6,5)1^{18}$
5. a) $8 \times 7 \times 6 \times 5$ b) $4^{16} - C(4,1)3^{16} + C(4,2)2^{16} - 4$
7. a) $S(9,3)$ b) $9!/(3!3!3!3!)$
9. a) $(3^{n-1} - 2^n + 1)/2$
    b) *Hint:* $2^{2n} - 1$ is divisible by 3.   c) Consider $n = 4k + 1, 4k + 2$.
11. a) $8 \times 9 \times 10 - 2$ b) $C(11,2) - C(4,2) - C(3,2) - C(2,2)$
13. $C(k,j)C(n-1,k-j-1)$
17. a) $S(m,k)$ b) $S(m,1) + S(m,2) + \cdots + S(m,k)$
19. $C(8,3)^4 - 4C(7,2)^4 + C(4,2)C(6,1)^4 - 4$

Chapter 3 Review

1. $7(8^{n-1}) - 6(7^{n-1}) - 7^n + 6^n$
3. $(C(19,5) - 5C(13,5) + C(5,2)C(7,5))/6^5$
5. $13C(48,9) - C(13,2)C(44,5) + C(13,3)40$
7. $36^n - 6(35^n) + C(6,2)34^n - C(6,3)33^n + C(6,4)32^n - C(6,5)31^n + 30^n$
9. a) $2^{11} - 1 = S(12,2)$ b) $12!/(3!4!5!)$ c) $12!/(6!6!2!)$
    d) $S(12,3) = (3^{11} - 2^{12} + 1)/2$
11. $C(7,2)C(6,2)C(4,2) - (6C(6,2)C(4,2) + 3C(6,2)C(5,2)C(3,2)) + ((3)(5)(5)C(4,2) +$
    $3C(5,2)C(4,2)2) - (C(4,2)3! + (3)(4)C(4,2)2) + 3(3!)$

CHAPTER 4

Section 4.1

1. 42
3. a) Since $a = qb + r$, then $(b,r) \mid a$ and $(b,r) \mid (a,b)$. In addition $a - qb = r$, so $(a,b) \mid r$ and
    $(a,b) \mid (b,r)$. Therefore $(a,b) = (b,r)$.
    b) Use a) and induction.
5. Input $a = a_1 a_2 \cdots a_n$, $b = b_1 b_2 \cdots b_n$.
    1. Set $i = 1$.
    2. Compare a_i and b_i.
    3. If $a_i > b_i$, output $a > b$ and stop.
    4. If $b_i > a_i$, output $b > a$ and stop.
    5. If $i = n$, output $a = b$ and stop. Otherwise increase i by 1 and return to Step 2.
7. 36!

9. **Hint:** Compare x_i and x_j for $1 \le i < j \le n$.
11. (a) **Hint:** Find the ith digit of the sum and the carry digit before computing the $(i + 1)$st digit.
  b) Compute the product by adding repeatedly.
13. Input $x = \{x_1 \le x_2 \le \cdots \le x_m\}$ and $y = \{y_1 \le y_2 \le \cdots \le y_n\}$.
  1. Let z be an empty list.
  2. Compare the smallest element in x and the smallest element in y.
  3. Place the smallest of these at the end of z and delete it from its original list.
  4. If one list is now empty, put the remaining elements of the other list, in order, at the end of z, output z, and stop.
  5. Otherwise, return to Step 2.
15. **Hint:** Start by comparing two sets of three coins.
17. Each question should eliminate half of the remaining possibilities. For example, question i could be: Is the ith digit in the binary expansion of the number equal to 0?
19. An inefficient method is to ask every person the same question and the majority must tell the truth.
21. **Hint:** Try $(a + d)(w + z)$, $(c + d)w$, $a(x - z)$, $(a + b)z$, $(c - a)(w + x)$, $(b - d)(y + z)$, $d(y - w)$

Section 4.2

1. **Hint:** $2^{(\log_2 x)^2} = x^{\log_2 x}$
3. **Hint:** $\lim\limits_{n \to \infty} \dfrac{\log n}{n^m} = 0$
5. For $n \ge N$, $f(n) \le (k + 1)g(n)$.
9. **Hint:** $(\log_b n)/(\log_b c) = \log_c n$
11. a) **Hint:** $1^k + 2^k + \cdots + n^k \le n(n^k)$ 13. **Hint:** Use calculus and consider $f(x) = \dfrac{x}{\ln x}$.
  b) **Hint:** $1^k + 2^k + \cdots + n^k \ge \int_0^n x^k \, dx$
15. $(2x + 1)(\log_2(x^3 + 1) + 5x^2 \le 3x \log_2 x^4 + 5x^2$
$$\le 12x \log_2 x + 5x^2$$
$$\le 17x^2$$

Section 4.3

1. a) before 372986541, after 374125698   b) before 453192867, after 453196278
3. 1234   1235   1236   1245   1246   1256   1345   1346
  1356   1456   2345   2346   2356   2456   3456
5. Find the largest j so that the jth digit is at least two more than the previous digit. Subtract one from the jth digit and for $i > j$ replace the ith digit by $n - k + i$.
7. 135, 156, 234, 246, 345, 456
9. Start with $123 \cdots k$ and end with $n(n - 1) \cdots (n - k + 1)$. Find the largest j so that the jth digit is smaller than one of the following digits or an unused digit. Proceed by replacing the jth digit by the smallest of those (not preceding the jth digit) that are larger than it. The final $k - j$ digits will be the smallest available $k - j$ digits arranged in increasing order.
11. To get to the next ternary sequence, add one to the right most digit that is not a two, and replace the twos to the right of it by zeros.

Chapter 4 Review

1. a) $8! - 2(7!)$ b) $5(6!)$ 3. a) $C(10, 5)5!9!$ b) $C(8, 4)4!9!$

5. **Hint:** First show that $(\log n)^2$ is $O(n)$.
7. a) Compare x with every number.
   b) Compare x with the middle number and delete half of the list after each comparison.
9. **Hint:** Use calculus and consider $f(x) = \dfrac{1}{x}$.

CHAPTER 5

Section 5.1

1. a) It has the largest degree.   b) It has degree 0.
3. a) It is a complete graph.
   b) Every pair of vertices are connected by a sequence of edges.
5. a) G has only $\dbinom{n}{2}$ different pairs of vertices that can be joined by edges.
   b) A vertex can only be joined to each of the other $p - 1$ vertices.
7. 1 with 0 edges, 1 with 1 edge, 2 with 2 edges, 3 with 3 edges, 2 with 4 edges, 1 with 5 edges, 1 with 6 edges.
9. In one graph the vertices of degree 3 are adjacent.
11. K_n^c is a graph with n vertices and no edges.
    $K_{m,n}^c$ is the disjoint union of K_m and K_n.
    b) K_6 has 15 edges so there is no self-complementary graph with 6 vertices.
    c) Otherwise K_p has an odd number of edges.
13. **Hint:** $\deg v_1 + \deg v_2 + \cdots + \deg v_{10} = 52$.
15. For any $p \geq 2$, there are p possible degrees, namely $0, 1, 2, \ldots, p - 1$ and 0 and $p - 1$ can't both occur in the same graph.
17. Use Corollary 3 to Theorem 5.1.
19. a) $p \leq 12$ b) $p \geq 11$
21. a) $q \geq pk/2$
    b) Because there would be an odd number of odd vertices.
    c) Take a regular p-gon and join diagonally opposite vertices.
23. If m of the degrees are odd, start with $m/2$ disjoint edges, and then add the appropriate number of loops to each vertex.
25. Show that there is a simple graph with a vertex of degree d_1 adjacent to vertices of degree $d_2, d_3, \ldots, d_{d_1 + 1}$, respectively.

Section 5.2

1. Starting with a (v_0, v_k)-walk W, show that it is possible to obtain a (v_0, v_k)-path by deleting edges from W.
3. If there is a path which starts in V_1 and ends in V_2, there must be an edge that starts in V_1 and ends in V_2.
5. a) Either two vertices are adjacent or they have a common neighbor.
   b) Take a disjoint union of two complete graphs with $p/2$ vertices.
7. Find a bipartition (X, Y) of G. First list the vertices of X, then the vertices of Y.
9. Every component of G has an even number of vertices of odd degree.

11. If there are nonadjacent vertices, find a shortest path between them. Take any three consecutive vertices u, v, w on this path.

13. Consider two vertices x and y that are not connected by a path with fewer than three edges. In G^c, x and y are adjacent, and any other vertex is adjacent to at least one of x and y.

15. *Hint:* If $a_{ij}^{(k)}$ is the (i, j)th entry of A^k, then

$$a_{ij}^{(k)} = a_{i1}^{(k)}a_{1j} + a_{i2}^{(k)}a_{2j} + \cdots + a_{ip}^{(k)}a_{pj}.$$

17. Otherwise the vertices of G can be partitioned into sets of k and $p - k$ vertices, respectively, with no edge starting at a vertex in one set and ending at a vertex in the other set. Thus G has at most $\binom{k}{2} + \binom{p-k}{2} \le \binom{p-1}{2}$ edges, which is a contradiction.

19. *Hint:* The edge e together with a path joining its endpoints in $G - e$ make a cycle containing e.

Section 5.3

1. Use strong induction to show that the edges of any closed trail can be partitioned into cycles.

3. Starting with any path, extend it from an end until a vertex is repeated.

5. a) It can be traced by starting at one vertex of odd degree and ending at the other.
   b) No such line is possible since four of the regions are surrounded by an odd number of edges.

7. a) No, since all 4 areas are incident to an odd number of bridges.
   b) Yes, since there are only two odd vertices.

9. Take an Eulerian circuit of G and color the edges alternately red and blue.

11. a)   b)

    c)   d)

13. a)   b)

    c)   d)

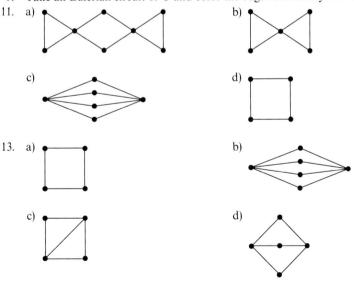

15. Start with a Hamiltonian path, and use it to construct a Hamiltonian cycle as in the proof of Theorem 5.4.

17. a) $K_{r,r}$ is the unique graph.
   b) Starting with a vertex v, consider the neighbors of v and the vertices adjacent to each of these.

19. a) Use each door at most once.
     b) Use each door at most twice.
21. If C is a cycle not containing v, then $G - C$ is Eulerian.
23. a) 25   b) 24
27. a) Use Theorem 5.5.
     b) A graph with $p - 1$ mutually adjacent vertices and one additional vertex of degree one has no Hamiltonian cycle.

Section 5.4

1. a) The smallest example has 6 vertices.
    b) The smallest example has 12 vertices.
3. If $q = 3p - 6$, the boundary of each region consists of exactly 3 edges.
5. Every simple plane graph can be made into a triangulation by adding new edges.
7. If $m, n \geq 3$, then $K_{m,n}$ is nonplanar.
9. There are $3n$ unused adjacencies at the start, and each move reduces this by one, so no game lasts more than $3n - 1$ moves.
11. Use Theorem 5.7.
13. Generalize the proof of Theorem 5.7.
15. $p = 10$
17. b) $cr(K_{4,3}) = 2$ c) $cr(K_6) = 3$

Section 5.5

1. Color the vertices in order so that each newly colored vertex is adjacent to a vertex that has already been colored.
3. a) Consider two cases, n even and n odd.
    c) For $n = 2$, $X(D_2) = 4$. For $n \geq 4$ and even, $X(D_n) = 3$. For all odd $n \geq 3$, $X(D_n) = 2$.
5. Use induction and start with a 2-coloring when $n - 1$ circles are drawn.
7. Use a bipartition of G to 2-color the vertices and vice versa.
9. Draw the appropriate graph and deduce that 3 colors are needed.
11. Use Theorem 5.11.
13. Show that the degree of each vertex is even if and only if the dual graph is bipartite.
15. Show that G is bipartite and then apply Problem 7.
17. Of all subgraphs H of G satisfying $X(H) = k$, look at the one with the smallest number of edges.
19. Order the vertices so that no vertex is adjacent to more than two previous vertices and apply the greedy algorithm.

Chapter 5 Review

1. a) $m = n \geq 2$ b) $m, n \geq 2$ and both even
3. a) 50 edges   b) 31 edges
5. a) $p(p - 1)(p - 2) \cdots (p - n)$ b) $p(p - 1)^n$
7. Let G be a planar graph with $p < 12$ vertices and let d_i represent the degree of vertex i. Then $d_1 + d_2 + \cdots + d_p \leq 6p - 12 < 5p$. Therefore G has a vertex of degree 4 or less.
9. a) n^2
    b) Given any two vertices x and y in G, they are either adjacent or there is another vertex that they are both adjacent to. Thus x and y are either connected by a path of length 1 or a path of length 2, so G is connected.
11. Degree 3

CHAPTER 6

Section 6.1

1. $3m3c \to 2m2c \to 3m2c \to 3m \to 3m1c \to 1m1c \to 2m2c \to 2c \to 3c \to 1c \to 2c \to *$.
3. A shortest path from u to v and a shortest path from v to w can be combined to give a walk from u to w.
5. 22:10
7. Start the breadth first search at a vertex u. Vertices receive a finite label if and only if they are connected to u.
9. Apply Dijkstra's algorithm, once for each city.
11. a) $2 \times 5! \times 5!$ b) $5!4!$ c) 0
13. A graph without odd cycles is bipartite.
15. a) Use a breadth first search.
    b) Apply the procedure in part (a) to every possible starting vertex.

Section 6.2

1. a) 6 graphs
   b) 2 trees with degree sequence $3, 2, 2, 1, 1, 1$
3. Prove by contradiction, since if G has a cycle, then any edge of the cycle can be removed.
5. $w - 1$ edges
7. 9 doors
9. *Hint:* Each neighbor of v is in a separate component.
11. 66
13. It is disconnected.
15. a) $2p - 2$ b) $2p - 2k$
17. *Hint:* Start with a spanning tree, and add one edge at a time.
19. *Hint:* Let e be the edge joining $n - 1$ and n. What can you say about the Prufer code of $K_n - e$?
21. $3H3WC \to 2H2W \to 3H2WC \to 3H \to 3H1WC \to 1H1W \to 2H2WC \to 2W \to$
    $3WC \to 1W \to 1H1WC \to *$

Section 6.3

1. a) The minimum distance from SC to SJ is 28.
   b) The minimum weight is 58.
3. Apply Huffman's algorithm.
5. Construct an optimal binary tree with weights $1/2, 1/12, 1/12, 1/12, 1/24, \ldots, 1/24$.
7. Analyze using a ternary tree.
9. Exhibit the tournament schedule on a binary tree.
11. a) 99   b) 7
13. Use a ternary tree, and consider all possible first weighings.
15. Analyze using a ternary tree.
17. Starting with the preassigned edge, continue by choosing the edge with smallest possible weight at each step.

Chapter 6 Review

1. For $p = 2$ vertices, a tree consists of a single edge, and its endpoints must receive different colors so a tree with 2 vertices has chromatic number 2. For some $p \geq 2$, assume that all trees with p vertices have chromatic number 2. Let T be any tree with $p + 1$ vertices. T must have some vertex u of degree 1. Since $T - u$ is a tree with p vertices, it has chromatic number 2, but any 2-coloring of $T - u$ can be extended to a 2-coloring of T by giving u the opposite color from the vertex that it's adjacent to. Thus T has chromatic number 2, and the result is true by induction for all $p \geq 2$.

3. 33 vertices of degree 4

5. a) 1   b) 3

7. First find the shortest path from u to w; then find the shortest path from w to v.

9. a) A breadth first search can be used to determine whether or not a graph G contains a cycle.

    b) To show that any two vertices in $G - e$ are connected by a walk start with a walk in G and replace the edge $e = xy$ when it occurs by any walk from x to y not containing e.

    c) Repeatedly remove any edge contained in a cycle until the resulting graph is a tree.

CHAPTER 7

Section 7.1

1. a) $(1 + z + z^2 + z^3 + z^4)^2(1 + z + z^2 + \cdots + z^6)$

    b) $(z + z^2 + z^3 + z^4 + z^5)(z + z^2 + z^3 + z^4)(z + z^2 + z^3 + \cdots + z^{10})$

    c) $(1 + z + z^2 + z^3 + \cdots)^5$

3. $(z^5 + z^6 + z^7 + z^8 + \cdots)^4$

5. a) $(1 + z + z^2 + z^3 + \cdots + z^9)^4$

    b) $(z + z^2 + z^3 + \cdots + z^9)(1 + z + z^2 + z^3 + \cdots + z^9)^3$

7. a) $(1 + z + z^2 + \cdots + z^5)^9$

    b) $(z + z^2 + z^3 + z^4 + z^5)^9$

9. a) $(z + z^2 + z^3 + \cdots + z^6)^k$

    b) $(z^2 + z^3 + 2z^4 + 2z^5 + 3z^6 + 3z^7 + 3z^8 + 2z^9 + 2z^{10} + z^{11} + z^{12})$

    c) $(z^2 + z^3 + z^4 + z^5 + z^6)(z + z^3 + z^4 + z^5 + z^6) \cdots (z + z^2 + z^3 + z^4 + z^5)$

11. $(z + 3z^2)^7$

13. a) $(1 + z + z^2 + \cdots)^{10}$

    b) $(z + z^2 + z^3 + z^4 + \cdots)^{10}$

    c) $(1 + z)(1 + z + z^2)(1 + z + z^2 + z^3) \cdots (1 + z + z^2 + z^3 + \cdots + z^{10})$

15. **Hint:** $(z + 2z^2 + 2z^3 + z^4)(z + z^3 + z^4 + z^5 + z^6 + z^8) = (z + z^2 + \cdots + z^6)^2$

Section 7.2

1. a) $\binom{k - 16}{4}$ b) $\binom{n}{k - 1} + \binom{n}{k - 3} + \binom{n}{k - 5}$

3. $(z^4 + z^5 + z^6 + \cdots)^4$; $a_{24} = \binom{11}{3}$

5. $(z + z^2 + z^3 + z^4 + z^5 + z^6)^{10}$

$$a_{35} = \binom{34}{9} - 10\binom{28}{9} + \binom{10}{2}\binom{22}{9} - \binom{10}{3}\binom{16}{9} + \binom{10}{4}\binom{10}{9}$$

7. $(1 + z + z^2)^3(1 + z + z^2 + z^3 + \cdots)^3$; $\binom{17}{5} - 3\binom{14}{5} + 3\binom{11}{5} - \binom{8}{5}$

9. $(z + z^2 + z^3 + \cdots + z^{10})(z + z^2 + z^3 + \cdots + z^{20})(z + z^2 + z^3 + \cdots + z^{30})$;

$$\binom{29}{2} - \binom{19}{2} - \binom{9}{2}$$

11. Show by induction that each product is equal to $1 + z + z^2 + \cdots$.

13. $z^5(1 + z + z^2 + \cdots)^2(z^2 + z^3 + z^4 + \cdots)^4 = z^{13}(1 + z + z^2 + \cdots)^6$; $\binom{17}{5}$

15. $(z^3 + z^5 + z^7 + \cdots)^4$, $a_n = 0$ for $n = 2m + 1$ and $a_n = \binom{m - 3}{3}$ for $n = 2m$

17. a) $(1 + z + z^2 + \cdots + z^5)(1 + z + z^2 + \cdots + z^6)(1 + z + z^2 + \cdots + z^7)$;

$$\binom{11}{2} - \binom{5}{2} - \binom{4}{2} - \binom{3}{2}$$

b) $(z + z^2 + \cdots + z^4)(z + z^2 + \cdots + z^5)(z + z^2 + \cdots + z^6)$; $\binom{8}{2} - \binom{4}{2} - \binom{3}{2} - \binom{2}{2}$

19. a) 31 solutions   b) 6 solutions

21. 31 ways; $(1 + z + z^2 + \cdots + z^{10})(1 + z^5 + z^{10} + \cdots + z^{50})$
$\times (1 + z^{10} + z^{20} + \cdots + z^{50})(1 + z^{25} + z^{50})$

Section 7.3

1. a) $(1 + z^2 + z^4 + \cdots)(1 + z^4 + z^8 + \cdots)(1 + z^5 + z^{10} + \cdots)(1 + z^7 + z^{14} + \cdots)$
   b) $(z^2 + z^4 + z^6 + \cdots)(z^4 + z^8 + z^{12} + \cdots)(z^5 + z^{10} + z^{15} + \cdots)(z^7 + z^{14} + z^{21} + \cdots)$

3. a) $(1 + z + z^2 + \cdots)(1 + z^3 + z^6 + \cdots)(1 + z^5 + z^{10} + \cdots)(1 + z^7 + z^{14} + \cdots)\cdots$
   b) $(1 + z)(1 + z^3)(1 + z^5)(1 + z^7)\cdots$

5. $(1 + z + z^2 + z^3 + \cdots)^3(1 + z^5 + z^{10} + \cdots)^2(1 + z^{10} + z^{20} + \cdots)^2(1 + z^{25} + z^{50} + \cdots)^2$

7. The transpose gives a bijection.

9. Use the bijection $n_1 + n_2 + n_3 \to (n - n_3) + (n - n_2) + (n - n_1)$

11. a) $(1 + z + z^2 + \cdots)(1 + z^2 + z^4 + \cdots)(1 + z^4 + z^8 + \cdots)\cdots$
    b) and c) $(1 + z)(1 + z^2)(1 + z^4)(1 + z^8)\cdots = (1 + z + z^2 + z^3 + z^4 + \cdots)$

13. a) $2n$ and $2n + 1$ have $n + 1$ partitions
    b) $n \geq 4$ has 4 such partitions

15. a) $(1 + z + z^2 + z^3 + \cdots)^6$ b) $(1 - z)^{-3}(1 - z^2)^{-3}(1 + 3z^2)$

17. a) $(1 + z + z^2 + \cdots)(1 + z^2 + z^4 + \cdots)\cdots(1 + z^5 + z^{10} + \cdots)$
    b) $(1 + z + z^2 + \cdots)(1 + z^2 + z^4 + \cdots)\cdots(z^5 + z^{10} + \cdots)$
    c) $(1 + z + z^2 + \cdots)(1 + z^2 + z^4 + \cdots)(z^3 + z^6 + \cdots)$

19. $(z^6 + z^3)((1 - z^2)(1 - z^4)(1 - z^6))$

Section 7.4

1. $(1 + z)(1 + z + z^2/2!)(1 + z + z^2/2! + z^3/3! + z^4/4!)^2$

3. a) $(e^z - 1)^3$ b) $((e^z - e^{-z})/2)^3$

5. a) $(5^n + 2 \times 3^n + 1)/4$ b) $(5^n - 4 \times 4^n + 6 \times 3^n - 4 \times 2^n + 1)/4$

7. a) $(1 + z)(1 + z + z^2/2!)(1 + z + z^2/2! + z^3/3!)(1 + z + z^2/2! + z^3/3! + z^4/4!)$
   b) $(z + z^2/2! + z^3/3! + \cdots)(z^2/2! + z^3/3! + \cdots)(z^3/3! + z^4/4! + \cdots)(z^4/4! + z^5/5! + \cdots)$

9. $1 + z + 2z^2/2! + \cdots + 2^{n-1}z^n/n! + \cdots$
11. Find the coefficient of $z^{10}/10!$ in $(1 + z + z^2/2! + z^3/3! + z^4/4!)^3$
13. Find the coefficient of $z^n/n!$ in $(e^z - z)^3$
15. Find the coefficient of $z^{10}/10!$ in
    a) $e^{3z}(e^z - 1)$ b) $e^{3z}(e^z - z - 1)$ c) $e^{2z}(e^z - 1)(e^z - z - 1)$

Chapter 7 Review

1. a) $(1 + x^5 + x^9)^{10}$ b) $10!/(7!2!1!)$
3. a) $C(8,2)$ b) 7
5. They are equal in number.
7. $(e^x - 1)(e^{2x})(e^x - e^{-x})/2$
9. a) $(1 - x)^{-6}$ b) $(1 - x)^{-3}((1 - x)^{-3} + (1 + x)^{-3})/2$
11. $(1 - x)^{-2}(1 - x^5)^{-2}(1 - x^{10})^{-2}$

CHAPTER 8

Section 8.1

1. $a_0 = 6, a_1 = 4, a_2 = 7/2, a_3 = 97/28, a_4 = 18817/5432, a_0^2 = 36, a_1^2 = 16,$
     $a_2^2 = 12 + 1/4, a_3^2 = 12 + 1/784, a_4^2 = 12 + 1/295{,}066{,}240$
3. a) $a_n = a_{n-1} + a_{n-2}$ b) $a_n = 2a_{n-1} + 2a_{n-2}$
5. a) $a_0 = 1000, a_n = 1.06a_{n-1}$ b) $b_0 = 1000, b_n = 1.06b_{n-1} + 100$
     c) $a_n = 1000(1.06)^n$ $b_n = 1000(1.06)^n + ((1.06)^n - 1)10{,}000/6$
7. $a_n = 2a_{n-1} + a_{n-2}, a_0 = 1, a_1 = 2$
9. $a_n = a_{n-1} + a_{n-2}, a_0 = 1, a_1 = 2$
11. a) $a_n = 2a_{n-1}, a_1 = 3$ b) $a_n = 2a_{n-1} + a_{n-2}, a_1 = 3, a_2 = 7$
13. $a_n = a_{n-1} + n(n-1)/2 + 1; a_n = \dfrac{n^3 + 5n + 6}{6}$
15. $a_n = 2a_{n-1} + 2^{n-1}$
17. a) $a_{n,k} = a_{n-2,k-1} + a_{n-3,k-1} + a_{n-4,k-1}$
     b) $a_{n,k} = 6a_{n-2,k-1} + 10a_{n-3,k-1} + 15a_{n-4,k-1}$
19. a) Use induction.   b) $L_{2n} - 2$
21. $a_{n,k} = a_{n-2,k-1} + a_{n-1,k}$
23. a) $(n-1)!$ b) $C(2n-2, n-1)/n$

Section 8.2

1. a) $x^2 - x - 6 = 0$ b) $x^3 + x^2 - x - 1 = 0$ c) $x^2 + 3x - 10 = 0$
3. a) $a_n = c_1 5^n + c_2(-3)^n$
     b) $a_n = c_1((3 + \sqrt{17})/2)^n + c_2((3 - \sqrt{17})/2)^n$
5. a) $c_1 + c_2(-2)^n + c_3 n(-2)^n$ b) $c_1 + c_2 2^n + c_3(-2)^n$
7. $(-n^2/8 + n/8 + 1)2^n$
9. a) $a_n = ((-3 + \sqrt{-3})/6)((1 + \sqrt{-3})/2)^n + ((-3 - \sqrt{-3})/6)((1 - \sqrt{-3})/2)^n$
     b) $a_n = c((1 + \sqrt{-3})/2)^n - c((1 - \sqrt{-3})/2)^n$
     c) Impossible, since $a_3 = -a_0$

11. a) $c_1(-1)^n + c_2(2 + \sqrt{3})^n + c_3(2 - \sqrt{3})^n$
13. $(1/2 + 1/\sqrt{3})(1 + \sqrt{3})^n + (1/2 - 1/\sqrt{3})(1 - \sqrt{3})^n$
15. $a_n = 2^n/3 - (-1)^n/3$
17. a) Solve $a_n = 2a_{n-1}, a_2 = 1$.
   b) Solve $a_n = a_{n-1} + a_{n-2}, a_2 = 1, a_3 = 1$.
19. Use induction to show that $A = \prod_{i=2}^{n-1} \prod_{j=1}^{i-1} (a_i - a_j)$

Section 8.3

1. a) $P(n) = -6n - 12$ b) $P(n) = -6n^2 - 24n - 36$ c) $P(n) = 3^{n+1}$
3. $c_1(-2)^n + c_2 n(-2)^n + 2^n/4$ $c_1 = 3/4$ $c_2 = -3/2$
5. $c_1 2^n + c_2 5^n - 3^{n+2}/2 + 1/4$ $c_1 = 4$ $c_2 = 9/4$
7. $c_1 2^n + c_2(-1/3)^n - n/4 - 13/16$
9. $a_n = 1.10a_{n-1} - 10n$
11. a) $-4\binom{n}{0} + 2\binom{n}{1} + 2\binom{n}{2} + 6\binom{n}{3}$

   b) $-4\binom{n+1}{1} + 2\binom{n+1}{2} + 2\binom{n+1}{3} + 6\binom{n+1}{4}$

13. $c_i = a_0^{(i)}$
15. $a_n = (3^n + 1)/2$
17. a) $a_n = \sqrt{2^n/3 - (-1)^n/3}$ b) $a_n = (-2(-1)^n/3 + 2^{n+1}/3)n$

Chapter 8 Review

1. a) 233   b) 927
3. $a_n = 2a_{n-1} - a_{n-3}; a_0 = 1, a_1 = 2, a_2 = 4$
5. a) Use the general solution $a_n = c_1 3^n + c_2(-2)^n$.
   b) Use the general solution $a_n = c_1 3^n + c_2(-2)^n - (2^n)$.
   c) Use the general solution $a_n = c_1 2^n + c_2 3^n + (3/2)n + (25/4)$.
7. a) $x^3 - 4x^2 + x + 6 = 0$ b) $x = -1, 2, 3$ c) $a_n = c_1(-1)^n + c_2 2^n + c_3 3^n$
9. Solve the recurrence $a_0 = 1000, a_n = (1.05)a_{n-1} + 100n$.

CHAPTER 9

Section 9.1

1. a) Multiply on the left by a^{-1}.
   b) Multiply on the right by a^{-1}.
3. Prove by induction on q.
5. a) $\begin{pmatrix} 1 & 2 & 3 & 4 & 5 \\ 5 & 3 & 2 & 4 & 1 \end{pmatrix}$ b) $\begin{pmatrix} 1 & 2 & 3 & 4 & 5 \\ 1 & 5 & 4 & 2 & 3 \end{pmatrix}$ c) $\begin{pmatrix} 1 & 2 & 3 & 4 & 5 \\ 1 & 3 & 2 & 4 & 5 \end{pmatrix}$
7. 36
9. a) It is cyclic, since 1 has order m.
   b) It is not cyclic.

11. Multiply on the left by a^{-1}, on the right by b^{-1}.
13. Show that every element $\langle i \rangle$ has an inverse.
15. $(7^4 + 3 \times 7^2)/4$

Section 9.2

1. a) $(1782)(46)(3)(5)$ b) $(1248975)(36)$
3. 30
5. 8 symmetries
7. $(2^8 + 6 \times 2^2 + 9 \times 2^4 + 8 \times 2^4)/24$
9. a) Identity, eight $120°$ rotations about an axis through a vertex and the opposite face, three $180°$ rotations about an axis through the midpoints of opposite edges
   b) $(n^4 + 11n^2)/12$

11. a) $(9 \times 2^5 + 2^9 + 2^4 + 6 \times 2)/18$ b) $\left(9 \times 4 + \binom{9}{3} + 2 \times 3\right)\Big/18$

13. $\left(\binom{8}{2}\binom{6}{2} + 4 \times 3\right)\Big/8$

15. *Hint:* See Problem 4, Section 9.1.
17. $(3^6 - 3 \times 2^6 + 3 \times 1^6 + \cdots)/24 = 30$.
19. a) 2^{16} b) $(2^{16} + 6 \times 2^{12} + 8 \times 2^8 + 6 \times 2^6 + 3 \times 2^{10})/24$
21. 3984
23. $(2^4 + 11 \times 2^2)/12$

Chapter 9 Review

1. a) $(3^6 + 3^3)/2$ b) $(C(6,2)C(4,2) + 3!)/2 = 48$
3. For example, let coloring 1 have vertex 1 red, vertex 2 blue, and all the other vertices white, while we let coloring 2 have vertex 1 blue, vertex 2 red, and all the other vertices white.
5. $(3^5 + 3^3 + 3^2 + 3^2)/4 = 72$
7. $(2^{10} + 2^4 + 2^4)/3 = 352$
9. $((n-1)^4 + (n-1) + n(n-1) + 2n(n-1)^2)/8$

CHAPTER 10

Section 10.1

1. To find a directed path of length k, start at any vertex and in each step proceed to a new vertex.
3. Any $p \geq 0$
5. Prove by contradiction. Otherwise a cycle can be found.
7. Exactly one of them is equal to 1.
9. Eliminate repeated vertices until a cycle is obtained.
11. Look at a Hamiltonian path.
13. Prove it by induction on k.

15. a) Any tournament has $\binom{n}{2}$ arcs.

19. The vertices are labeled by blocks of length 2.

Section 10.2

1. Prove by contradiction. A walk with repeated vertices must contain a cycle.
3. Successively find and remove a source vertex until either no vertex remains or no source can be found.
5. b) 46 hours.
7. $y_1 = 0$, $y_2 = 4$, $y_3 = 5$, $y_4 = 8$, $y_5 = 11$, $y_6 = 15$
9. *Hint:* Adapt the maximum-weight path algorithm of this section for arbitrary networks.

Section 10.3

1. *Hint:* See the proof of Theorem 10.7.
3. To construct a transport network, start with a bipartite graph that has vertices representing ships on one side and types of equipment on the other.
5. *Hint:* Start with initial matching M and use the labeling method to obtain a maximum matching.
7. Construct a transport network by starting with a bipartite graph that has boys on one side and girls on the other side.
9. Construct a transport network by starting with a bipartite graph that has objects on one side and sets on the other.
11. *Hint:* Consider the marriage puzzle.
13. Use Problem 12.
15. Look at the associated digraph and analyze the corresponding network flow problem.

INDEX